THE WAY

INTRODUCTION BY ROBERT COLBORN

PHOTOGRAPHS BY HEKA

OF THE SCIENTIST

Interviews from the World of Science and Technology

SELECTED AND ANNOTATED BY THE EDITORS OF
INTERNATIONAL SCIENCE AND TECHNOLOGY

SIMON AND SCHUSTER · NEW YORK

All photographs are by courtesy of International Science and
Technology. *Except for the following, all are by Heka.*

*Photographs of Abdus Salam, Lord Todd, F. C. Williams,
Richard Crossman, and Lord Snow are by Ron Appelbe; photographs of Guy Ourisson are by Jacques Richardson; photograph
of Myron Tribus is by Heinz Kluetmeier; photographs of Jerome
Wiesner are by Noel Clark; photograph of I. G. Petrovskii is
by Dan Cooper.*

FIRST PRINTING
LIBRARY OF CONGRESS CATALOG CARD NUMBER: 66–27585
DESIGNED BY EVE METZ
MANUFACTURED IN THE UNITED STATES OF AMERICA

Contents

Contents

The New Community

A couple of decades ago, in that confused time just after the Second World War, the style of our society took some sort of sharp turn. Now, twenty years later, things are nothing like what we expected them to be when we were young and wise.

For just one instance, it still seems strange to me to live in a world where the poor are freaks, commanding our concern from outside the main stream of society; those of us past forty grew up thinking that the poor were the main stream of society. It is strange to live in a world that could end at any moment, in quite describable nuclear ways, but never does. A world where some of the liveliest of our sons and daughters seem more interested in LSD and marijuana than in such sensible comforters as alcohol and tobacco. A world containing a couple of machines, particle accelerators, on Long Island and in Switzerland, whose purpose is to manufacture unexpected kinds of matter, kinds which may never have existed until now in all the ten billion or so years that time has run. A world where the centuries-long improvement in the human food supply has just now ended, tipping us down onto the dark course toward running out of food.

I could go on with this catalogue of strangeness for a long time. And in a way I would like to and to brood over these instances, because it would be a fine thing to be the man who managed to make sense out of America in the sixties, of the world in the sixties. By any indication I can see, that task is still unmanageable. But what this book, this collection of interviews, does have to offer is the record of a somewhat random exploration of one of the queer new territories of the queer new world we live in.

This territory is an important one, because the things that go on in the community of science and technology have a strong impact on the rest of us. Now, that alone might not be a very good justification for another book; we are knocked around by impacts from many directions. But I believe an exploration of this particular territory can offer some revealing clues to what is happening to the whole society. For many of the puzzling changes in our motivations seem to be most vigorously and visibly at work in the technical community.

It is easy to miss the novelty of what is going on here. The people involved have mostly forgotten that the life of the scientist or the engineer wasn't always the way it is now. And few who are not involved in it have had much chance to understand the large role the technical community has come to play. It is worth remembering that before the war an educated man who was not in a university was about as likely to encounter a professional physicist as he was to encounter a professional poet.

There are some standard numbers I could trot out at this point to describe the change I'm talking about, but I have become as bored with them as everyone else has. They did come alive for me a couple of months ago when I dug out the old pages of an article I wrote in 1946. I was just getting back to work then as a reporter in Washington and was trying to sniff out the new things that had appeared while I was away. My article was headlined "Science Dons a Uniform," and I felt very good about it at the time, because it seemed to me that I had identified one of the important postwar changes. When I reread it twenty years later I felt good all over again, because I really had put my finger on something.

The article said that research in the natural sciences and in advanced engineering had been taken over by the federal government and that it was going to remain a primarily fed-

eral function. Before the war, most of the cost of research had been met by industry, either directly or through the flow of industrial fortunes into university coffers. Now the source had become the federal government, which was paying for an overwhelming share of all the research being done. This, the article said, would prove a permanent and important change.

That far, it was dead right. Which is enough of an achievement so that I'm not ashamed that the article also completely missed one important consequence of the change I had spotted and was wrong about another.

Writing in 1946, I failed to foresee the immense increase in the sheer amount of scientific research and of developmental engineering which would follow the infusion of government money. At that time no one was breaking down expenditures on research and development as a special category, but as near as I was able to tell, the federal government was putting in something close to a billion dollars, which was a lot. Nowadays, federal spending of this sort runs to some $15 billion, and even in a $100-billion budget that is a very great lot of money. Particularly when you bear in mind that this is dynamic money, money which expresses decisions. Jerome Wiesner, who was President Kennedy's science adviser and who appears as an interview subject in this book, has pointed out that something like half of all the money the government spends each year is routine; it's locked into the budget and goes on from year to year without anybody having to think much about it. So he concludes that, of the flexible money whose spending is argued about and decided on, almost a third is for discovery and innovation.

Now anyone who compares any kind of numbers across two decades expects to find a manyfold increase. Yet even in a society whose wealth and whose problems are in the midst of explosive growth, a fifteenfold increase is something to think about. For comparison, that touchstone number of the economists, capital spending on factories and machinery, merely tripled during that same period.

Clearly, my old article missed something pretty important, and not just in the size of the numbers. For the growth of society's technical arm has been so rapid, so much greater than the expansion of other organs of society, as to change the basic character of the technical enterprise—and to change the role it plays as a whole.

I do give myself this much credit: I understood, twenty years ago, that a change in the sponsorship of science and of advanced technology was sure to change their character and direction. As a young reporter specializing in economic matters, I had a firm grasp on the principle that the man who pays the piper calls the tune. Science was going to have to dance to the tune its new paymaster called. And the tune was bound to be a military one, since most of the federal money for research was passing through military hands. Inevitably, I wrote, the nation's best technical minds would be lured or pushed away from work motivated by scholarship or civilian usefulness and steered onto paths which led directly or indirectly toward weaponry.

It was very solid and logical thinking. So logical that even today a great many people assume that this is exactly the way things have gone. How could it be otherwise? And indeed, looking at the situation from the outside, it can be extraordinarily difficult to tell whether or not things really have gone this way, for the bookkeeping of the federal involvement with science has become almost hopelessly tangled. Air Force money supports an international conference on cosmology, or the Navy backs up studies of antarctic geology and meteorology. Or look at high-energy physics: This is just about the purest pure science there is, preoccupied with the ultimate nature of matter, and because it has to work with very powerful particle accelerators it is also one of the most expensive kinds of science; high-energy physicists get most of their money from an agency charged with building nuclear bombs—for no more obvious reason than that the baby accelerators of thirty years ago helped unravel the structure of the atomic nucleus and so led to the atom bomb and the Atomic Energy Commission and its budget officers.

You can't tell from budgetary statistics whether science really has donned a uniform. You have to look at the fruits of the research effort. What sort of discoveries, what big changes, have come out of all this intellectual activity?

*When you do examine the fruits, the first thing you dis-
cover is that the art of weaponry is no longer one of them.
That art is now pretty nearly stagnant. The early fifties saw
the development of the hydrogen bomb, which involved some
fairly solid science. In the second half of the decade, a surge
of engineering effort produced workable intercontinental
missiles. Through the same years an electronic fence of
detection and warning systems was put around the country,
and the submarine became fast and atomic-powered. But
about the beginning of the sixties, the technology of warfare
reached a plateau. Harold Brown, who was then coordinating
research and development for the Defense Department and is
now Secretary of the Air Force, talked about this plateau
several years ago in an interview which is republished in this
book. Just a few months ago, President Johnson's science
adviser, Donald Hornig, used the same expression in another
of these interviews. Hornig himself is convinced that sooner
or later some breakthrough will open up new military possibilities, and therefore he wants the military people to go on
supporting fundamental research. But he has no idea where
the breakthrough might appear, and the reason he encourages
military research sponsorship is simply to keep military men
aware of what's going on in science, just in case. Meanwhile,
current military research is aimed at things like a high-pre-
cision radar to keep fast low-flying airplanes from bumping
into chimneys, or at ways to detect enemy infantrymen in a
jungle, or deeper-diving submarines, or more accurate ways
to count the trucks in a parking lot from a surveillance satellite a hundred miles up. To a man in uniform, things like this
are important. But in technical terms, they are not where the
action is.*

*Where is the action, then? I have put this question to a
lot of knowledgeable people and to myself. And I think most
would agree that after twenty years of mostly government-
sponsored research and development the hottest action is in
the following areas:*

*(1) Medicine and biology have to head the list. As an
applied science, postwar medical research has effectively
eliminated all but two or three diseases as serious threats. Of*

course we all die, eventually, by violence or of one of the two or three unsolved diseases—but the human and political significance of eliminating the daily fear of sickness is something we are just beginning to experience. At the theoretical level, molecular biology has come to the very verge of understanding what makes living matter live and perhaps of synthesizing it and is beginning to accumulate hints on how the brain works.

It is one of the weaknesses of this collection that it includes few people working in this area—a result of the emphasis on physical science and engineering of the magazine from which the interviews were drawn.

(2) I have already spoken of high-energy physics. The particle physicists are exploring a level of reality at least one step deeper than the prewar and wartime investigations of atomic structure. When you read the interview with Victor Weisskopf, you can sense how very far removed the goals of this sort of work are from those of medical research. Nothing that Weisskopf and his colleagues are doing suggests any workaday usefulness. You need specialized training even to see the point of the questions they are trying to answer. And yet this science exerts an intense pull upon some of the most attractive and subtlest young minds around. The pull is felt, as Abdus Salam reminds us in another interview, even in underdeveloped countries which are in desperate need of more useful science. Out of all this, ideas and results come flooding so fast that The Physical Review *has had to add a biweekly supplement.*

(3) An equally active but completely different kind of physics is the study of the solid state. In a way, this is just as simple as it sounds—how is a solid chunk of stuff put together, and what goes on inside it? But these ancient questions come to life when you apply to them the insights of theoretical physics about the behavior of individual atoms— sometimes in ways as simple, as intuitive as those Bernd Matthias talks of in one of these interviews. It turns out that very complex and useful things are going on inside quite inert-looking lumps. The transistor radio that hangs around half the high-school-age shoulders in America is one out-

growth of this, but only one. For a little crystal of this material or that, if the atoms in it are arranged just so, can operate as the equivalent of a complicated electronic device —promising some of the longest steps toward simplicity and reliability that technology has ever taken. Of all the really active fronts of technical advance, this one probably contains the largest element of private investment. It got its start—in a classic of planned research—as a deliberate effort by the telephone company to find a replacement for the radio tube. It has continued to be the sort of field in which a man can get rich, and a lot have.

(4) The body of technology which has been wrapped around the computer belongs on this list for two different reasons. The more obvious one is the rapid progress which is being made on machines which manipulate information instead of material or energy, machines which store information, rearrange it, draw logical conclusions from it, make decisions about it. Such machines are in a burst of advance and so is our understanding of ways to use them.

There is a second and potentially a more important sense in which mechanized information-processing is a place where the action is. A computer technology is beginning to appear which permits almost anyone who is doing intellectual work, whether he is designing appliances or investigating history or doing research in chemistry, to have very cogent machine help available to him, minute by minute. This man-machine collaboration is a radical new tool of thought and may be comparable to the invention of writing itself in what it does to the manner in which people think. Just as general literacy has made rote memory a fairly unimportant skill, so information-processing machines seem likely to assume most of the intellectual burden of strictly logical analysis, leaving intuition and imagination as the valued elements in human thinking.

(5) In the last few years a group of old and rather stodgy sciences—geology, oceanography, meteorology—has come suddenly to life under a new name, environmental science. Its practitioners are among the most ebullient around, talking freely about controlling the weather, predicting earthquakes,

exploiting the oceans. Here is a field of science which changed radically as soon as really large funds became available to it; at that point investigators could send aircraft to fly through storms or could shoot rockets into the outer atmosphere or could assemble observations of planetary phenomena on a worldwide basis. This too became one of the places where the action is.

(6) I put the exploration of space—of the moon and the planets of the solar system—here at the end of this list simply because every television viewer is bound to have looked for it at the beginning. There is no question about the scale of activity; the interesting question is about the purpose of it all. And the almost unbelievable fact is that no one can say with any confidence what the purpose of the space program is. There is a vague feeling around that its importance is military. And indeed a significant military space program does exist and has already made Eisenhower's open-skies proposal an accomplished fact, with U.S. surveillance satellites watching what goes on in Russia and vice versa. But this is one small part of a huge enterprise which has little military meaning otherwise.

It is common, also, to speak of the space enterprise as a scientific research program. Scientists are not the ones who speak that way, though. Most of them would settle happily for a much cheaper program of unmanned, heavily instrumented space probes. They either resent the effort to put a man into space or welcome it half cynically because their research can be a passenger on a far bigger program with quite other motives.

When the argument over support for the space program gets bitter—and the odd fact is that it rarely does—enthusiasts are likely to fall back on the rather unsatisfactory defense that if we don't plunge into space the Russians will get there first.

To a great many sophisticated non-technical people, this haziness about motives has an almost psychotic sound. The space program seems a crazy, an inexplicable perversity, a way of evading the tragic problems of earthbound reality. I don't share that feeling. If Edmund Burke couldn't find the way to draw an indictment against a whole community, I think one should be just as cautious in making a diagnosis of schizophrenia concerning two powerful nations. Admittedly, universal madness does seem a plausible hypothesis at times, yet I think it is more interesting to inquire what this lack of a describable purpose for an enormous national undertaking may be telling us about the driving forces at work in society today.

It is almost fair to say that in modern times any large social enterprise has traditionally demonstrated its right to exist in one of two ways: It has an economic justification, providing useful goods or services; or it has a military justification. (I limit myself to modern times to avoid talking about the pyramids, the cathedrals, and the Crusades.) All through these last couple of centuries, of course, artists and scientists have done their work, churches have got themselves built, sportsmen have raced yachts or hunted the source of the Nile, philanthropists have endowed hospitals, and all for reasons which were neither economic nor military. But such activities have been small, marginal, unofficial, in some sense outside the main stream of the serious workaday world. The only large respectable enterprise I can think of that has enforced a non-economic, non-military claim for thoroughgoing social support is public education.

Now if you think about my sketches of six technical fields where the action is, an odd thing emerges: None of them is backed up by a clear-cut military justification. Only two of them suggest any large degree of economic motivation. Two others have made or promise to make important contributions to welfare, though not of the sort that are readily measured on a profit and loss sheet. Two, and they are the most expensive, have quite other motives.

It seems to me—and here is where this discussion has been leading—that the science-technology-discovery segment of postwar society, a segment now absorbing some 3 per cent of the national income, simply fails to operate a good deal of the time by standards which can be measured along military or economic axes. Some of its most important values are measured in other directions.

Just what values do govern the technical world? Clearly, it will take more than two decades to uncover the full dynamics of really large resources devoted to technical innovation and discovery. But it does look as if in some substantial measure the enterprise is governed by values that used to be thought of as characteristic of the artist, of the scientist, of the adventurer—and that the present technical enterprise involves the most sweeping support for such values that our society has ever been willing to grant.

Read the interview with science adviser Donald Hornig and you'll see something of how this works. We had asked him about the objectives which govern the distribution of federal money for research. The most basic goal he could point to was this: to ensure that every person with scientific talent gets the resources he needs to do the work he wants to do. Now this is a rather amazing statement, and the amazing thing about it is that it was not expressed as a pious hope; Hornig is of the opinion that this is just what present allocations are accomplishing, if you exclude investigations that require multimillion-dollar equipment.

For a generation or so most of us have been willing to take it for granted that educating as many people as possible up to the limit of their abilities is a good thing in itself, a goal which need not be justified by appeal to more practical purposes. Now it appears that, with hardly any debate and hardly noticing what we were doing, we have adopted the view that the free exercise of society's best minds is also a good thing in itself, worth supporting for its own sake with public dollars. No one has come right out and said this, but it is the basis on which we seem to be operating.

If this has happened, and I think it has, it is a useful insight for anyone concerned to understand the technical community. Beyond that, it suggests to me that quite a few people who have hardly any interest in the technical community as such can learn interesting things about the way their society is evolving from glimpses of the way the men of the technical community are feeling and behaving nowadays, which is what this book really has to offer.

I am beginning to be conscious, at this point, of a some-

*what simple-minded and Philistine grin on my face. I have
been making the technical enterprise sound pretty sweet and
well-meaning. And I am imputing very high-minded motives
to a tough, confused, and growth-wracked nation.*

*I do impute such motives, and I expect to see them endure.
But it is clear that they have evolved out of some ignorant
and ill-founded hopes and fears about the results to be expected from progress in the natural sciences. War-born fears
that weapons even more horrid than we have yet seen are
lurking in the wings, waiting to be discovered. War-born
hopes that enough money for high-brow science could ensure
that we would be the ones to make the discovery. That is
why the rather magnificent awareness of human potentials
which glimmers through present federal policies toward science and technology has not yet shown itself in public deal-
ings with other sorts of creative work. Perhaps there have
been some beginnings the past year or two in relation to the
arts—beginnings reminiscent of the hesitant steps toward a
National Science Foundation twenty years ago. But public
support of the humanities and the social sciences is trivial.*

*Undeniably, too, the technical community itself lost some-
thing when it got rich. Sciences which were once little en-
claves of noble monomania are diluted with competent men
building honorable conventional careers. Engineers with an
intuition for the way things work are succeeded by men with
more feeling for mathematics than for the heft of a steel bar.
You can sense a mournfulness about this between the lines of
an interview with a brilliant ex-Hungarian physicist like
Szilard, a German Nobelist of the old school such as Debye,
or with engineers like Nixon of Rolls Royce, or Sporn of
American Power.*

*Again, the emergence of science from the university into
the workaday world has necessitated the appearance of a
sometimes disturbing Establishment, men of science policy,
enlightened and often skillful administrators who have left
the laboratory and the classroom a long way behind. The
attitudes and the preoccupations of this new manipulative
style of technical man show up in interviews with Harold
Brown and Harrison Brown, with Wiesner, or with the group*

17

of presidents of small science-based companies whom we gathered around a table for a joint interview.

It would be naïve to ignore such crosscurrents. And yet the total effect from a reading of these interviews, I find, is an extraordinarily pleasant one. These are men of breadth and, naturally, high intelligence. They are also men who intensely enjoy the work they are doing, in ways as diverse as those you'll see expressed by Wilson, Williams, Massey, and Townes. There is nothing alienated or defensive about them; they respect the work they are doing; they know that other people respect it; they seem to feel at home in society. They are also—despite popular belief—thoroughly lucid. They talk well, organize their ideas with clarity, and precision. The scientist's reputation for obscurity is only justified when he is talking about the details of his own work; there he has been trained to a style of discourse which takes no account of the outsider. Get him on to broader matters, and his native intelligence and good will take command.

Perhaps, as a group, these men lack a sense of tragedy or of the limitations of life. I'm not sure; you can catch a whiff of that too in Abdus Salam or in the group interview with émigré British scientists. Presumably one does not look to society's favored children for the tragic vision. And perhaps the interview situation is not calculated to call it forth if it exists.

I should say something, finally, about the origins of these interviews. They were all conducted by members of the editorial staff of International Science and Technology *and were published in that magazine, which is addressed to professional scientists and engineers. In this book an explanation has been added in the margin, here and there, to make the ideas more readily accessible to lay readers, but the interviews themselves are unchanged. The editors involved with the interviews were, besides myself, David Allison, Daniel Cooper, Evan Herbert, Charles Lynch, Howard Mattson, Ford Park, Seymour Tilson, and Michael Wolff.*

One or more of the editors conferred at length with each interviewee, sometimes in the office of the magazine but more often on the interviewee's home ground. A few of the con-

versations were as short as forty-five minutes, a few stretched into several hours; an hour and a half was a typical length. Although the editors always began with an idea of what they wanted to talk about and sometimes stuck to it, no questions were ever submitted to a subject in advance. One or two subjects preferred to have an aide along, but most faced the tape recorder alone.

All the pictures in this volume were taken at the time of the interview and so, insofar as pictures can, they reflect the subjects' reactions to topics discussed. Most of the pictures were taken by Regula Davis, staff photographer of the magazine, who works under the professional name of Heka.

The tapes of the interviews were transcribed, and each transcript was edited by one of the interviewers. Editing was mostly a matter of shortening. We cut the subjects' language freely, eliminating repetitions and topics that turned out to be blind alleys. But we made almost no outright alterations; what you read is what the man said. We did alter the text of our own questions quite freely in the editing whenever we thought such a change would clarify the answer.

The edited text always went back to the subject for review before it was published. Surprisingly, and with hardly any exceptions, we were asked to make only the most minor changes. Perhaps I should not be surprised. These are men who know their minds, who think fast, and who stand by what they say once they have said it. What I am truly surprised at is that they resisted the temptation to pretty up their language, to make themselves sound stuffier or more elegant than they are. For this I am grateful as well as surprised—almost as grateful as I am that a very rewarding group of men were willing to undergo the ordeal and to seem, most of the time, to enjoy it.

Robert Colborn

A
WAY OF THINKING

What the life of science and the content of science feel like to the men who live it and work at it

Leo Szilard

*I*n *the brief time between his surprising recovery from cancer and his death about two years ago, Leo Szilard had been spending most of his time in Washington, working sometimes in the sunny lobby of the Dupont Plaza Hotel where he lived, sometimes in the cluttered little study next to the service elevator where we interviewed him. He was professor of biophysics at the University of Chicago, but the post involved no teaching. (Actually, in his long scientific career, he never taught, which is an extraordinary thing to realize when one recalls the intellectual influence he had throughout the scientific community.) So he was free to do pretty much as he pleased. Mostly he pleased to divide his time—he knew how short it was likely to be—between research into the molecular mechanisms of biology and searching for ideas on how to avoid war.*

The latter search was stimulated by his own scientific contributions to the production of the first atomic bombs. In 1939 Szilard conducted some of the first experiments that demonstrated the possibility of a chain reaction in uranium. Later, with Enrico Fermi, an outstanding contributor to atomic physics who came to the U.S. from Italy, Szilard devised the first working atomic reactor.

Through a lifetime of scientific work in his native Hungary, Germany, England, and this country, Szilard seems to have had an uncanny talent for getting into the fields where exciting discoveries were being made, and for creating excitement wherever he went. So our first question to him was:

One thing we're anxious to talk about, Dr. Szilard, is your shift from nuclear physics into biophysics. As background to that, would you tell us about your involvement in the development of the atomic bomb?

In January 1939, when I learned of the discovery of fission by Hahn and Strassmann, it immediately occurred to me that neutrons might be evaporated in the fission process. This would make a chain reaction possible.

Where were you then?

I was nowhere, really. I lived in New York, thinking what I should think about, when the discovery occurred. Now, I had thought about the possibility of a nuclear chain reaction in 1934, but by 1939 I had given it up. When I heard about the discovery of fission, the first thought that came to my mind was that we ought to look immediately whether a chain reaction is possible—and if it is possible, then we ought to keep it secret.

Did you find the idea of secrecy repellent?

I invented secrecy. I had written a number of letters, and we proposed both to the English and the French that if neutrons are emitted in the fission of uranium, this fact should be kept secret. There was considerable resistance, and the resistance became insurmountable after Joliot published his results and showed that neutrons are emitted in fission. I was still in favor of adhering to this policy—because, I said, if we did this, Joliot would have to fall in line; if he didn't, we would know his results and he would not know ours.

During that period was anything published which significantly helped the Germans?

No, except the one paper by Joliot.

Why do you think the Germans did so badly?

I really think that the German scientists got so little pleasure out of contemplating giving a bomb to Hitler that they failed to make those simple inventions which you had to make before you could say with any degree of assurance that you could make a bomb.

Are you saying the German physicists really did not want to find a bomb?

It was not a conscious decision. I think there was a sub-conscious impediment against putting steam behind this. I can give you an example: For instance, the Germans did one experiment to determine whether the uranium-graphite system would sustain a chain reaction. They concluded wrongly that it would not, and they dropped it. It is one single experiment. Now I tried to find out what happened, and I talked to Professor Heisenberg who made the theory for this experiment. Heisenberg told me that even today he doesn't know what was wrong. You see, with real interest, it would not have been conceivable to do just one experiment.

As to your own role in the bomb work, after the Manhattan Project began . . .

The Manhattan Project didn't take over until the middle of 1942, and by that time we knew that we knew how to make a chain reaction. Essentially, we knew the answer to all the major problems, and this is fortunate, because if we had been organized too early we would have been hindered, I think, to the point where we may not have found the answers. It is important to note that we were unimpeded by the Manhattan Project during the formative phases of this work—when the ideas had to germinate, you know. After ideas are all down, then you can organize it; but if you organize it too early you have to go to so many meetings you have no time to produce an idea.

You shifted from work at Columbia to the problem of pro-ducing enriched uranium at the University of Chicago in 1942. And you left the Chicago Metallurgical Project after 1945. Was it then that your interest began to shift from nuclear science into biophysics?

No, I was always interested in biology, and in 1933 when I went from Germany to England, I thought of shifting to biology. But then I had the thought about the possibility of a chain reaction—and the discovery of artificial radioactivity made physics too exciting, and I couldn't leave. But during the war I made up my mind that when the war was over this would be a good time to make the shift.

Was this entirely a return to an old interest?

No. When somebody does something, there are usually many motivations involved. It is not a single motive. Physics has had a change of character. The interesting portions of physics have moved to higher energies where you have to have a Committee and Planning and Getting The Machine and Getting the Money for The Machine and the Committee deciding which Experiment should be done first—you know. This is not the kind of physics I enjoy. I like the physics where I can think up an experiment today and do the experiment tomorrow. This I could do in the beginning of neutron physics in '34, '35. My neutron source was a little beryllium mixed with radium at the end of a long glass rod. I came into the room and held the source away from my body as well as I could and said, "Well, boys, what experiment do we do next?" Today you can't do that in physics.

See comments on the jockeying over the location of the current machine in the Wiesner and Hornig interviews.

And the basic charm of biology in 1945 was that you could still do this.

Yes, and others. I really find the mysteries of biology more intriguing than the mysteries of physics.

Was there a specific biology problem that appealed to you?

There was no one single problem. It was rather a feeling that I can come to grips with interesting problems very fast if I go into microbiology, which is a very young science. If you go back to Pasteur, in the early days of biology, the microbes were not studied for their own sake; they were studied because they cause disease, and it was more or less an applied field. Just before the war, people began to study microbes for their own sake, and this was what I wanted to do.

How did you get started?

I teamed up with a young colleague, a physical chemist, Dr. Aaron Novick, who is now director of the Institute for Molecular Biology at the University of Oregon. I knew nothing about his interests, and he was at the time employed by the Argonne National Laboratory. I called him up and said, "Novick, I decided I want to go into biology and want to start out by learning microbiology. Would you like to come along with me?" And he said, "Yes." We had never discussed this before. I just called him up on a hunch, and it worked.

Why did you seek out this particular man?

Well, I don't like to work alone. I'm not too good working with my hands. So working in partnership I thought was better.

Is two the magic number for you?

No, three would be all right, even five. I don't like large programs if I can help it.

Is Novick younger than you?

He is much younger than I am, but I don't know how old.

At the time of the interview, Novick was forty-three, Szilard sixty-four.

At that time not many people with training in physics were working in biology, were they?

A few, but not many. As a matter of fact, when I visited Moscow a year ago last December, Tamm, the distinguished nuclear physicist, said, "Tell me this, Szilard. Today everybody knows that biology is very interesting and that physicists ought to move into biology. But how did you know that in 1945?" I was probably the first physicist with notable achievements in physics who made this jump—and at an advanced age, you see. I was forty-seven years old at that time. I could not have known for sure that I could make good.

Well, how did you know?

It was not too difficult to know. Such things depend not so much on your intelligence as your character. If you don't fool yourself, then you'll see a number of things which other people may not see because they prefer to fool themselves. At forty-seven, I took a certain risk here. If I had lacked the courage to make the change, I would not have admitted this to myself; instead I would have underestimated the possibilities of biology. I could not have seen clearly the potentialities of biology if I had been reluctant to make this step through lack of courage.

There's a theory that very young men make the discoveries. By moving into a new field at forty-seven, did you get a freshness of viewpoint equivalent to that of a younger man?

Yes, of course, I was young in biology. It's the excitement of novelty, you know.

It's not that we're brighter when we're younger?

I think both are true. I think we are brighter when we are younger; and also we aren't prejudiced when we first come into contact with a problem. Once a man has missed the solution to a problem when he passes by, it is less likely he will find it the next time.

Are you as good a biologist as you were a physicist?

Yes. But I am older and therefore less productive. I have not yet come as far as I could have, but I am satisfied mainly as a result of three papers I published the last few years. These I like very much.

How did you learn biology? You didn't tackle it like a graduate student?

I didn't go to classes except in summer. I picked up the techniques in the summer. The Cold Spring Harbor biological laboratory offered summer courses in bacterial viruses, and I took one of these courses. After one such course I started to experiment.

You learned the techniques. How about theory?

Any theory that exists you can learn in two days.

DNA is the biochemist's shorthand term for the complex molecular substance that controls heredity generation after generation, essentially by duplicating itself repeatedly. It is found in the genes of all living things.

But you weren't working as a physicist, studying these things as physical systems?

No. I think what I brought into biology—and this is quite important—was not any skills acquired in physics, but rather an attitude: the conviction, which few biologists had at the time, that mysteries can be solved. If secrets exist, they must be explainable. You see, this is something which modern biologists brought into biology, something which the classical biologists did not have. They often were astonished, but they never felt it was their duty to explain. They lacked the faith that things are explainable—and it is this faith, you know, which leads to major advances in biology. An example is the

Watson-Crick model for DNA, a model which immediately explains how the DNA can duplicate. Everyone knew that DNA can duplicate, but nobody asked how it does. The desire to know how led these men to fool around with the structure of the molecule, and when they did that, they saw that a particular structure would explain the duplication.

Does the DNA breakthrough mean that the great days are over and that biology will now settle down again?

No, I don't think the great days are over. We haven't even scratched a problem like differentiation.

I'm not sure what you mean by the problem of differentiation.

Well, we have a single cell, an ovum, which is fertilized, and from this ovum we get an organism which has a great variety of different tissues. This is called differentiation— during embryonic development. Even if you understand the single cell, the microbe, you still don't understand this. Now this is a very big portion of life. So we are far from over.

What problems are you yourself concerned with in microbiology?

I published a paper on the theory of aging in January '59. It may be a wrong theory, but it is a theory—in the sense that it has made hard and fast predictions.

This is at the macrobiological level?

No, because in this theory aging is considered as a process which goes on in the individual cells. Not the organism, but the individual cells, are the seat of it, and particularly the chromosomes. So it is really a molecular biological theory. I don't know whether it is right or not. It is very difficult to say; we don't have the right experiments to show. But if I say that this is the only theory of aging in existence, I mean that this is the only theory which is quantitative enough to be proven by the right experiments. So I like this theory because it is a theory which can be disproved—proved or disproved.

Neither does any one else, yet.

You said you had three biology papers . . .

Yes, in March of '60 I published two more papers. One describes a mechanism that would enable us to understand how a microbial cell regulates the level of different enzymes.

29

In a classical experiment, you take a bacterium, *B. Coli,* which lives in the gut; if it is grown in a nutrient medium in the absence of the sugar, lactose, it will not make the enzyme, lactase, which splits lactose. But if you add lactose to the medium, then this bacterium makes a very large amount of the enzyme which it needs to split this sugar. This is called enzyme induction, and in this paper I gave a model of how the process of enzyme induction occurs.

Again, a molecular model?

Yes. Now I had had this model already in my head but I had never felt impelled to publish it, because I was not able to connect it with another phenomenon—antibody formation in rabbits—which I felt must be somehow related to enzyme induction in bacteria. You know if you inject foreign protein into a rabbit, it responds by making an antibody which can specifically combine with this foreign protein. How does the cell make the antibody which fits the particular antigen you inject in the rabbit? I tried to make a theory, but something was missing.

So what happened?

In a plane flying back from Stockholm to London, in the fall of '59, I suddenly had an idea. Everything fell into place, and I thought, Now I might be able to understand how the antibodies are formed.

Just what was the problem?

The trouble is that in antibody formation you have to explain two phenomena simultaneously. One is that if you inject protein into a rabbit and then inject the same protein a month later, the rabbit responds with a much stronger antibody formation. It's called the secondary response. At the same time you have to explain a phenomenon which is called tolerance—when you inject large quantities of a foreign protein into a newborn rabbit, when that rabbit grows up, he cannot make antibodies against this specific protein.

So your theory had to explain both phenomena—tolerance and secondary response.

Yes, and the idea of how to do this came to me, you see, on this airplane flight. My explanation of the secondary response invokes a mechanism which is endowed with memory; the rabbit "remembers" that it was exposed to this protein before. I had a model for induced enzyme formation, but I had failed to see earlier that if I just changed a constant in it, made it bigger, the model became endowed with "memory." Now at the time when I returned from Stockholm, I knew I was slated for surgery, but they didn't think I was seriously ill, so I said, "Give me six weeks or two months; I have an idea and I want to write this down." And so I wrote these two papers. I told you, on my aging paper, that I just wouldn't know how to bet whether it is right or wrong. But the experiments which have been done since I published this paper on antibody formation have strongly increased my belief that this paper is really right.

The work you have been describing seems to be pure science, motivated by curiosity. Do you expect your basic discoveries in microbiology to produce applications?

I will answer this by telling you a story. A year ago last December I was in Moscow to attend the sixth Pugwash conference. . . .

Dec. 1960.

The one on disarmament, the one Wiesner also attended?

Yes. And while I was there I was invited to talk to a writers' club about my work in molecular biology. One of these writers said, "Now what practical consequences does this have?" So I said, "As far as I can see it has no practical utility whatever—but of course if you had asked me that about nuclear physics in the 1930's I would have told you the same thing." And then the Russian said, "Well in that case, wouldn't it be better if you stopped right now?"

Jerome Wiesner, science adviser to the late President Kennedy, also mentions this conference in the interview with him.

The idea of controlling life processes could be just as disturbing as the idea of controlling nuclear forces. Do you worry much about that?

No, I don't worry about that, but I am aware of it. What's the use of worrying about it? You may have seen my little book *The Voice of the Dolphins*. There is one story in there, called "The Mark Gable Foundation," about a foundation set up to retard science. You can make a strong case that science is progressing too fast, that we should retard its progress so that social advances can catch up.

How did retardation work in the story?

The method described is to create a foundation with a very large endowment, and every year you take every creative scientist and put him on a committee to pick out from submitted applications for research grants the most deserving. A system that is very similar to what is now in operation in America.

Most of the Dolphin stories get into the area of disarmament. You seem to put your serious thinking into the form of satire quite often.

It used to be that if I said something serious, people thought I was joking; but now if I joke people think I'm talking seriously.

Aren't you, usually?

The point Szilard makes here remains substantially valid in spite of the conclusion of the treaty banning nuclear tests everywhere but underground.

Sometimes. Today you see the world is on the verge of an all-out arms race. We stopped testing for a period, and this somewhat slowed down the arms race. But now we are starting to think in terms of antimissile missiles and decoys to neutralize them; this really is the beginning of a new kind of arms race. I think that people in the administration know that this is not the solution, and they are considering how they could get some sort of arms control.

Are you?

I have attended practically every Pugwash conference, because I wanted to find out what our Russian colleagues are like and how they think. So far I have found that the Russians aren't very interested in what you call arms control. You see arms control means that you slow down the arms race, but it doesn't say what level of expenditure you are stabilizing; many of my American friends talk of stabilizing the arms at a very high level. I couldn't get any spark of enthusiasm for that out of our Russian colleagues. What the Russians are interested in is to achieve a considerable measure of economic saving through disarmament.

You really think that's a major motive?

I'm convinced of it, and you can understand why this should be so. The Russian national income is about 40 per cent of ours, and they spend about as much as we do on

arms. This amounts to, say, 10 per cent of our income, 25 per cent of theirs. This is even worse for Russia than it looks, if you consider that their industrial production may be a smaller proportion of national income than ours. I'm quite convinced from all the conversations I had while in Russia that they are very much interested in the kind of disarmament which would enable them to lift this burden of heavy expenditure from their economy.

How much variety of viewpoint have you encountered in your talks with Russians?

There is only one viewpoint—that it's impossible to solve the housing shortage with the arms race as it is, that consumer demands cannot be satisfied, and that there cannot be aid to underdeveloped nations on an adequate scale except if there is disarmament. I have heard no other view in Russia.

But this is not an important motive in this country?

There is no indication so far that any American in a responsible position would accept disarmament, as against arms control, even if a satisfactory inspection were included. I think the basic reason for this is all the uncertainty of how peace would be secured in a disarmed world; obviously, disarmament does not automatically secure peace. An army equipped with machine guns and other conventional weapons can spring up overnight.

You can negotiate successfully only if you have some goods which others want to buy. The only goods I have discovered which the Russians want is an economic saving which disarmament would bring about. This they want to buy, and I think they would pay a commensurate price for it in terms of political accommodations. Obviously, if we have disarmament, we in America cannot retain our military commitments to defend nations which are geographically remote from us and in the proximity of Russia. So to make disarmament politically acceptable to America, it will be necessary for Russia to agree to the kind of political settlement which enables America to withdraw from these commitments without too much loss of face and without sacrificing the security of the nations involved.

You've been spending most of your time in Washington for some months now, thinking and talking about this. What would you like to see done first?

I think the most fruitful thing would be the establishment of a group of scientists and scholars composed of Americans and Russians to talk about how the peace may be secured in a disarmed world. It must be done with the blessing of the governments. Particularly the Russians couldn't do it otherwise. I am often asked if the Russians can talk freely—and the answer is, "Yes, if they are so instructed by the government!" Such a private study could take something like four months. It could end up in a working paper in which Russians and Americans list various solutions, and pointed out in each case what could go wrong—because almost every solution has some weak points—and then they would turn this all over to the governments, which could take over from there.

In these efforts, Dr. Szilard, do you feel you are in an almost hopeless, last-ditch struggle? Or do you feel hopeful?

I think all I need to be fully effective is a 10 per cent margin of hope. It's enough to make you concentrate your efforts. This much hope I think we have, but I won't say we have much more.

Bernd Matthias

*B*ernd Matthias is a physicist who concerns himself primarily with solid materials—crystals, metals, and organic solids. His approach to physics is straightforward, almost primitive. He looks for clues to a material's behavior in its simplest atomic properties—the number of electrons orbiting around the nucleus, the weight of the atom, or its structure—rather than to measurements of electrical, magnetic, or other secondary properties. All such measurements are suspect, in Matthias' eyes, since they can be affected by irrelevant factors such as impurities, shape, or strain.

This way of thinking has brought him an enviable record of discovery. For example, some metals show a peculiar property called superconductivity when they are chilled to temperatures near absolute zero. When superconducting, they lose all electrical resistance, and an electrical current started in a superconducting "doughnut" will continue to flow indefinitely. Matthias has discovered more superconducting materials than any other man alive.

Not only that, he devised a rule to predict the transition temperature at which such materials become superconducting, and discovered the materials with the highest transition temperature. This factor has great practical significance, because it is far easier to cool something to, say, 18° above absolute zero than to 1° above.

Like many other scientists who spend their waking hours (and sleeping hours too, but more of that later) dealing with materials at an atomic level, Matthias has his occasional problems with the practical aspects of life. We met him in a Sears, Roebuck store in New Jersey a few years back, trying to figure out how to install the dry cells in a flashlight he was buying; he also expressed mild astonishment over the fact that we were buying supplies to do an electrical wiring job, obviously far too complicated for a layman.

This time we found him in his office at Bell Labs, preparing to leave for Brookhaven National Laboratories, where he is a consultant. (He is also on the faculty of the La Jolla campus of the University of California.) Not wanting to waste time on generalities, we jumped right into the interview—and, as promptly, put our foot in it.

What interests us most about you, Dr. Matthias, is your intuitive approach to some of the fields in which you have made discoveries. I know you hold a generally low opinion of theorists, and we . . .

You shouldn't say that. I have great love for theorists, provided they have a certain scientific foresight. A good example is the experiments Ted Geballe and I did on the isotope effect in superconductors here at Bell Labs. We had predicted years ahead that the transition temperatures in some superconductors would vary from one isotope to another with the mass of the isotope. We predicted it on the basis of the statistical occurrence in the periodic system, by just looking at the way things happen in the periodic system, and then we knew. Some theorists said, "Oh no," but in the end we were right. They then said, "Oh yes, we can explain that"—after the fact. That happens quite often. For the real theorists, however, I have an enormous respect.

Isotopes are different forms of elements that vary only in their mass (weight), because of extra neutrons in their nucleus.

What's your definition of a "real theorist"?

A real theorist, in my opinion, is more an applied mathematician than an experimental physicist. I just look at how nature occurs in a systematic way, and draw conclusions. I think there must be very general, very simple features of everything that happens in nature. The moment things are complicated, the moment you read a formula that extends for lines and lines, you know it is all wrong. The true formulas are all simple—whether it's refraction of light through glass, or the wave equation, or Einstein's equation, they're all simple, because they're true.

Do you think that there are certain people, perhaps including yourself, whose way of thinking has a certain parallelism to the way nature operates?

I just don't think nature is very tricky. I don't believe that one phenomenon or another is an enormous coincidence, or accident, or just happened to happen. Everything that is true is very simple, once we understand it. It's only complicated when we don't. I look for simplification, because that's the only way I can understand it. This may be my own limitation.

Isn't your idea of simplicity relative to a particular person or to a particular way of thinking, though? In other words, what seems simple to you isn't necessarily simple to another?

The periodic table is a graphic method of arranging the elements according to their electronic structure. It also emphasizes their chemical relationship.

No, that isn't true. Most people agree that the way I look at things is about the simplest and most primitive way anybody can think about them—except for those people who don't understand the periodic table or who don't know the elements, of course. They think it is very complicated to look through so many elements. The elements are really nature, and the periodic system is the most natural way of presenting them.

But you do have a rather phenomenal record for finding materials with unusual properties. How do you explain it?

Strictly for one reason—I'm willing to look. Most people are not willing to do this. You see, I like to gamble, and I do the same thing in physics. I look for new things. If you do this, there are three possibilities. Either you find what you are looking for, or you find something else, or you don't find anything. If you don't find anything, there is nothing you have to show for it. Oh sure, today people want to publish negative results, but it is always an anticlimax. I'm quite willing to gamble. If I find things, fine; if I don't, well I've just lost.

Most people don't work that way . . .

When I started on superconductivity along these lines, I was in Chicago. There was not much sympathy for this kind of approach there, with the exception of Fermi, who actually had suggested it, and John Hulm. The rest of them thought superconductivity was not a particularly good field. They felt that so many people had done it before. But they really hadn't; they had always looked along certain lines, either predicted by the theory, which insofar as superconductivity was concerned invariably predicted the wrong things, or they looked at the things that other people had been looking at before. Most experimentalists don't look in that way; they tend to believe the theory, and try to verify it. That's one way I may be different from the rest.

Enrico Fermi was the Italian-born physicist who first brought about a chain reaction in uranium.

You neither try to verify or disprove?

My idea is—if the theory can predict, fine. Since the theory couldn't predict superconductivity, it wasn't so fine, so I set out to look for myself.

When you're looking for superconductors, you don't just look at random. You seem to have the poker player's feeling —"This is a good hand, we'll bet it." How do you get that?

I didn't make any assumptions except that I thought that there must be a simple rule for the occurrence of superconductivity if it is a general phenomenon. The answer to both was affirmative, and out of it came a simple rule.

Is this rule of yours a theory or a criterion?

It's just a criterion for the transition temperature. Basically, it states that the transition temperature for elements in a given group reaches a maximum when the number of valence electrons is 5 or 7. You can see the number of electrons strictly from the periodic system—you just count the number of electrons outside the filled shell. These exist whether the element is isolated in a gas or is in a solid phase. The detailed configuration of the electrons, as it is effected by neighboring atoms or molecules, is really completely irrelevant, as long as the element exists at all. Of course, if it forms an insulator it doesn't work. When you plot the transition temperature against the number of valence electrons, it looks like

Electrons around a nucleus tend to arrange themselves in stable "shells." Those outside the shells are "valence electrons" and are involved in chemical reactions.

this (see marginal) with a peak just below 5 and below 7. There are none at 3 or 9. The data we had didn't support this symmetric curve at first, but I was convinced that nature had to be symmetric, and I just drew it like that. The later compounds filled out the curve.

How did you first get the feeling for your rule? Was it something you reasoned out, or was it more the way an artist might say, "If there's a line here, there has to be one there" . . .

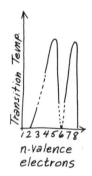

I wanted to find the underlying features that predict superconductivity without weaseling. For instance, if I had stuck to measurements of, say, electrical resistivity, for one given element there are a hundred different measurements in the literature. I then could have chosen the ones which suited me best. I decided instead to use only those features which are universally known, those which you can see from the periodic system. Then there is no longer any argument, no discussion, for example, that molybdenum doesn't belong in column VI. When people give you a value for the resistivity of molybdenum, you can argue that it wasn't pure, or it was strained, or they didn't measure it right. I wanted to rely not on recently measured values but on features of the elements that were beyond any doubt, that were fundamental. I was just waiting until I would see a feature that was common to superconductors with high transition temperatures.

Did the rule come to you all at once, or gradually? Do you know when it happened?

Oh yes, I know. It was at night, but I was awake at that time. Some superconductors I found when I was asleep, but this time I wasn't. I was reading a book, something quite different, and suddenly I knew that it was the number of valence electrons that was the common feature.

The next step, of course, was to see what the rule would actually do for you. How quickly were you able to verify it in the lab?

Oh instantly, we made some just like that. I had two points, one for niobium at 5, and another for technetium at 7. They were, of course, known previously. Then there were other elements here and there. I spent about ten hours going through these maximum transition temperatures, and suddenly I realized this curve, and predicted several compounds. Two of them, niobium$_3$-tin and niobium-zirconium, are the ones everybody is making superconducting magnets from now.

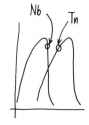

What are you most interested in nowadays?

At the moment I'm doing many things. I'm trying to prove first of all that superconductivity is really a very general phenomenon.

You're looking for another rule?

I'm convinced that every metal, provided it's very pure and very cold, eventually should go through some kind of condensation—a condensation where suddenly all the electrons pair up, with opposite or parallel spins, and the material becomes either superconducting or ferromagnetic—providing it's pure. The normal state of a pure metal at low temperatures, I think, is superconductive. Now and then, in a few rare cases, it will become ferromagnetic. Ferromagnetism is another kind of condensation, an ordering phenomenon of the electrons, only here they are paired with parallel spins. Apparently superconductivity is the more favorable situation, because most metals are superconductive rather than ferromagnetic. My question now is: Will they always have to do one thing or the other? I think yes, and if they don't, then there are two reasons only: either they are too dirty, because if you get too dirty you don't reach an equilibrium situation,

In a "condensation," valence electrons spinning at random pair up with their axes of rotation parallel. If they spin in the same direction, the material is ferromagnetic —you can pick it up with a magnet. If in opposite directions, they are antiferromagnetic and unaffected by magnets.

or they are not cold enough, because then the thermal motion disturbs the ordering.

How are you attempting to show this?

I'm trying to show that many metals which have not been found to be superconducting until now, do become so when purified sufficiently. That's how Ted Geballe and I discovered superconductivity in molybdenum and iridium. I'm trying to find ways of showing superconductivity without going to extremely low temperatures. I try to extrapolate from temperatures of between, say, 0.3 and 1°K, to what would happen at 10^{-3}°, and there are many ways to do this. In the cases of molybdenum and iridium, we extrapolated, then made the samples, and then verified the prediction. But that's a lot of work, and extrapolating is much easier. So right now I'm trying to extrapolate the rest of the periodic system to see what should become superconducting.

0°K = absolute zero
10^{-3}°K = 0.001° above absolute zero.

Anything else?

Yes, during the last ten years, ever since I made niobium$_3$-tin, the last superconductor with a high transition temperature, 18°K, a lot of people have looked but nobody has been able to raise the transition temperature by even as much as a tenth of a degree. I'm trying to find out if this is a fundamental limit, or if it is just our own shortcoming. There are still things to be made that, according to the rule, should have higher transition temperatures. Now I'm trying to get other people to make them, because today the techniques are getting more and more complicated. The easy things I did a long time ago.

You're still fascinated by superconductivity?

Of course. At the same time, I think ferromagnetism is much more interesting, because it's so much harder to find. There was nothing known that became ferromagnetic that didn't contain one of the five elements, chromium, manganese, iron, cobalt, and nickel, or one of the elements containing so-called *f*-electrons. I've found two new ferromagnets, and they were very interesting. The first one was zirconium-zinc$_2$; here the two constituent elements are superconductors at 0.7 and 0.9° respectively. The second one was scandium$_3$-indium. Scandium isn't superconducting, yet indium is.

"f-electrons," to a physicist, defines an electron in a certain quantum mechanical energy state. Its exact meaning isn't essential to the argument here.

Do you feel that all the constituents should be superconducting?

I once thought they should be. The conditions that cause both phenomena are closely related, I'm sure. You can have compounds which are both ferromagnetic and superconducting, but then they are only weakly ferromagnetic. A strong ferromagnet would inhibit the antiparallel alignment of the paired electrons, and therefore the phenomena would be essentially mutually exclusive.

Much of your interest then arises from the fact that ferromagnets are so rare?

Yes, free-electron ferromagnetism was considered theoretically by Bethe, who concluded that it was unlikely—the balance was too delicate. It's in his handbook article. Theoretically, he said, one could visualize them, but it was unlikely that it would ever be observed.

Hans Bethe, one of the great living theoretical physicists, was chief of the Theoretical Physics Department at Los Alamos during the war, and member of PSAC under Eisenhower. He is now at Cornell.

Were you challenged to try to prove him wrong?

No, because Bethe is one of the great names in physics of this century. He has created many theories, every one of which has predicted results that were true—there were no modifications, changes, and amendments afterward.

Who else would you put in the category of ideal theorists?

Einstein, of course. Fermi, in spite of the fact that he said he was an experimentalist—he was one of the greatest theorists that ever lived. Bohr, of course, and Heisenberg. . . .

Niels Bohr proposed the atomic structure model with a nucleus and orbiting electrons in 1913.

In 1927 Heisenberg postulated a principle that stated you couldn't know both the speed and the position of an electron at the same time.

Who falls into the category with you, of "simplicitists"?

I don't know of anybody else. The other day I had to give a speech, and I said, "A hundred years ago, I really would have been very popular." Today I'm anathema to many people, but a hundred years ago my approach would have appealed to a great many, because it is a rather pragmatic approach, based however on intangibles. For example, once many years ago when I was still in Zurich, Scherrer came to me and said, "There may be a new ferroelectric crystal, barium titanate. See if you can make a single crystal." So I went to the library—Zurich has a marvelous library—and I looked up what people had been doing along these lines. I found that a guy named Bourgeois had grown crystals of

MATTHIAS

Zurich 1942-47
MIT 1947-48
BTL 1948-49
U. Chicago 1949-51
BTL 1951—
U. Calif 1961—
(La Jolla)

43

barium titanate, but he didn't quite know it. He just mixed everything together, and looked at what came out, and described it. He thought he had something very complicated. He didn't; he had barium titanate. I repeated his experiment, and that was how I discovered how to grow barium titanate crystals.

Isn't that somewhat the same situation you found yourself in with ammonium sulfate and its ferroelectricity?

That's really one of the bitterest stories of my life, but if you want, I'll tell it. Ferroelectricity is a peculiar behavior of insulating materials which is similar to the magnetic behavior of ferromagnets. Kurchatov discovered the first one, Rochelle salt. Well, in Switzerland we looked. Busch found one crystal —potassium phosphate—that was ferroelectric, after a long search. People were thrilled at the discovery, but it turned out to be just an intermediate step to the insight that ferroelectricity was not an isolated, but a very general phenomenon. Perhaps because it seemed so rare, for the next fifteen or twenty years no ferroelectric crystals were found. Then during the war, Wul in Russia (he didn't publish until the end of the war) and von Hipple in this country discovered ferroelectricity in barium titanate. Then I found guanidine aluminum sulfate at Bell Labs by looking through Alan Holden's drawerful of single crystals, hundreds of them. The second crystal I looked at was ferroelectric. None of the others were, even the rest of those in the same bottle.

You say it's a bitter story?

Well after that I thought, What about the alums? I asked the experts, who were certain the alums were not ferroelectric; many people had looked at the alums. But that was how Ray Pepinski discovered the ferroelectricity of the alums— he didn't care that all these people had looked! I couldn't believe it. I thought, Hell, everybody had looked at the alums, how come they didn't find it? I spent a few days with Ray at State College, Pennsylvania, and true enough, the alums were ferroelectric. Then, to go home, I rented a car and drove to the airport—it's way out in the country—and I drove past a farm where a man was fertilizing with ammonium sulfate. And I suddenly thought, That's impossible; it couldn't be as simple as all that! So when I got back to Bell Labs, I went to Joe Remeika, one of my best friends, and said, "Listen, probably ammonium sulfate is ferroelectric." You know that until then there had been four hundred papers published on ammonium sulfate—every year between ten and twelve papers were presented on the extremely complicated mechanism that provoked the transition in ammonium sulfate. Well, to make a long story short, we made the ammonium sulfate crystal, which took three days, and we measured it, which took us half a day, and we showed that it was also ferroelectric.

It is rather unbelievable.

Now, if you assume that there are three people involved in a scientific paper, you have to assume that over a thousand people overlooked this. If you come to this conclusion, you sort of feel like getting out of such a field. If that number of people look for something and don't find it, and really spend an enormous amount of time looking, then there is something basically wrong. That is why I said that I am convinced that everything is ferroelectric. Since I said that, they have found nearly a hundred new ferroelectric crystals—potassium nitrate, sodium nitrite, on and on.

Because the inhibitions are down?

I don't know, but the funny thing is that after our short letter to the editor, there was nothing more to say, except that everything that had been published in the past was wrong. For three years there wasn't a single paper. Sometimes, a wrong or negligent paper is much worse than no publication since it will be taken seriously and not re-examined.

That's what I meant by the inhibitions; they prevented people from doing work that should have been done.

Pompousness is probably a better word. People overrate their own thinking. My attitude is this: If I find something, fine. Otherwise it doesn't really amount to anything. This is where the gamble comes in, but most people don't want to gamble, they want to publish.

Robert R. Wilson

*I*s physics pleasurable? For those outside the science it hardly seems possible. And yet, as with any creative activity, there is pleasure of a high order in doing physics. The physicist seeking clarification of nature's ways is a brother to the artist seeking proper expression of a vision half-formed within him. The Scientific Method—that idealized succession of hypothesis, experiment, and interpretation—ill describes the actual error-ridden route along which new knowledge is gained. Certainly it gives little sense of science as a human enterprise, of the contest of ego against nature's intransigence.

Physics is pleasurable and physicists are human. That message emerges clearly from our interview with Robert R. Wilson of Cornell University. Wilson is a nuclear physicist, one of the best around. He got his start at that fountainhead

of American nuclear physics, the Berkeley campus of the University of California, under Ernest O. Lawrence, who invented the cyclotron. One or another of these atom smashers has formed the background for his activities ever since. They were working at Columbia University and Princeton University, where he shared in the early researches on uranium fission and isotope separation. In wartime, at Los Alamos, he headed first the cyclotron group and then the entire research division. After the war he went to Cornell University, where he heads the Laboratory for Nuclear Studies. There he does research with one very large accelerator, while he and his students design another that is to be a hundred times as powerful. These large accelerators he uses to study the smallest bits of matter, the so-called elementary particles. These are the pieces out of which are formed—in a way not yet clear—the neutrons and protons that are themselves the building blocks for all atoms.

In recent years the complexity of accelerators has tended to make the building of them a specialty in itself. The team that builds the accelerator is seldom the one that uses it for research. Not so with Wilson's group at Cornell—he has insisted on designing his own accelerators, alternating periods of machine-building with machine-using research.

The interview was conducted in our editorial offices in late January 1965. Wilson was in New York for the annual meeting of the American Physical Society, the physicists' professional organization. There was a boyishness about him, a frank, non-self-conscious way of exploring his own attitudes that helped us to penetrate quickly to just how he feels about his subject.

Professor Wilson, you seem to have a very special, almost private, way of looking at physics.

Well, to me physics is, among other things, a form of personal expression. When I see what other physicists do, I don't think of it as just physics, but I think, Well, so and so's doing such and such a thing. I always identify it with a particular person . . . hopefully with some friend. If I don't know the man who is doing the work, it doesn't mean as much to me. But even then I try to imagine qualities and characteristics so he will have a definite personality for me.

You seem to be saying that physics is not so much an expanding body of knowledge as something that people do, that you do.

A recent article in a physics journal had fifty-one "authors," another listed no human author—just the laboratory where the research was done.

I'm sure if there were no other people in the world, I wouldn't do it. I wouldn't do physics in a vacuum. I don't like to think of physics as something that I'm devoting my life to. I do think of it as a form of human activity, and I've thought of physics as a way in which I've expressed myself not only to others but also to myself. There's much more to it—but this is an important part.

I guess I find the most gratification when I personally have done something. I can take pleasure if I can get up before other men and make an announcement of it with a certain flavor, some style. Then, perhaps, somebody will attack me . . . if a controversy starts, so much the better. There's pleasure in that too, you know. Then back into the laboratory, to think and work hard, to have—almost—to have enemies, to have competitors. What a joy; how much more intense is the work when there's a human involvement.

To me the style *is* important. If the work doesn't have style—if you don't identify with it, it might as well not be done. I can't stand the present trend toward multi-authored papers—anonymous physics.

Is it important to you that this is connected with some physical object . . . would you be as happy about equations on a blackboard?

Certainly. I have always done a certain amount of theoretical work, not highly mathematical. I have gotten just the same gratification from the theoretical work as I did from the experiments.

Another thing, I find that just the writing down of a nice piece of physics . . . there's joy in that too.

The language . . . ?

It's the language. If I could express it well, or if I could present it well at a meeting. Even if I presented something that wasn't very important, if I felt that I had presented it well and with style, then that would be a pleasure.

Can you ascribe some of your considerable success with accelerators to being able to see a mental model of them more vividly than others have?

My thinking about accelerators does tend to be intuitive rather than logical. And perhaps this does amount to thinking in terms of a visualized mental model. Acceleratology, as I like to call it, is much more concrete, much simpler, and much closer to the surface than is the practice of physics itself.

Accelerators ("atom smashers") impart high speed, high energy to atoms. Wilson worked on the first cyclotron, now works with what are called synchrotrons.

Are these ways of thinking so different—thinking about machines and thinking about particles—as to explain why some people tend to specialize in one and some in the other?

Maybe for others. For myself, I've found all my life that I've gone back and forth . . . emphasis on physics, then emphasis on technique. I often found that doing a particular experiment with a machine involved changing the machine. So the two get very much mixed up, and with it myself as a physicist, myself as a machine builder. Lately we've started at Cornell a new 10-billion-volt machine, a much larger machine than we've ever built before. I find that I've gotten farther away from physics and closer to the machine. That has made me more of a machine builder, but less of a physicist; and I am not sure how I feel about this.

"Machine" is physicist's slang for "accelerator."

The Cornell machine is slated for completion in 1968; it will accelerate electrons.

Then there's not a great personal payoff in putting the last touch on a very elegant piece of machinery?

Oh no, there's a great esthetic satisfaction. However, to me there's a greater satisfaction in having the original conception. Once you've had that, then there's the fun and excitement of making the design. At Cornell we have developed a style of designing accelerators not by having detailed drawings made in a drafting room but rather by going into the machine shop and working closely with the men there. So the design happens in three dimensions, and we make our changes in three dimensions—sometimes directly with a cutting torch. It's gratifying and stimulating to see these things actually being constructed in front of you, to participate directly in the construction. There's a great deal of give and take at Cornell between the technicians and the physicists. Sometimes this reaches a frenetic state, though, that is more characteristic of one of these new "happenings" —the kind that are put on by the artists.

Do we understand correctly that on one of your machines there never does exist a real set of working drawings?

Bev = billion electron volts, a measure of the energy the machine imparts to each particle. 10 Bev is a lot.

Certainly in the past this has been pretty much true. We probably do it differently than it's done in other places. The national laboratories, for example, seem to be more professional, have engineers. As yet we do not have any engineers in our laboratory at Cornell. Sometimes we have no drawings except for back-of-envelope sketches. In designing the 10-Bev machine, where much of the construction will be made elsewhere, we put most of our effort into the building of a full-scale prototype of some part—a fraction of the magnet ring, or a resonator, or whatever. When that is satisfactory, then drawings are made of the prototype. Then further prototypes will be made from those drawings to see if the drawings are any good. Then we'll make the whole thing. Actually the process all runs together much more than this. The point is that a small group can work together quite efficiently when the formalities are reduced to a minimum and when the responsibilities of individuals are maximized.

The building of the machine has this marvelous, climactic moment when you turn it on and it works. How does that feel?

Frequently you turn on a machine and it doesn't work, and then there's the long plodding business of making it work. With our 1-Bev electron synchroton, which we built back in '54, it took only about one year from the concept until we turned it on—then we just broke our hearts in getting it to work right. However, we have learned. The one we built at Cornell last year, the one to give 2 Bev, was different. We put it together in our usual happy manner. Then we were ready to try to look for a beam. All of us said farewell to our wives and went off prepared to work for weeks or months to get it to go. Well, it worked in a few hours, almost immediately—to our complete surprise. So we all went out and got silly drinking beer. We were in an ecstasy—but we were drunk long before we had any taste of beer.

How does that compare with putting together the data that tell you whether there is or isn't a core in the proton?

It depends on how it comes. If you've finished the long business of putting together lots of data, then, as a picture gradually emerges, you do get a certain pleasure. But the real kicks come, of course, when you have the more typical creative experience. When you've filled yourself with a particular problem, and—you know—you have a great desire to have some clarity in it. You go through this long, hard period of filling yourself up with as much information as you can. You just sort of feel it all rumbling around inside of you, not particularly at a conscious level. Then—it can happen at any time—you begin to feel a solution, a resolution, bubbling up to your consciousness. At the same time you begin to get very excited, tremendously elated—pervaded by a fantastic sense of joy.

You can't wait to tell somebody about it, to hear what it is that you're going to say to him, or to write it down and read what it is you're going to write. All of these go through your mind at the same moment. It may last for twelve hours or just two hours or a few minutes; but for the time you're really swinging. Those are the great moments.

There can be a lot of self-delusion in all this. All too often there is the morning after when you realize that it was all wrong. But the pleasure is there in any case. Those moments certainly help you along.

Are there two or three identifiable moments of this sort in your own career that you look back to and think, Boy, that was a nice one!?

I can certainly remember one. It was during the war. Somebody came over from England—it was Simon, from Oxford—and he visited Princeton, where I was an instructor. I was working at the time with Fermi on his atomic reactor

A problem to which Wilson has long devoted himself concerns the internal structure of the proton, the nucleus of hydrogen: Is it a uniform smear of matter and charge or is most of it lumped in a "core" at the center?

Now (1966) he thinks it looks like this:

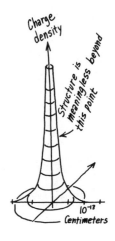

Cross section is the target area a uranium nucleus presents to an oncoming neutron—the larger the cross section for fission, the easier to make a bomb.

Remember, U-235 is the fissionable species of uranium, but it's also the rare sort; it has to be separated from the plentiful U-238.

project. He was at Columbia, but I was using the Princeton cyclotron. Anyway, Simon said that the values of the cross sections of uranium which had been assumed by us in the United States and which indicated that atomic bombs were completely out of the question, were quite wrong. Instead he presented new results of measurements, which subsequently also proved to be wrong—ironically enough. Nevertheless, his numbers indicated that if you could just get a few grams of uranium-235, separated uranium-235, then you could make a bomb.

This must have been very early in the atom-bomb project.

It was late 1941—right in the worst moments of the war. The time of Pearl Harbor. The Battle of Britain was just over, but things were still at a very low point. If one could make a bomb, that would be the salvation of the world, not the damnation of it.

So with this idea and in that desperate situation, I thought, My God! I just have to learn how to separate isotopes! I thought long and hard—intensely for a number of days. My thoughts turned to the electrical methods. I can still remember vividly the clear cold air and the experience of walking through it and thinking, By God, it's going to come. And come it did. I was conscious that the idea was there within me before it finally revealed itself to me. That idea subsequently became known as the Isotron.

Ion is an atom that has been stripped of one of its electrons; an electrically charged atom.

Just what was this Isotron?

It was a method of separating isotopes, by the use of electric fields. It came to me how to make an ion source that would produce a big beam of uranium ions, then how to bunch the uranium-235 ions separately from the 238, and then how to deflect the two kinds of bunches off into different cans. It all came out just as revelation and in a complete and fairly final form.

I became extremely excited, and, as I walked along, my ego became all involved. I felt, I, a young man of about twenty-five, would almost personally win the war. In a few months, if we worked hard, we at Princeton could test this thing, we could get a few grams of U-235, and then we would make a bomb and stop the war. And we could have. It *was* possible—had the neutron cross sections worked to be larger, as the British thought, it *could* have happened.

With that fantastic feeling that I'd had, I remember working like a demon and, with the full help of Harry Smyth, assembling a group of very good young people, who tried awfully hard to make that scheme work. We almost did. Within a month we made it work in a prototype for small currents, then we ran into horrible difficulties—space charge I think it was. It just didn't work.

Space charge has nothing to do with outer space. It just means that so many electrical charges are crowded into a small space that their mutual repulsion causes trouble.

A failure!

Yes, a failure, but that didn't take away from the thrill of creativity, and the strong identification of oneself. Through it I had become involved suddenly with all humanity. It's a peculiar way of thinking about yourself and the rest of the world—that you're just going to change everything around. I don't think I've ever recovered from that experience. It changed my whole personality. I never recovered from that moment of delusion.

How do you carry yourself out of the period of discouragement that must follow on finding that it doesn't work—or don't you have that?

No, that's much later. Because the principle of the Isotron was all right, I wasn't too disappointed; that is one of the nice things in life. I think the disappointments don't cancel out the moments of elation. The intensity of the elation lifts you far out of yourself—the disappointment is a more normal reaction—one you're quite accustomed to. In this business of creativity, it's pretty much all pleasure. But there's an aspect of terror too in these moments of creativity. You must come pretty close to—can I call it the life force? Being shaken out from your normal experience enhances your awareness of mortality.

Do you think there's a qualitative difference between this scientific creativity and the more familiar artistic creativity?

No, I don't. I would guess that they're identical. When I am doing physics, as I said earlier, I don't think of it as science with a capital S. I am only conscious of myself as a man doing what I am doing in a manner nowise different from that when I do other things than physics. I don't like that connotation, I wish we weren't known as scientists. I

Wilson was first president of the Federation of Atomic Scientists, which fought for civilian control of atomic energy in 1945-6.

think of myself only as a person working in a personal manner. I'm sure if I could make a good poem, I would experience the same feelings.

For example, I dabble in politics. When I've figured out some political move, I've had that same pleasure of creativity. I don't see a difference in my thinking or feeling; it's only the results that are different.

I think there's something universal about the experience of something coming from your subconscious almost fully formed. It's like throwing up when you're sick. You know it's going to happen long before it does, and when it does happen there's a satisfaction—almost a pleasure. Creating is a pleasure, just fantastic fun. But I think this is something that has basically to do with people, not physics.

What of the perhaps lesser pleasure of the one who merely contemplates it—who reads the poem rather than writes it.

After all, we get all kinds of satisfactions. Certainly we all have this pleasure, if only secondhand. For example, reading some kinds of mathematics—I get pleasure out of that. When the Russians put a satellite in orbit—that gave me a lot of satisfaction, a real kick. Or when someone paints a picture and I see it—I'm delighted. Or I read a new book or go to a play. You get a pleasure, which is not only the joy of reading, or looking, or listening, but there is the feeling of identifying yourself as a man. What men have done has raised the stature of all of us. You get a tremendous satisfaction of identification as a man, as people.

If I feel that I personally have done something, then that gives me the most pleasure. After all, I'm a particular man, one I'm particularly interested in, and I do like to have my ego boosted by doing things. Yet I identify not only with myself, but with other men, with Man. Whenever any man does anything, in the past, or anywhere, or in any country, that makes me feel better, because I am a man, a member of the human race.

I feel larger and better. It makes me feel more complete— less a stone.

Charles H. Townes

*A*s he tells it, it was very early on a Sunday morning while
on a business trip in Washington. He had awakened at 5:30
and, finding himself unable to go back to sleep, left his hotel
room for a morning walk along the rain-damp streets. It was
while he was sitting on a bench in Franklin Park that the idea
came to him—the idea for a new way of amplifying radio
waves that has since been shown to have great practical importance.

There is a matter-of-fact tone in his voice when Charles
Townes describes that predawn experience in Washington
in 1951. But he is a physicist, and to a physicist there is
nothing particularly surprising or novel about a new idea—
physics, after all, is a creative enterprise, and ideas are a
physicist's stock in trade. As it happened, however, this idea
proved to be an unusually rich source of new technology. It
has already spawned a number of new electronic devices,
from an extremely sensitive amplifier that allows astronomers
to "listen in" on the feeble radio waves that come to us from
the stars, to a source of light intense enough to burn through
a steel plate. The devices are called masers (or sometimes
lasers, if the principles are being applied to a light source).
Townes's idea, and his subsequent research, won him the
Nobel prize in physics for 1964.

His matter-of-fact tone also reflects his appreciation that
such ideas are not the spontaneous act of creation they ap-

*pear to be, but are a synthesis of facts, ideas, observations,
both related and unrelated, collected over many years. In
fact, the sources in this instance are not too difficult to trace.
For the three years prior to 1951, Townes had been professor of physics at Columbia University where he had been
studying the way materials behave when exposed to high-
frequency radio waves. In connection with these studies, he
had also been interested in finding ways to generate radio
waves of higher and higher frequency. The maser, being a
device that uses a material's response to radio waves to
amplify extremely high frequencies, is a natural combination
of these interests (or so it seems in retrospect).*

*Undoubtedly, Townes could also point to other sources
for the inspiration. In all probability, the idea owes something to his earlier days at Bell Telephone Laboratories,
where he first learned to apply his training in physics to the
solution of practical problems. It may even owe something
to his long interest in music (he studied music and voice for
a time while a professor at Columbia), or to his earlier training in languages (his first degree was in modern languages
and he still maintains a working knowledge of four languages). There is also his natural inquisitiveness, his yearn-
ing to explore and to understand. It was this explorer's
instinct, probably, that prompted him to climb the Matter-
horn once while on a trip to Europe; and the story is told
that when he first took the teaching position at Columbia, he
deliberately moved from one part of New York City to
another every three months better to explore the city.*

*Today, Townes spends much of his time doing research in
his new position as Institute Professor at Massachusetts Institute of Technology. When we interviewed him in 1964,
however, he was dividing his time between research and
administration as Provost of MIT, a position that put him in
charge of all the teaching and research done at the Institute—
everything, in fact, except the Institute's financial matters
and its capital equipment.*

*Whether seated behind his desk (as we found him) or
standing before an assembly of his fellow physicists (as we
have often seen him), he talks calmly and deliberately with
just the slightest trace of a Southern accent to betray his*

North Carolina origins. But there is a special enthusiasm in his voice when he speaks of his research, and it is this prevailing interest that caused us to begin our interview by asking him:

You've done research in industry and in universities and in circumstances where you've had to split your time with administrative work. How do you see the differences? Which have you liked most?

I have tried my hand at a variety of things, all right, but what I enjoy most is fundamental research, teaching, and university life. When I finished school in 1939, a very attractive offer and prospect took me to the Bell Labs. This was an amazing experience to me; suddenly I was being *paid* to do research. I could do just what I had wanted to do in a pleasant environment, with good equipment and stimulating associates and some money in my pocket. It seemed almost sinful. Of course one gets accustomed to such luxuries.

All that was what drew you into applied research?

No, the idea was that I was to settle down and do some physics. But then the war came and I was immediately assigned to the task of developing radar bombing. It was just an idea at that time, but it was terribly important—to bomb through clouds and at night. Dean Wooldridge and I went to work, and for about five years I was very busy learning electronics, and designing analog computers and radar systems.

How did you feel about that?

This wasn't the kind of work I would have chosen in peacetime. But it was still very important to my education because I became familiar with electronic techniques. Many physicists benefited from this same type of war experience; after the war they were familiar with electronics.

Has that had an effect on physics?

I think it's had a very important influence. Immediately after the war a number of specific things came out of that contact between electronics and physics. Of course it also affected electronics considerably, because physicists brought certain new approaches. Microwaves were developed to a high state during that period.

The transistor, tape recorder, computer, and, to some extent, television have all been developed since the war.

59

So you were away from fundamental work for most of five years.

I managed to find a little bit of extra time during that period. I got interested in trying to understand the observations Jansky had made on radio noise from the galaxy. I decided this was a good problem to start thinking about, and worked out the so-called free-free electron transitions which produce certain types of radio-astronomical noise.

He is speaking here of the beginnings of radio astronomy, in which the astronomer gathers and examines the radio waves that originate in the stars.

Something quite separate from your regular work.

Yes, but the radar experience itself got me interested in the possibility of microwave spectroscopy.

The two are related in the first instance because microwave spectroscopy uses radar-like radio waves to examine the structure of materials.

What was the connection?

We were seeking better radar resolution, and hence went from 10-cm microwaves to 3 cm. And after that, there was a push to go down to about 1 cm. I thought at the time that we would get into trouble because of absorption of the radio waves in water vapor. The decision was to go ahead anyhow, but as a result of looking into it, I realized that this kind of absorption provided the basis for a very high resolution spectroscopy which could examine the structure of molecules in great detail. At the same time the spectroscopy would be useful to technology, because the interaction between waves and molecules, particularly at the shorter wavelengths, was bound to be more and more important in engineering. But my primary interest was in fundamental work, and I hoped to get at this as soon as I could get through designing radar bombing systems.

Absorption
lines, the
narrower,
the better

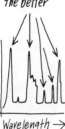

Wavelength →

And did you?

I managed to get started four or five months after the war stopped. I had worked out a theory which showed that, as one decreases the vapor pressure, the intensity of the absorption lines should not decrease, but the lines should become exceedingly narrow. This was exciting because it meant one could do very precise work on molecular structure. It took only about three months to verify this, after I got started. And I persuaded Bell Labs that the research effort was sensible for them because of the possible eventual payoff in engineering electronic circuit elements involving interaction between molecules and atoms.

Were they hard to convince?

I had to work at it a little, but I wouldn't say it was any harder than normal. I had to write up a memorandum. I think Bell Labs was an excellent place for this type of work, and one can see in my experience there the importance of the interplay between the applied work and the fundamental work—without the techniques and components developed during the war we wouldn't have been able to get started.

Do you conclude that—at this time anyway—an industrial laboratory was the best place for this sort of fundamental work?

As I got farther into the fundamental work, I found that I was interacting more with university physicists than with the Bell Lab physicists. So, when I got an attractive offer from Columbia University, I went there. The center of interest there coincided a little more closely with my own center of interest.

And that took you well away from applied work?

Actually, no. After about 1948, when I went to the university, the backlog of wartime techniques was beginning to run out. I felt the need for still shorter wavelengths—generated coherently by oscillators. So from time to time I tried to think of ways one might generate shorter and shorter waves, by harmonic generation and new types of tubes and so forth. This got me back into applied work—but for the purpose of producing tools for basic research. In this struggle to find new ways to produce shorter waves, eventually I hit on the idea of the maser. You see the interplay. Shortly after, I picked up the thread of my original interest in radio astronomy—the Jansky radiation—because the maser amplifier was an enormously valuable tool for radio astronomy, allowing one to detect weaker signals. So I built some amplifiers. We were also busy on the optical maser. But about this time I was caught by Washington. This was 1959.

Shorter Waves

That was when you became vice president and director of research of the Institute for Defense Analyses. Did you welcome administrative responsibility?

I had never objected particularly to administrative work, but I was interested more in teaching and in research. Yet

I felt strongly that we were in perilous times, and I agreed to take a two-year term—with the proviso that I could maintain one day a week to continue to do research and work with students at Columbia.

How did you like it?

I considered the Washington job hard work. It was not a pleasure in the way teaching or research was. It was very instructive and interesting, but not something I would want to do as a lifework. I was looking forward to going back to Columbia and to giving up all administration, when I was propositioned by MIT to come here to do administrative work on a much more permanent basis.

And yet you took the assignment. Why?

Because MIT is a very challenging institution and one where administrative work by a scientifically trained person makes sense, I think, and can be useful in a unique way. MIT is changing so rapidly, its impact on science and technology is so important, that I find administrative work here enjoyable. I'm willing to give up the research time.

What is your work as provost like?

In this institution, the provost is approximately a vice president in charge of academic affairs. I am concerned with the teaching and research program of the institute, and I report to the president. Financing and buildings are not my direct concern, although there's very little at the institute that doesn't eventually revolve around teaching and research. I try to help make decisions on what should be done and to help see that things get done. This means talking with faculty members at great length, attending committee meetings, discussions with the deans, the president. . . .

Do you teach any courses?

I'm only involved in a seminar, and I give an occasional lecture. I do supervise some undergraduate and graduate student theses and work with a few postdoctoral colleagues.

How has all of this affected your own research?

It has obviously been bad for it. It's difficult to do successful research on a part-time basis. On the other hand, I have built up a certain backlog which I can capitalize on. . . .

Backlog?

Of knowledgeability, ideas, skills which I can use with some success in a part-time way. And there are lots of exciting things to be done in my field. So I would hate to stay out of it. I recognize that I'm only limping along, but it's still fun.

There has been a lot of part-time research since the war. Has that caused much loss?

In one sense, yes. On the other hand, administration is terribly important to the success of other people, and of course, in a university, to the training of future leaders, teachers and research men. I have no doubt that in many cases it's a sensible career for a scientist. But it does detract from his direct and personal contribution.

In proportion to the time he spends away?

I think research effectiveness goes up more than linearly with the time available.

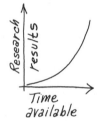

So a half-time researcher gets less than half-time results?

Usually, yes. But you have to add in the time one spends in odd moments while dressing in the morning or while driving to work, or at lunch. The effectiveness of a scientist depends a lot on how he spends these moments.

It was during one of those moments that the idea of the maser came to you, wasn't it?

Yes, it was. I think this is typical of science, engineering, or most creative work. In this way I still put in a good deal more research time than would meet the eye.

How much actually would meet the eye?

I suppose on the order of a day per week.

When you are in the middle of research, do you dream a lot about your problem?

I don't dream, but I don't sleep as much. If I'm busy with a very interesting problem, I'm likely to work on it moderately late at night, and then I'll wake up early in the morning and start thinking about it. Sometimes I get up at 4:30 or 5:00; sometimes it pays off, sometimes it doesn't.

Much of your own research nowadays seems to take the form of suggestions to many other people. Your publications seem less concerned with specific results, more with suggestions, speculations . . .

I know what you mean. There was a time when I felt it was rather poor taste simply to publish a suggestion. If the idea is good you ought to work it out thoroughly and then publish. In the case of the maser, I was active in the laboratory, and we went ahead and made a working system before publishing anything. But when I went to Washington, I didn't have time to work out ideas—which I thought might be good or interesting to other people—so I felt it was sensible to discuss them in the open literature, where they could be helpful to someone else even though they had not been experimentally investigated. The same thing is somewhat true now. Of course, when one has students or associates, one can try to persuade some of them that an idea is good, and this is one way an individual can be crucial in making a powerful attack in a large field. I have always talked quite freely about my ideas. If I have enough resources, I or my close associates work on them; otherwise it's fun to see other people make progress on them.

On the matter of resources—how does the university situation compare with the industrial laboratory?

In universities the resources in money are not as good, and I think universities are going to have to change this if they are to stay in the forefront of some areas. But the universities are strong on people. In a sense the government and industry labs have to compensate for that with money and equipment.

Strong on people? I should think the money factor would weight the scales the other way.

Yes—if you need large numbers of people in a tight organization. For a specific goal, industry can usually do better. But in terms of alert creative minds of the highest order, you find resources in the large universities somewhat better. It's the influx of young people, many of whom are very good. Only some of them stay permanently, but they all stay for a while. They don't have much to live on, but they frequently work hard and are in a period of their life when they are alert and eager to work.

Early in your career, you did a lot of nuts-and-bolts work, and it seems to have helped you. Would it be a good thing if more researchers were forced into that kind of work for a time?

I would hesitate to talk about forcing people to do things. Engineering design did give me experience with equipment and an insight into what kinds of things are important in practical applications. But I think people accumulate experience in whatever they do; some of them are wise and lucky in the combinations they make. But you never know. They might have done even better with something different.

What sort of research do you find yourself working on in your present circumstances? You have a relativity experiment under way?

Yes. This is one I proposed some time ago and now we are carrying it out. It's a fundamental experiment which takes precision. I think it can be done efficiently by continuing to work at it over some period of time.

What is really involved here?

It can be thought of as a test of special relativity. For a thorough test of the nature of space and of the effect on it of velocity, one needs to measure three things: how time changes due to motion, how distance changes along the direction of the motion, and how distance changes perpendicular to the direction of motion. Those three things provide a check on the Einstein-Lorentz equations.

These simple but important equations show that the length of a rapidly moving object shortens in the direction of movement and that a rapidly moving clock runs more slowly—in both cases as seen by an observer not moving with the object.

Now you have been using masers in these experiments because of their very pure output—because the purity of their output allows you to detect what happens to the output when the maser moves.

Yes. A while back I measured the change in time in IBM's Watson Laboratory at Columbia, using the ammonia maser as a clock. That's completed to good accuracy. The one we are working on now measures the difference between the

The maser here is acting as a highly precise clock. The experiment will determine if the clock ticks very slightly faster or slower when it changes its direction of motion.

direction parallel to the velocity and the direction perpendicular to it. This is what the Michelson-Morley experiment really measured.

That is, you are trying to detect a change in frequency resulting from a change in the distance between the end mirrors of an optical maser as it is rotated?

Yes, the way the lengths change due to some "absolute" velocity. I have in mind a third experiment and it will use optical masers too. The third one will allow us to compare time and length—or, if you like, it will allow us to measure the absolute change in a single length rather than comparing two of them.

The experiment will monitor a moving clock and a moving yardstick to see if they change when they move.

How will you do that?

One needs two optical masers, one of which has a frequency determined primarily by an atomic line, the other a frequency determined primarily by the separation between two mirrors. Most optical masers have their frequency determined by the length, but it is possible now to design one whose frequency will depend primarily on the atomic frequency. If you put them both on the platform and compare frequencies, you can compare the effect of velocity on time with the effect of velocity on length.

This is a fairly leisurely long-term program of research.

Professor Javan and I are doing the experiment together, and I expect it to last several years. But there are many other interesting facets to the program. And there are other things we're doing that are shorter term. I'm quite interested right now in what might be called phonon masers. This is generation of intense sound waves of high frequency, up into the infrared frequencies. It involves an understanding of the interaction between light waves and sound waves and molecular vibrations in matter. I'm working more intensively on this at the moment than on the relativity experiment.

One million million cycles per second.

For a part-time researcher, how do the long-term and the short-term projects compare?

I suppose the short-term things are a little harder. On the long-term things you can take your time, work on it when you have a week's vacation—or put it off. Short-term things need to be worked on more intensively.

Abdus Salam

*H*ere and there among the many men who are concerned
about the dreadful dilemmas facing the underdeveloped parts
of the world are a few who speak with special authority.
They are products of the unindustrialized world, they speak
for it, but they have also excelled at the West's own game of
physical science.

Abdus Salam is one of these men.

From the viewpoint of the part of the world which is
struggling to industrialize, Salam appears as a thirty-nine-
year-old Pakistani. He is a graduate of Punjab University in
India and has taught at Lahore University in Pakistan. He
is a Moslem and is quite likely to wind up a speech or public
paper with a quotation from the Koran. He is the science
adviser to the President of Pakistan.

In Western eyes, Salam is an important theoretical physicist. He has been associated with two of the world's most
distinguished scientific organizations—as a member of the
Institute for Advanced Study in Princeton, New Jersey and
a fellow of the Royal Society in Britain. At the time of his
admission to the Royal Society, he was its youngest fellow.
He is professor of theoretical physics at London University's
Imperial College of Science and Technology, the nearest
thing there is to a British equivalent of the Massachusetts
Institute of Technology.

To a scientist, Salam is one of the architects of the octet
model of physical reality. Like Wilson (who is interviewed
on page 46) and Weisskopf (page 87), he is concerned
with the question of what matter really is, at the most basic
level. He is a theorist who does not share Wilson's concern
with experiments; and, as a theorist, he is less traditional in
his views than Weisskopf. The problem all of these people
face at the moment is that when atoms of matter are broken
up in the extremely energetic collisions now possible, dozens
and dozens of different sorts of fragments or traces of fragments appear—with no obvious indication which ones are

Abdus Salam

fundamental, or whether any of them are, and which might be constructs or special states of the fundamental ones. Salam is among those who avoid the search for an especially fundamental particle and seek instead to introduce order among the confusing fragments of matter by assigning them to groups whose properties bear symmetrical relationships to one another, in ways quite obscure to a layman or indeed to most other scientists. At the time of this interview, in 1964, groups of eight were preferred, a situation referred to by its practitioners as the Eightfold Way.

Such problems are remote from the immediate needs of a country struggling to establish an industrial base, and as a Pakistani, Salam cannot avoid concern with such needs. One of the links between his two preoccupations is a new international institute of theoretical physics which the United Nations has set up in Trieste and which is intended to be of particular help to the underdeveloped countries. When we interviewed him, Salam had just been appointed to head the institute. But he was still in his college offices in London. His windows look out on the Victorian museums and university buildings which were built with the profits of Prince Albert's great fair, but Imperial College's physics building is in that sleek glass and concrete mode that says "science" anywhere in the world.

Salam has a warmly personal manner and made a point of getting acquainted for a few minutes over cups of rich Turkish coffee before the tape recorder was turned on. His speech conveys the impression of a man with a thorough command of a language not quite native to him. Any new subject brings a pause, almost a stammer, while he gathers his thoughts, then an enthusiastic rush of talk.

In our first question, we were probing for the link between Salam's humane and scientific concerns.

Is there any opposition between the character of an Asiatic society and the spirit of modern technology?

I would like to say no. Take Japan. But . . . let me limit myself for the moment to Pakistan. Now, Islamic society was highly technological in the eleventh and twelfth centuries, when the Arabs were strong in the sciences. Even later, in the Turkish days, the technology of the Turks was not poor compared to the emerging European states. After I have said this, of course, I have to admit there are a number of factors in the way life is organized which will have to change if Asia is to become technologically modern.

The question is how.

Up to a level technology is easy. After one starts living in a technological society, one develops a sort of contempt for the thing. It's not hard. It can be acquired easily once the mental attitude toward it changes. It's not like scholarship, which needs a long tradition to develop. Now take tradition: I keep telling my boys in Pakistan, "Do not despair if you do not produce, for example, mathematicians like Hilbert. You still might produce mathematicians like Raminujan." Raminujan was, if you like, relatively untutored. . . .

David Hilbert: German mathematician who laid logical foundations for non-Euclidean geometry and so for much of relativity and quantum theory.

S. Raminujan: largely self-taught Indian mathematician who made startling contributions to number theory.

Intuitive.

An intuitive person, one who could be produced anywhere at any time given a minimum of mathematical training. We could not produce overnight the solid tradition of scholarship which is typified by a Hilbert or a Weirstrass or a Gauss. Luckily, most technology does not need that long tradition of centuries; scholarship does.

But where did you yourself come from?

I come from Pakistan.

I mean—how did Pakistan produce someone like you?

I don't put myself in the category of Hilbert. My subject is theoretical physics, and theoretical physics at the moment is in an intuitive state. It's at a stage when we are sitting on the top of experiments. We are utterly impatient. We don't want to wait from one resonance to the next. As soon as three resonances turn up, we make a complete theory. That theory is upset tomorrow; we don't worry; we start all over again. If you make mistakes, you don't worry. That is the intuitive milieu in theoretical physics. You need different types of gifts; you need good imagination, intuition, perception, seeing a correlation between facts. You do not need that long tradition of erudite knowledge.

A resonance is a phenomenon observed in the aftermath of an atomic collision which might be a particle or might be an excited state of a particle—or might be neither.

This is a temporary condition, of course.

Probably, in another few years things will change; the basic laws will have been established; the thing will become classical, less exciting. We shall need duller people with deeper scholarship. This just illustrates my point. For in technology, you are not looking for depths of erudition. Apart from a few basic things, the faster technology changes, the better it is.

How do you make it start?

The most important step is breaking the mental barrier. You see, in my country, you preach a thing for five, six, seven years. You go on talking. Nobody listens. And suddenly you find . . . For example, take the civil service in Pakistan. The civil service was a legacy of the British Empire —men with liberal education, responsible for law and order and revenue collection. Sterling men, first rate administrators. But men with no appreciation of engineering, technology, or science. Not the men best suited for development. I personally do not wish the system to perpetuate. It is the sort of thing we have been crying out against for five, six, seven years. But in the last few years, suddenly we begin to find that a majority of the civil service men are sending their own sons to read physics, chemistry, mathematics, engineering . . . for research. You begin to wonder whether the barriers have suddenly begun to fall down.

What are the numbers like? How many young Pakistanis are studying technical subjects?

Let's take the PhD level. And let's concentrate on those being trained in the U.S.A. or the U.K. Through our Atomic Energy Commission, which does not merely function for the atomic energy program, we have succeeded in training, in the last three years, something like five hundred men at the PhD level. Now that's a tremendous number for a country like ours.

Will these men go back to Pakistan?

Oh yes. They are all employees of the Atomic Energy Commission. They will go back to Pakistan. We are trying to throw them into the universities and into other spheres. So I should say we are taking care of the chemists and physicists and partly of the engineers. We are not taking care of biologists—that's a tremendous loss.

Not even agriculturalists?

Not at the moment. We have no organization to do for them what, for example, the Atomic Energy Commission does.

That seems absurd.

It's absurd—absolutely absurd.

There seems to be an element of old-fashioned intellectual snobbery in the choice of an education.

You are quite right. As a rule it's the glamour subjects which get developed first. That seems to be the pattern all over the world. It's something to be deplored, in the abstract, but you can do nothing about it in a free society. First of all, the boys get more attracted toward the glamour subjects. Second, the government always puts up more money for them. But I do not despair. Once we get the government and the public used to the idea of spending on science, once that tradition develops, then that brings in the second round; the biological sciences, the prospecting sciences, the ones which are economically important get their share too.

And meanwhile, the thing is to encourage the glamour sciences?

I am afraid one can't help it. There is a private enterprise in scientific selection, if you wish. One good man turns up in a country, and he has a bee in his bonnet—he only knows physics, he only knows nuclear engineering. These are the only things he can put his heart into. His force and the energy go in this direction. What can you do? Stop him giving of his best? Ask him to go back and read medicine?

Often this seems to mean into theoretical physics.

I am glad you said that. For it brings me to the venture just now closest to my heart. Theoretical physics is one of the few subjects where even a country with very little tradition of science can produce reasonably good people. Japan is a prime example; it wasn't as developed when theoretical physics started there. The Japanese school of physics preceded the heights Japanese technology has reached now. The same thing is happening elsewhere. There are one or two very good physicists in Turkey—one I know is commuting between Columbia and Ankara. A couple of very good Koreans; people from Lebanon; people from India, of course a number of very good people. Some from Pakistan, some from South America—one or two outstanding men in Brazil, some very fine men in Argentina, and so forth. To my mind, these men are very much worth saving—not only because they are good scientists, but because they are the central . . .

What do you mean, saving?

Saving for good science, within their own countries. They have the following problem. Theoretical physics is a subject in which—there's a Biblical phrase which expresses it— in which speech is the important thing, not the written word. You have got to go around and talk with people and be in contact if only to learn that this particular mess of papers here on my desk is rubbish and these others are the important thing. You can scan the whole blasted lot and never find out what is important. But going to an active place for a day, you can easily get to know the significant from the non-significant. So a man living in isolation or with a small group has every chance of just deteriorating.

He has students but no teachers.

Yes. When I was teaching in Pakistan I had exactly the same problem. In Cambridge and at the Princeton Institute I had done reasonable work. But at Lahore, I found myself getting out of the subject altogether. So when I was invited to a position at Cambridge, the only choice was to migrate, to make myself an exile. Now if somebody could guarantee those people who are living out there that they can maintain continuity, guaranteed continuity to come out once a year, for three months let us say, and to work in a stimulating atmosphere, they will stay on. They will not have the cruel choice of either giving up physics or their countries.

This is what your new institute will try to do.

This is the project which is dearest to my heart at the moment. You see, in the world of theoretical physics there is the Western group, the United States and Europe, and there are the Eastern European physicists. No one recognizes that they exist, but there is also this third set of people. They may be as good in physics as some in the West or the East, but they have very unequal opportunities.

Do they also represent a different way of thinking?

I definitely believe that every cultural tradition of the human family brings to science a different way of thinking. In theoretical physics I see some of the great Chinese physicists bringing the subject their pragmatism. Or take another example I was recently discussing with Oppenheimer— though he did not necessarily agree. In mathematics or theoretical physics I do not know of any great Jewish complex variable men, or real analysts, but there are great Jewish set theorists, group theorists, and number theorists. This must come from the great Talmudic tradition. We speak now about symmetries in particle physics. When great Negro physicists arise, I wonder, in my lighter moments, if they will introduce the concept of "rhythm" and "harmony" in elementary particles.

So you see a third group in both an intellectual and a political sense.

I do not wish to labor this point about intellectual diversity. But it seemed to me it would be an excellent idea to have an international institute of theoretical physics and one with a special emphasis on this need of underdeveloped countries. The idea started out at the Rochester Conference of High Energy Physics in 1960 with a remark by Mr. McCone. He was then chairman of the U.S. Atomic Energy Commission, and in his after-dinner speech, he said that it was time now to think of international particle accelerators. A few of us who met after the speech were commenting on it and we said, this is very fine, but let's start at least with a U.N.-run institute for theoretical physics.

How was the idea received then?

It was opposed at first by the U.K. It was opposed by France, by Germany, by Australia, and by Canada. It had only a lukewarm support from the U.S.A. and the U.S.S.R. We had no friends whatsoever among the great countries. But the idea caught the imagination of the developing coun-

Robert Oppenheimer, wartime head of the Los Alamos atom bomb laboratory; later, head of the Institute for Advanced Study.

To a mathematician, analysis involves artful, more or less algebraic, calculation.

Set, group, and number theory call for careful reasoning about subtle logical entities.

tries—then nothing could stop it at the International Atomic Energy Agency meetings in Vienna.

But it wasn't set up at that time, was it?

It was decided that governments should make offers of sites for the institute, and then IAEA would choose the most suitable among those offered. A bad way of proceeding . . . there was no rational discussion of the ideal place. The governments that made offers were Denmark—a million dollars for a building and about $100,000 toward annual costs; Italy offered buildings and a quarter-million dollars for annual costs; we also had an offer from Pakistan and an offer from Turkey. The Italian offer was linked to Trieste. Financially it was the handsomest so the decision was that the institute will be set up in Trieste for four years, and after that the situation will be reviewed, and if necessary it may possibly go to a developing country.

Would that be desirable?

I would like to get the experience of seeing the thing run first. Trieste has some attractions. Somehow Eastern Europe is nearer; it's a semi-international city. Already we have had a tremendous demand for fellowships and senior positions from Eastern Europe—from the Poles, the Hungarians, the Rumanians, the Yugoslavs; also from South America; also from Asia. The institute will function at the beginning with a senior staff of about fifteen to twenty-five (mostly PhD) fellows. There is also a new type of fellowship we have instituted. We call it "associateship." The "associates"—several dozen of them—are men from developing countries with the privilege of coming to Trieste at periods of their own choosing from one month to four every year. We shall pay their stay and travel.

It does seem strangely remote from the practical world as a way to help a developing country.

Let us not confuse the full problem with a part of it. I did not suggest this was a panacea for all scientific deficiencies of the poorer countries. If I were an administrator in charge of science in Pakistan, I would certainly do my utmost to stress the basic agricultural and biological sciences. But let me make no bones about it. One needs, in addition, good scientists, first rate scientists in pure subjects too.

The important thing is to develop a scientific tradition, no matter what science it is?

It's not that. In a free society it is a matter of the example. You must not underestimate what a great physicist can do for the morale of young people in a developing country. They come flocking in to read sciences, rather than literature or law. And as another aspect of precept and example, I am pretty certain that this institute, if we can get the word spread that it is functioning the way we want it to, will breed a network of international institutes in other subjects—in practical subjects, like plant breeding or tropical medicine. Idealistically, it's the beginning of a U.N. university. So I don't despair.

A slow process. A generation.

You don't need a generation. In some ways things are easier in a poor country; they happen in four or five years. That's a generation for us. With us, the people you are trying to convince are few—paradoxically perhaps—but the pace is faster.

Peter J. W. Debye

*F*ew *living scientists have had as long or productive a career as Peter Debye. He was sixty-eight in 1952, when he was named professor emeritus at Cornell University, for most people a euphemistic term for retirement. Not so for Debye. Since then he's published almost as many technical papers as another scientist would in a fairly productive lifetime, and he's not through yet.*

His career breaks conveniently into halves: The first thirty years he spent in Europe, working primarily in what we would call physics (what he calls it we'll see later). He came to the U.S. in 1939, as did many other European scientists, and has been contributing importantly here to the physical aspects of chemistry, especially polymer chemistry, ever since.

Debye has affected the fundamentals of almost every field in which he's worked. One measure of this effect is the number of fundamental units and equations named in his honor. For example, his name is appended to the theory that explains how and why strong acids and alkalis conduct electricity, and another that explains why this conductivity changes with the frequency of the electric current. The mathematical product of the magnetic or electrical charges on a molecule times the distance between them is measured in "debyes." There is also a "Debye formula" for the amount of heat a standard amount of any particular substance will absorb or give off as it is heated or cooled one degree, and others to explain the way ultrasonic sound waves are scattered, the way x rays are "bent" as they pass through a crystal, and the way magnetic materials are demagnetized under constant energy conditions.

With such a list of fundamental contributions in diverse fields, it's no surprise that he has received just about every prize professional societies have to offer, including the 1936 Nobel prize for chemistry. In fact, you get the feeling that societies occasionally award him their highest medals more to increase their own prestige than his. Debye sometimes takes advantage of the award ceremony to present one of his latest papers or to puncture another scientist with whom he doesn't agree. He loves to bring up references to obscure literature when questioning a speaker, knowing full well that no one nowadays reads the literature of the nineteenth century, even when it's relevant. (Mendel's work on inheritance might not have lain so long neglected if Debye had been working in biology in the 1800's.)

Debye's office at Cornell is dominated by an enormous library table laden with stacks of journals and with reprints sent him by colleagues. One whole wall is lined with books and more journals, but the other side and the window sills are covered with violets and cactus, which he nurtures passionately. At home he grows more cactus, especially the varieties that survive outdoors. (Cornell is too busy tearing up the campus for new buildings to give him ground space near his office.) When we approached him, it was with some concern:

With a person like you it is difficult to know where to start, since you have been involved in so many different fields.

I don't feel that I have ever really changed fields. It's true that I started as an electrical engineer, and was taking courses in electrical engineering, but during that time I was really doing experimental physics with Max Wien, and trying to do some theoretical physics under Sommerfeld. Sommerfeld was professor of mechanics at Aachen, Germany, but he was really interested in mathematical physics and later more theoretical physics.

Max Wien (1864–1928), a famous German physicist, helped explain the nature of electrons. He was once counseled to become a pianist by Max Planck (the even more famous physicist who first formulated the idea of packages of energy called quanta), because everything there was to discover in physics had already been discovered.

What do you mean when you say theoretical?

I mean finding new things, not just taking the mathematical formulation and finding your fun making mathematics out of it. The problem is to make theories first, and then formulations. I have nothing against someone making a good mathematical formulation, but I don't like it much if he

Schrödinger devised an equation which is fundamental to quantum mechanics, that describes an atom's behavior in terms of its energies.

applies it too strictly. For instance, a lot of people now use Schrödinger's equations in quantum mechanics to calculate the characteristics of a single atom, but what are they trying to show? They are trying to show that in the end their equations are good. Well, we know that already—nothing new comes out of that. I think they're doing engineering with their equations, and this is not the thing we need most.

With this background, how did you get into polymer physics?

At the beginning of the Second World War, R. R. Williams of Bell Labs came to Cornell to try to interest me in

Polymers are substances with giant molecules, and include such things as rubber, plastics, and most biological materials (protein, gelatin, etc.).

the polymer field. I said to him, "I don't know anything about polymers, I never thought about them." And his answer was, "That is why we want you." They wanted to do something in a general way about polymers and about synthetic rubber. I had just come over from Germany, after having lost my old laboratory, the Physics Institute of the Kaiser Wilhelm Gesellschaft.

How did that break come about?

Well, I was a Dutch citizen at the time I was appointed director, and normally, if you took a professorship at a German university, you had to become a German citizen. Also, as a Dutch citizen, if you took a position in another state, you lost your Dutch citizenship. I didn't want to do either, so first I had to get permission from the Queen to accept the position. Secondly, I had to get the German Foreign Minister to give me a paper assuring me that I would not become a German citizen by accepting it. Then, when I had built it up, and we were just starting to get it going well, a man came to me and said he was very sorry, but I could not use my laboratory any more—I could stay at home, get all the money I wanted, write a book, but I could not enter my lab. Just about that time, I was invited here, to Cornell, to give the J. T. Baker lecture, so I came, just as a temporary thing. Of course, after I had been here a while, Germany declared war on Holland, and I could not go back. Then Cornell asked me to head the department of chemistry.

The chemistry department?

Yes. This is an old story—when I am in Europe, everybody says I am a physicist, when I am in the U.S. they say I am a chemist. Why? Because I once got a Nobel prize for chemistry. I never made much distinction between the two— I always say that what nuclear physicists do is really chemistry of the nucleus. In chemistry, of course, you had to remember a lot more, especially in organic chemistry. And you had to use your feelings—what does the carbon atom *want* to do? You had to remember all that. But it is more important to find the interrelationships between these various things, to get a picture of what is happening. I can only think in pictures. Physicists today don't want to think in pictures— there is a tradition of thinking the other way, in mathematics. And maybe they are right. Some things are natural for me, but that does not mean they are right for physics. Even in mathematics there are two kinds of people—one group talks geometrically, and others, as in number theory, talk algebraically. They both do good things, but right now, algebraic-thinking physicists are in the foreground.

Lord Todd talks about organic chemistry in his interview on page 100.

Debye seems to have a unique gift for visualizing situations in terms of models—pictures—that immediately makes omissions apparent and relationships obvious.

How would you contrast the state of theoretical physics with, say, that of solid-state physics?

I feel that there is not much new in solid state. What is new there is only in the field of electrons and conductivity. But most of the questions which are dealt with now were dealt with long ago. There is also the problem of language. We have two kinds of language in solid-state work, you see. One language uses phonons, while the other talks about vibrations and how they have to be quantized. Now these two things come out to the same result in the end, but most of the people now think about phonons, because they think it is more modern. In the real model, you don't have phonons floating around. If you want to calculate anything, you can't use individual phonons—you have to introduce waves anyway, or a spectrum of phonons at least. You cannot just take one phonon and another, and let them hit each other like billiard balls.

Considering that the whole transistor revolution is based on solid-state physics, this is a surprising statement, but typical of Debye's knowledge of the old literature.

Phonons are simply "packages" of vibration created by quantum mechanics to explain why high-frequency sound, like light, often acts as though it were composed of solid particles.

Are scientists today as personally and intensely involved in their work as they were in your younger days?

Perhaps not as personally, but where someone is convinced that something is right, then he tries hard to convince others.

But does the audience enter into this?

Oh, the audience, the audience—in a big audience there are never more than two or three who really think. In the early days it was absolutely the same. There are many more involved now, so you should have the probability of new things coming up faster, but I don't think there is any difference in the general way of thinking. There have always been a lot of "hangers-on," and they publish much too much, and much too fast. They think about something, and then they have to see it printed, and it comes out half-baked. They don't take time to let it ripen. In a way, it was different in the early days—there was not so much competition. There were far fewer people—although there were also fewer rewards. Now they publish because they want to get ahead, especially with the people who count publications instead of looking at their content. A friend of mine in the Rhineland said of such people, *"O Herr Gott, wie gross ist Dein Tierreich; die meisten fressen Heu."* (O dear God, how large is Thy animal kingdom; most of them eat hay.)

You were lucky enough to have tasted of finer fruit.

Well, I would not say lucky, but I've always had the sense to do only the things that I found were fun. I never wanted to do a thing because I had to do it. I have offended many people by that attitude, but I still feel it is the right one.

What makes a particular problem fun to you?

Let me give you an example. A man gave a paper at the Physical Society meeting in Kansas City recently, about the scattering of laser-light in a mixture of two liquids. In it he mentioned that the width of the central line gets narrower as you come nearer the critical temperature of the liquid. Now I didn't understand that at all, but this is always the start of something. When you have something that you cannot understand, even though you try, you get angry with yourself. Then you forget all about it because other things come up, and all at once you know it. In this case, I have since found out the reasons.

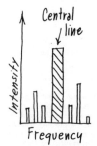

Lasers are new light sources that provide a uniquely pure light, light of nearly all one frequency. The "central line" is that frequency that would be the only one present if it were absolutely pure, but there is always some spreading. Debye worries here about why the spreading varies.

Have you ever run across a problem that really titillated you, and yet you never did solve it?

None that in the end I did not understand. Now that can have two explanations. One is that I only thought about simple problems and not about the very difficult ones.

What effect on graduate education do you see from current emphasis on using instrumentation and computers in contrast to your own graduate days?

I think calculating procedures are very nice, and very good for what I call "engineering work." I tell Henry Eyring, "When a man has no ideas at all, then he starts working with a computing machine." Now this may be a joke between Henry and me, but it is true to a certain extent; say someone is working with computers to determine the structure of a compound like lithium hydride. He works a long time, and does very complicated computations. Now during that time, he certainly cannot be doing anything else. And he should be able to do better things. In this sense, I don't like it. But you must remember, doing a PhD is not a preparation for what you are going to do in the end . . . all you really want to show is that in this special field, you can do *something*. And in this sense, *anything* is good enough for a PhD. It is just the same in industry. You should not ask for people who have already done in the university the things which they are going to apply in industry—this is the most nonsensical way of doing it. You should ask for people who have enough brain power that they at least have a feeling of how to handle a new problem. The specific nature of the problem is not important.

Henry Eyring's major field is physics of liquids; he's at the University of Utah.

Some observers have felt that today's student "hides" behind his equipment, and so never really comes to grips with his problem.

If so, this is a poor thesis and falls back on the professor, not on the candidate. There is another problem I see now, though. If a man wants to be ready with his thesis in, say, two years, I cannot give him a thing which is not absolutely clear in my own mind. One project might have a much bigger impact than another, if he got through with it, but I cannot guarantee him that he is going to have "the idea," if I don't have it myself. Oh, if a man has a lot of money, and he does the whole thing for the fun of it, then you can ask him to do it, but not the ordinary student today. To a certain extent, this too was different at the turn of the century, because then there were a lot more people who were financially independent who wanted to do things. Think of all the people like Lord Rayleigh, who only worked for fun. And there were a lot of graduate students who were independent in their means, and another three or four years did not matter.

Lord Rayleigh was one of the great "compleat" scientists of the nineteenth century. He contributed importantly in chemistry, physics, and acoustics.

Isn't this function now filled by postdoctoral fellowships?

No, it's not filled at all. The real sense of independence comes only with great wealth, or with a man who says, "It does not matter to me." I always compare such a man to a drunkard, who cannot keep away from alcohol. In the same way, this man wants to do things in chemistry or physics, regardless of whether there is much money or little money. It's also like going into a monastery. There are far fewer of this kind of people around today, because money has such a big hold on us here.

But you are not saying that things are terrible these days?

Not at all, they are very good in many respects. But there are some things which are not so good. For instance, there is really something back of it when people say there is a little too much money given to projects which are not really fundamental—where a man has to do a lot of things just because the money is available; if he were left alone under some kind of stipend, he might sit down and get much more important things done. It is relatively easy to get money, you see, but only for things where you can predict the outcome. And it is not easy to get money for a thing which is wild— where you cannot say, "This is going to have results."

Debye here decries the "grant system" for federal research funds, a system in which a man has to state fairly clearly what he hopes to discover before he gets his funds, and the granting agency must decide on the feasibility of the project. For a defense of the system, see the interview with Donald Hornig.

And yet this is where the future lies.

Yes, yes. And many of the things which do come out and are good are being done by a certain kind of faking. Oh yes, you do the things that are written down, but you don't do them the way they are written. You use the opportunity to do something different. If something comes out of it, well, everybody is happy.

*I am struck by the size of your library. How do you feel about
the literature situation?*

Well, I don't read all this literature you see. I learn about
most new things by talking with other people, and then I
look it up—not by just getting the new journal and going
through everything in it. But I want to have it here, because
when I want to know something I cannot even wait a day.
I want to put my hand on it right away. At the same time,
when I attack something new, I don't think it is a good
idea to sit down and read all the literature first. It is much
better to start the thing, and after you have started to get
some results, then look up the literature. You will find in
80 per cent of the cases that somebody else thought about
the same thing before and did it. There is nothing wrong
with that, because you learn much more that way. Also, you
may have attacked it from a little bit different point of view
and gotten other good things out of it. The fact that you
have duplicated work is not important. Nor is it really important who does the problem. If the problem is important,
then it is important that the problem, as such, is done.
Whether A or B does it really isn't crucial.

*Do you have the feeling that your younger colleagues haven't
read as much of the literature of physics as they did in your
time?*

That is true, but it is only because we university professors
are so bad we don't give them any time. When I was studying for engineering in Aachen, we had to do a lot of drawings and all the other things an engineer had to do (I designed
a 200 kW turbogenerator for my diploma), but still I had
time to go to the library and read. Now they don't have that
time. When I was head of the department here, there was one
hour free in the schedule, and I said, "Let the boys have
this one hour free, because then they can go to the library
and do something." One of the men said, "When they have
free time, they go out and drink beer." Now, that may be
true for many of them, but for some it will not be true. And
they should have that time. I have nothing against beer, but
I do have something against trying to fill all the time a
man spends in a university trying to put something in his
brains—as if this were so important. The amount is not important, it is the type of thing and the quality.

*Designing an electric-
power generator was
standard practice for
engineering and physics
majors in earlier days. No
university worthy of the
name has such a
requirement today.*

Along this line of quality, I've been amazed at the number of equations and units named after you. Just looking briefly I found seven.

Well, you really have to measure these things differently. You see, you have to take the number of things which are known to have happened to a man, and then divide them by the number of years he has been living. Then you can estimate the "density of discovery," and come up with a new unit of measurement.

Victor F. Weisskopf

S*ome of the simplest observations about nature require the most profound of explanations. In this interview one of the foremost physicists of our time seeks to explain why matter has characteristic properties—why, in a sense, sugar is always sweet and why all iron atoms are like all other iron atoms. These are questions so fundamental that one expects the only answer to be an axiom—an assertion that that's the way things are, and that is all there is to it. Yet in fact there is an explanation.*

The answer lies, Victor Weisskopf tells us, in quantum theory and, more particularly, in the idea of quantum states. At the atomic level, matter can be arranged only in certain precisely defined ways, just which ways are determined by the laws of quantum mechanics, the laws of motion at the atomic level that Schrödinger and Heisenberg introduced into physics in the mid-twenties.

It's ironic that many scientists, outside of physics, tend to associate quantum mechanics with uncertainty. They remember Heisenberg's assertion about the impossibility of knowing both the position and the velocity of an atomic particle—the uncertainty principle. They learn that the definite, planetlike electron orbits of Bohr's 1913 picture of the atom gave way to the spread-out electron clouds of Schrödinger's more refined 1926 model. So, not unreasonably, they think "uncertainty," "fuzziness," when they think of quantum

mechanics. Weisskopf knows better. Quantum mechanics, he teaches us, leads to definiteness and precision and predictability as much as it does to uncertainty.

In the interview, Weisskopf associates the definite states of an atom with the rungs of a ladder, a quantum ladder. He then guides us up the rungs of this ladder to states of higher energy, which correspond to progressively finer subdivisions of matter. We end contemplating the ultimate constitution of matter, a still unresolved problem of modern physics.

This man who steadies our figurative quantum ladder has ofttimes performed a similar function for his colleagues in physics. The outpouring of research papers in all fields in recent years has placed a particular premium on the scientist who can detect the trends amidst all that detail. Time and again Weisskopf has been the man who caps a meeting of specialists on some nuclear topic by summarizing the state of the field. That sort of contribution, which may escape public attention, is extremely important to the progress of science.

In 1961 Weisskopf took leave from his post as professor of physics at the Massachusetts Institute of Technology to serve as director-general of CERN, the European Organization for Nuclear Research founded in 1954. CERN is a remarkable institution; the nations of Europe have joined to support research into the ultimate constitution of matter. The result has been not only a flourishing of high-energy nuclear research on the Continent, but a reassertion of the European spirit.

Weisskopf brought to the direction of CERN not only a deep understanding of its mission in physics but a deft talent for handling its political problems. Some of this can be ascribed to the fact that Weisskopf is a European who gained American citizenship. Born in Vienna, educated in Göttingen, a postdoctoral student of Wolfgang Pauli's at the Technische Hochschule in Zurich, he came to the United States in 1937 in the wave of European scientists who fled totalitarianism. He headed one of the theoretical groups at Los Alamos Scientific Laboratory during World War II, working on the theoretical design of atomic bombs. He returned to MIT in January of 1966, leaving CERN at the threshold of a new era of investigation into the state of things at the topmost rungs yet reached on the quantum ladder.

Our interview with Weisskopf took place in his old office at MIT early in 1963, during one of his frequent trips back to the United States. There was a shabby couch in the office, an incongruous and even shabbier overstuffed easy chair, the inevitable blackboard, and bookcases laden with physics journals—the green-covered Physical Reviews, *the orange* Reviews of Modern Physics, *a dozen others. Weisskopf, a tall, genial man, sometimes sprawled in the easy chair, sometimes darted to the blackboard to amplify with pictures what could not be described with words alone. Through it all he was gentle—considerate of our ignorance, yet eager to have us share not only his knowledge but his sense of wonder.*

Quantum physics is very different from classical physics. How do you see the difference?

I like to say it in the following way: Before we got to quantum theory our understanding of nature did not correspond at all to one of the most obvious characters of nature, namely, the definite and specific properties of things. Steam is always steam, wherever you find it. Rock is always rock. Air is always air. This property of matter whereby it has characteristic properties seems to me one of the most obvious facts of nature. Yet classical physics has no way of accounting for it. In classical physics, the properties are all continuous.

Classical physics is pre-quantum physics, based on Newton's laws of motion and Maxwell's laws for electromagnetic radiation.

What do you mean by "continuous"?

There are no two classical systems that are really identical. Take the planetary systems of stars, of which we all know that there are billions. According to our present knowledge, you can be sure that no two of them are exactly identical. In some the sun will be a little larger, in some the planets would be a little larger, the orbits would be a little different. . . . Why? . . . Classical physics allows us an immense range of possibilities. The behavior of things depends on the initial conditions, which can have a continuum of values.

Now quantum theory changes this fundamentally, because things are quantized. No longer is "any" orbit possible, only certain ones, and all the orbits of a particular kind are the same. Thus in quantum theory it makes sense to say that two iron atoms are "exactly" alike because of the quantized orbits. So, an iron atom here and an iron atom in Soviet Russia are exactly alike. Quantum theory brought into physics this idea of identity.

I'm struck that you stressed the word "exactly," because for many people it's a certain inexactness that characterizes quantum physics. They remember the uncertainties.

I'm an old fighter against this interpretation of the uncertainty relation. Quantum theory brought in just that exactness.

Heisenberg's uncertainty principle states that it is impossible to measure precisely both the speed and position of a particle. One but not both.

The classical Greek approach was apparently based on sound intuition. The Greeks had a picture of discreteness in nature.

Yes, but the Greeks postulated the existence of atoms; they did not explain it. One cannot understand on the basis of classical physics how it is possible to have a mechanical system of one kind and a mechanical system of another kind and no mechanical system in between.

So that atoms, which were axiomatic to the Greeks, remained unexplained assumptions through the nineteenth century. You had experiments on atomic weights and had the kinetic theory of gases but that did not mean that atoms were understood.

Maxwell's kinetic theory of gases assumed that they were made up of free-moving colliding atoms.

They remained axiomatic up until 1913. If you look a little under the surface, you hit the same problem always. You mentioned gas theory. Now before quantum theory, people rightly looked at gases as colliding atoms. Yet how come such collisions don't change the nature of atoms? Atoms must have a structure, a mechanism, inside, and the collision must leave some change in it. Yet we know that it isn't so. The stability of the atom is something that is not understandable in classical theory.

Was this question posed at all before 1913?

Oh yes, in the famous Boltzmann paradox: Classical mechanics leads you to expect that, for a system of atoms in thermal equilibrium at a given temperature, the thermal energy should be shared equally among all the possible modes of motion. *All* modes. In a piece of heated material the electrons should run around faster, the protons should vibrate more rapidly within the nuclei, the parts of which the protons are made should vibrate more strongly within their bounds, and so forth. Thus the specific heat in any ordinary piece of matter should be extremely large. In actual fact

Ludwig Boltzmann: nineteenth-century theorist, worked on heat.

The Way of the Scientist

Specific heat is a measure of the amount of heat energy a particular piece of matter can absorb as it gets hotter.

the specific heat has just the size that can be accounted for by the external motions of the atoms alone. It was not understandable how the heat energy doesn't get into the atom and excite the internal degrees of freedom. This Boltzmann paradox came in 1890, well before quantum theory. There was no explanation.

Your implication is that there had already been advance beyond the Greek idea of the atom as the uncuttable one. Did the nineteenth-century physicists imagine there was structure within the atom?

Yes. The atom emits light, and after the discovery of the electromagnetic nature of light, it was clear there must have been some motion inside the atom that emits the light, so there must have been internal structure. And there was also a philosophical idea behind it; namely, the concept of an imaginary atom without internal structure doesn't make much sense. One must ask, "What's inside?" Now, one could have said it is solid, but even if it is solid, we know the solid has a structure.

So the philosophical question of what happens if you cut the atom remains.

To my mind, quantum theory for the first time indicates how one has to deal with problems of this kind. Quantum theory tells us that an atom is a non-divisible entity, *if* the energies applied to it are below a certain threshold. If the processes inflicted upon the atom are below a certain threshold, the atom is really indivisible, in the real sense of the word. It means that if atoms collide with energies less than the threshold, they bounce off completely unaffected, in exactly the same state that they were before. This is the new idea. That's the quantum idea.

However, when you are way above the threshold, the atoms go to pieces, and they behave like ordinary classical systems containing parts and particles. For example, at very high temperatures an atom is completely decomposed into its parts, the nucleus and the electrons. Consider a sodium atom and a neon atom. The former has eleven electrons, the latter ten. Below the threshold they are in their characteristic quantum states; very different. One is a metal, the other a gas. Above the threshold—at high temperatures—they are

92

both a gas of nuclei and electrons. It is what one calls a plasma. In this state there is not much difference between a sodium plasma and a neon.

And just as there are threshold energy levels for disrupting an atom, so there are levels above which the nuclei would be split.

True enough, there is also a threshold above which the nucleus goes to pieces. This threshold is much higher than the atomic threshold. The atomic thresholds are of the order of a few electron volts; the nuclear threshold is at much higher energies—a few million electron volts.

An electron volt is a unit of energy, a very small one. It is the energy acquired by a single electron moving through a potential difference of one volt.

I like to use the term "quantum ladder" for this. These are two steps of the ladder.

The quantum ladder has made it possible to discover the structure of the natural world step by step. When we investigate phenomena at energies characteristic of atoms we need not worry about the internal structure of their nuclei. And when we study the behavior of gases at normal temperatures and pressures we need not worry about details of the internal structure of the atoms that make up the gas. In that way the quantum ladder solves the Boltzmann paradox. The finer structure of matter does not participate in the exchange of energy until the average energy has reached that rung on the ladder.

Our whole experience in daily life is down low on your ladder, within the atomic level of the quantum ladder.

Yes. That or even lower. I started with the atom, but there are also steps farther down the quantum ladder, which are important for our life. Molecules, macromolecules, crystals. All life consists of macromolecules. The lower you go on the quantum ladder the more pronounced becomes the specificity of the structures: nucleus—atom—molecule—macromolecule—life.

How do these specific structures come about? This is a central point, it seems.

The quantum is an important precondition of the structuralization of nature. The particles fall into definite patterns, the quantum orbits of the nucleus, the quantum orbits of the atom, the quantum orbits of the molecule, the quantum orbits of the macromolecule. Our hereditary properties are nothing else than the quantum states of the parts of a nucleic-acid chain, the so-called DNA. In some way the recurrence every spring of a flower of a certain shape is an indirect expression of the existence of certain quantum orbits in the DNA molecule—a consequence of the identity and uniqueness of quantum orbits.

Is it an accident or is there some deeper reason for the spacing of rungs on the quantum ladder?

One of the consequences of the uncertainty principle is that the more energetic a particle is, the smaller the space it occupies.

Oh yes, there is a very good reason. It lies in the size-energy relation, that the smaller the system is, the higher the quantum energies are. For example, it is not an accident that the quantum energy of the outer electron shell in an atom is only a few volts, whereas the quantum energy of a nuclear system is a few million volts. It's because of their size.

But, there must be a reason that atoms and nuclei have that size.

Well, the reason the electron shell exists is the electric attraction between the nucleus and the electrons, and the reason that the nucleus exists as a unit is the nuclear force between nucleons, that is, protons and neutrons.

Up to 1930 we dealt with two forces in nature. They are very well known to us on a macroscopic level—namely gravity and electricity. Bohr had found in 1913 that the chemical forces—the forces within the atom—are electric. Only in 1930 when we first experimented on the inner structure of the nucleus did a new force come in, the nuclear force. It is the force that holds the protons and neutrons together when they form the atomic nucleus.

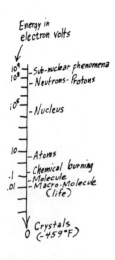

So the answer on the particular level of your question is, I think, the existence of these two force fields. Why these force fields? That is an unsolved question, and a question which I have a very definite feeling will be solved in our high-energy research.

There is a next step on the quantum ladder higher than the one which breaks the nucleus.

Yes, there is. Recently experiments with big accelerators have shown us that the proton and the neutron have a structure too. These particles can be changed into different states, they can absorb energy; in short, a world within the proton has been discovered. That is the next higher rung of the ladder.

What is the energy threshold for that step?

You can get at it only if you go to energies way beyond the temperatures and energies in the center of the stars. We don't know where the universe displays such energies . . . well, we have it in cosmic rays—very rare events. We have it at the target of our accelerator at CERN, and maybe the center of the galaxy is of such type. We just don't know.

With the 30-billion-volt machines you have just broken into a new highest level of energy. The immediate effect has been the discovery of thirty or forty particles. The new machines seem to cause more confusion than anything else.

I don't accept your premise. The statement that high-energy physics has found thirty or forty particles has brought this field into disrepute. But that reputation is wrong—for several reasons. One is that everybody counts the antiparticles as extra particles, which is as if you would double the number of animal species by calling the mirror image of an animal another animal. And there's more than that. I think it is wrong to call an excited state of a system a new system. It's as if we would say that the excited hydrogen atom is another atom. It's becoming clearer and clearer that many of these particles are nothing else than the excited states of other particles.

Which particles are fundamental and which are excited states?

For example, the sigma particle, the lambda particle, and the xi particle are all excited states of the proton. I would go so far as to say we have only two elementary particles, the baryon and the lepton, and these particles have different states, different configurations, just like the hydrogen atoms. The proton and neutron are two states of the baryon, just like the spin up and spin down of the electron in the ground state of hydrogen. The lambda, the xi, and the sigma are excited states. The systematics of all these new states is what I like to call the "third spectroscopy." We have atomic spectroscopy, the quantum levels of the atom, nuclear spec-

The CERN machine at Geneva, Switzerland, and the Brookhaven machine on Long Island are both in the 30-billion electron-volt range. The U.S. is now planning a machine of 200 to 300 billion electron volts. Compare the interview with Donald Hornig.

Many physicists would disagree with Weisskopf's position on this. He is presenting one of several conflicting interpretations of what the present multiplicity of particles really means.

Baryon: from Greek βαρυς, meaning heavy. Lepton: from Greek λεπτος, meaning small or weak.

troscopy, the quantum levels of the nucleus, and now we have the third spectroscopy, which is the quantum levels of the nucleon.

The leptons also occur in different forms: as electrons, as neutrinos, and as heavy electrons (sometimes called mu mesons).

Where do the pi mesons and the K mesons fit in your picture? Aren't they also particles?

I would rather not call them particles. They are field quanta. Just as the light quantum is a quantum of the electromagnetic field, so the pi meson and the K meson are quanta of the nuclear field.

What is a field?

Classical physics distinguishes particles of matter and the fields of force that act on them. In quantum theory, that distinction is lost, since a field of force takes on many of the properties of a particle.

Fields began as a way of expressing the force between particles. The attraction between two unlike electric charges can also be expressed in terms of the action of the field of one on the other. But the field is not just a mathematical fiction, it is as real as its particle sources, and we can speak of its energy, and so forth.

Now, every field has a quantum. When a field propagates in space, when it is emitted in form of radiation, it propagates in form of quanta. The very best known field quantum is the photon, the quantum of the electromagnetic field. The nuclear force seems to require two quanta—one is the pi meson and the other is the K meson. They both play an important role. The pi meson is responsible for the outer reaches of the nuclear field, and the K meson for the force at very close distances.

You're not troubled that there are two quanta for this field?

I'm troubled, but not as much as one might think. The field is just somewhat more complicated. The electric field falls off inversely with distance, it's just straight $1/r$; you see, the nuclear field is a complicated field, so no wonder two quanta. What is complicated is that the quanta carry isotopic spin and another quantum number which is called hypercharge or "strangeness."

Isotopic spin and strangeness are properties of subatomic particles akin to electric charge— except that they are not observable in the man-size world, as electric charge is.

It's not just as if you had the two quanta of that field, but also you have to adduce new quantum numbers.

Yes. These quantum numbers play an important role in

the "third spectroscopy" we mentioned before. The excited states of the baryon can be classified according to these new quantum numbers.

But the basic idea is the same as in the spectrum of excited states of any atom, say hydrogen. The ground state is of course the proton or the neutron—the neutron has a little more energy. Then there are several excited states—the names originally given them make no sense any more so we call them by their various quantum numbers.

Stable

Unstable

Metastable

There's a nice historical parallel, isn't there? Just as the early history of optical spectroscopy was marked by the naming of spectral lines according to their appearance, so the names of nuclear particles have grown with their experimental discovery.

Exactly . . . now there are also excited states which have a different strangeness quantum number. And they have names—the lambda, for example. But they have names only because of the fact that their different strangeness makes them metastable and they last long enough to be observed as an apparently different particle. It's like an atomic state which is metastable.

You get these extreme energies from CERN and Brookhaven accelerators at intensities that apparently do not exist in the universe otherwise. When you are doing physics of a sort that nature doesn't do, what are you doing?

I am deeply convinced that nature has such a variety that any process we find on earth will be of importance somewhere. And that's why I think that the experiments we are now doing on these highest rungs of the quantum ladder will have significance in one of those unsolved problems, such as the problem of the expansion of the universe, the creation of matter, or the fundamental structure of matter. It may be that the problems of the creation of the universe are connected.

You are now perhaps experimenting with conditions which, 20 billion years ago . . .

That is a matter of interpretation. As you know there are two views—which I would like to call two "religions." One is the Big Bang theory where the universe started billions of years ago with tremendous pressure and energies in a small volume, and the other is the Continuous Creation theory. I'm sure that the true answers to the questions would be neither one nor the other. But it is correct to think that if the Big Bang has something to do with reality, some of the early phases might have had to do with the latest rung on the quantum ladder. My religion probably is Continuous Creation religion—but I'm not sure you had better put that in.

You say "religion" to indicate a real difference between those parts of physics which have the authority of physical experi-

Both theories attempt to account for the observed continuing expansion of the universe.

Big Bang: Everything began 10 to 20 billion years ago, very small, and has been expanding ever since.

Continuous Creation: There is no beginning or end; galaxies get farther apart and the space between is filled by newly created matter.

ment and those parts that are extrapolating to conditions that in no sense we can duplicate.

Exactly. One must really draw a serious line there. Although I also believe that these speculations are the most exciting one can imagine. But they are really different from physics itself. Sometime, when we shall know more about these things, they might become true physics.

Readers who wish to know Weisskopf's thinking better might try his Knowledge and Wonder, *Doubleday, 1962.*

Is the line of progress inevitably toward the still higher and higher levels of energy; or does your ladder have a top rung?

A last quantum rung? I cannot tell. It is always the highest hope, maybe a hope only, of physicists that at the next step of the quantum ladder you will find the all-embracing principle. Heisenberg thought so. In every physicist there is an element of belief that you will sometime come to the recognition of some fundamental facts which close it, from which you can explain everything. I'm not so sure. It may be that nature is inexhaustible. But it might not be. How do we know?

You're saying there would be a last step if you could predict what would happen if you used a hundred times as much energy?

Yes. But in order to reach that state of affairs we must also have a Heisenberg or a Bohr of the future who gives us the theory that explains all phenomena in terms of what we know. Until we have that theory, we will never have a guarantee that there is not a new world coming up. We would have to build higher-energy accelerators to find out.

Earlier you said that atoms are philosophically unsatisfying because you can always ask what is within them. If physics is not inexhaustible, then at some point you will truly have elementary, non-divisible particles.

I wouldn't call it the elementary particle, it might be something else. A field, or even some new thing which is as far from the field as the field is from the particle, consequently something new, but that embraces the whole. What it will be we don't know—we are just at the beginning.

A theory which enjoys some favor in 1966 sees all the particles as describable in terms of each other, no one more "fundamental" than another. This bootstrap theory promises a closed, self-consistent description of matter . . . in another way.

Lord Todd

*L*ord Todd is like Olde England, and yet he is not, just as the University Chemical Laboratories at Cambridge which he heads are like and unlike the historical image. The buildings housing the laboratories are crisp and modern, Todd's offices more reminiscent of corporate Detroit than of the banks of the Cam. Even the books in their glass cases line up smartly, implying an ordered approach to life.

While Lord Todd has held his post at Cambridge since 1944, he has spent much of his time either away from his office or on other business in recent years. He was chairman of Britain's Advisory Council on Scientific Policy from 1952 to 1964; when Harold Wilson was elected Prime Minister, Todd was replaced by Sir Harrie Massey, who is interviewed elsewhere in this book. During the years from 1963 to 1965, he was also president of the International Union of Pure and Applied Chemistry.

In spite of his administrative work, he has managed to continue an impressive research program, which culminated in the Nobel prize for chemistry in 1957, with special reference to his pioneering work on nucleotides, those building blocks of DNA and RNA, which are fast becoming household words (almost).

Todd, a Scotsman originally from Glasgow, is a towering six feet four inches, powerful in appearance, friendly in demeanor. He speaks thoughtfully, yet spiritedly, in a voice whose amplitude matches his frame.

Chemistry divides sharply into two parts, organic and inorganic. Todd is an organic chemist, and we wanted to get an idea of how an organic chemist thinks, so we started right off with . . .

Lord Todd, just what is organic chemistry?

Well now, you've asked me something. Because organic chemistry is two things. At the beginning of the last century, chemistry was divided. The inorganic was to be the chemistry of the substances in the non-living world. Organic chemistry was defined by Berzelius as the chemistry of substances found in living matter. Between ourselves, at the time that meant

Jöns Berzelius, 1779–1848, famous Swedish chemist.

nothing more than that these substances were a bit funny, and it was convenient to separate them. It was discovered very soon that *all* the substances in living matter contain carbon, and you couldn't do very much about them unless you understood the chemistry of carbon. And the chemistry of carbon turned out to be such a multifarious and marvelous thing that after a bit people redefined organic chemistry as the chemistry of carbon compounds.

But why the separation?

One was beginning to appreciate, about then, in a dim sort of way, the constancy of proportions in a given inorganic material, that one composition meant one material—but this just didn't apply to these organic substances. It was obvious one was dealing with something complex and apparently quite different from what one deals with in copper sulfate, say.

John Dalton, another Britisher, published his law of definite proportions in 1808, from which came our concept of indivisible atoms, and molecules of definite combinations of multiples of these atoms.

What is it about carbon that causes it to have a chemistry all to itself?

The feature of carbon that differentiates it from all the other elements is, of course, its internal atomic structure; it has a valence of four in most of its compounds and it has an astonishing capacity for joining up with itself. There are compounds with hundreds of thousands of carbon atoms in them. You don't find atoms of other elements joined together in large numbers in chemical compounds.

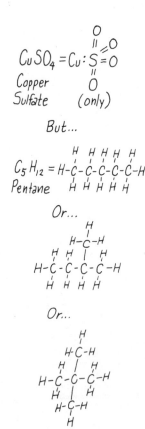

Not even the elements that share carbon's place on the periodic table, that have similar combining properties?

No. Silicon can do a bit of this, but not really. You can get two or three silicon atoms to join, but then you come to a stop. You can only make big silicon compounds by introducing carbon and oxygen. It's difficult to imagine any chemistry that could conceivably be like the carbon chemistry. No other element could give the complex systems we find in life.

How many organic compounds are known?

I don't know offhand, but certainly more than a million. Do you see that bookshelf, starting there and running right along? That is just part of our dictionary of compounds for

1930 to 1945. The complete *Beilstein Handbook* would cover the whole run of these shelves, and that simply contains the general facts on each organic compound, how to make it and some properties. After all . . . a carbon atom can bond to four other atoms . . . they can be carbon atoms, nitrogen, oxygen . . . or mixtures of these. Remember that that process can be repeated indefinitely, as far as we know. You take all the possibilities of that—from a practical point of view it's infinite.

A huge industry is built on that. Which came first—the industry or the science?

One of the great features—I would almost call it one of the glories—of organic chemistry is that it has grown up side by side with the industry. It was only between 1850 and 1860 that organic chemistry got its basic theory. It was only then that people realized that isomerism could be rationalized . . . that there were two or three different ways in which you could join, say, five carbon atoms . . . and that each of these arrangements would represent a distinct compound. In the course of studying that fact, by accident, substances were made that had a clear practical value. One example is the thing that Perkin did in 1856. He was trying to synthesize quinine by oxidizing a simple coal tar base. And he got a purple dye called mauveine. He realized this was something new, and he started to manufacture it.

On his own?

Yes; he started a company. A few years later, in Germany, Liebermann looked at the so-called Turkey red, the red dye which had been made from madder root. He wanted to see what was in it that gave the red color, so he isolated the red substance from it and showed it to be a compound we now know as alizarin. Then—to prove he was right—he did what the organic chemist always does. He made it in the laboratory. Artificially. In ten years the madder industry in Europe had disappeared.

It seems that synthesis has been a characteristic of the art from the beginning. But I'm curious about the rationale of the synthesis. When Liebermann was seeking Turkey red,

Beilstein, German chemist, began compiling his books of data on organic compounds in 1881. Since then, they run to dozens of volumes.

Isomers are compounds containing the same number and kind of atoms, but arranged differently, like the pentane on page 102.

Perkin was only a teen-aged student at the Royal College of Chemistry when he had his "accident," while doing some experiments at home during Easter vacation. With his father and brother, he formed a company to produce his dyes, got so rich that he "retired" at thirty-five to go back to pure research. This is the classic example of serendipity.

103

did he have a theory that said that such and such a molecule would look red?

No. What he did was just to isolate from the madder root the actual chemical compound which gave it a red color. Then he used the standard method of the organic chemist, which is to degrade the molecule of an unknown substance. In other words, he broke it up and looked at the bits, and then inferred from that what the structure of the original substance must have been. Then he set about in the laboratory to prepare something of that structure from simple materials. When he got it, it was identical with the stuff he had isolated from madder. This is one of the great satisfactions of the organic chemist, you see.

Great satisfactions?

To understand the differences between the way chemists and physicists think about the subject of certainty and levels, read the interview with Victor Weisskopf.

Unlike many scientists, in our field we can very often prove that we are right. This isn't a case of there being any doubt about it. You deduce that a certain compound has a certain structure, and you make that structure, unambiguously. Now if your product is identical in all respects with the substance you set out to investigate, you know that your structure is right. You may say that this isn't a very fundamental level of knowledge; the chemist doesn't bother about anything below the atomic or the molecular level. That's his base. But assuming his base, he knows that he's right. He can't be challenged. There's a peculiar satisfaction about finishing a piece of work and knowing the right answer. Not, as in so many sciences, saying, "Well, this looks as if it could be the right answer."

By now, I gather, the pursuit of that satisfaction has meant that, on the industrial side, you do have a theory to guide synthesis. Today, if an organic chemist wants a green dye, does he know how to put the molecules together to make green?

Yes. If you say to an industrial dyestuff expert, "I want a substance that is green and I want a substance that can dye wool directly," he can probably make you one. What I don't think he can do just yet is to say that the one he is going to make you will be fully satisfactory from a practical point of view. We know the kinds of groupings that give you color, and we know the kinds of molecules that are likely to dye wool direct; but there are features like the light-fastness and resistance to washing which aren't entirely predictable. He might have to make two or three variants on this dye to find the right one. But every year we are getting closer to being able to specify in advance that such and such a molecule will do the job.

These new powers—what new fields of research do they take you into?

To give you an example: I started with my people, just at the end of the war, to go into the so-called nucleotides, which led us to setting up the general structure for the nucleic acids. Now people had been working on this for a long time; but not many organic chemists had worked on it. Biochemists and biologists were working, and they couldn't make head or tail of it because it was essentially a chemical-structural problem. A great many of the findings that we used in setting up the structure of the nucleic acids had actually been in the literature for years. Now the reason organic chemists had totally neglected that field was that until about the time when we started, it had been virtually impossible to work with these compounds. Most of them are soluble in water rather than in organic solvents . . . they don't have melting points . . . from the older point of view their characteristics are fairly dubious. We realized that with the development of techniques like chromatography and certain new types of reagents, we were now able to handle compounds of this type; so we went in.

Nucleotides are the building blocks of the protein of living matter; nucleic acids are long strings of nucleotides, but not as long as most proteins. DNA and RNA are the most widely publicized nucleic acids today.

Organic solvents include things like alcohol, kerosene, gasoline, or glycerine.

Chromatography is a new analytical technique with which you can detect tiny amounts of substances in a complex mixture.

I'm surprised by such a gap in communication between two kinds of chemists—biochemists and organic chemists. Why weren't they reading your papers?

Of course, you understand that this division is much less now. But the reason is historical. In the latter part of the last century, partly under the spur of industrial development, the organic chemists largely ignored living matter. There is a famous statement made by a German chemist at that time: *"Tierchemie ist Schmierchemie."* Biochemistry is muck chemistry. Meanwhile, there were a few hardy spirits—the so-called physiological chemists—who struggled to look at things in plants and animals. And it was clear, whether chemists liked it or not, that eventually they would have to be concerned with these complex and difficult materials—things that don't crystallize, things we now know are macromolecular.

The physiological chemists, from whom the biochemists are descended, played around with these things, were scorned by the organic chemists, and incidentally developed a chip on the shoulder. Over the years they developed different types of training from the orthodox chemists. Biochemists did not have the strict chemical training which was absolutely essential if they were to make maximum progress in their own subject; and the organic chemist was getting that strict training, but the biological side was ignored. This is all fading away now, thank goodness.

But now, finally, the organic chemists are turning toward biochemical problems.

We've reached a point in organic chemistry today where our methods are so powerful that determining the structure of a non-macromolecular substance is a pretty straightforward operation. If you show me a chemical molecule, then, if you consider that it is worth the effort, I can almost certainly synthesize it. This means that from the point of view of progress in the pure science—as distinct from progress in the industrial science, where the production of new compounds is the lifeblood of the business—in the pure science we are at the end of the phase of pure structural work, in my opinion.

So where do you go next?

We are moving forward, I think, into the area of what I always call structure-and-function. We are moving much closer to biology. I think that in the future an organic chemist is going to be concerned more and more with trying to explain—in detail, in real chemical terms—what in fact does go on in living systems.

Macromolecules are simply molecules that go on and on, forming long strings that sometimes cross-link with each other to form networks. Proteins are macromolecules; so are plastics and rubber.

There is one area that presents a tremendous challenge. It hasn't yet, in general, been taken up. That's the challenge of the macromolecular substances. Organic chemistry has got to the point where you can take a sample of a small protein and tell what the structure is, in detail.

How small is a "small protein"?

Well, one with about thirty amino-acid residues in it. You can even make it in the laboratory. But the big proteins and the nucleic acids—these molecules have hundreds of units joined together, and a problem is presented to the organic chemist that he hasn't yet solved. Take the example of a nucleic acid. There is evidence to suggest that DNA has a molecular weight of 10 or 15 million, as compared with carbon itself, whose molecular weight is only 12.

A different sort of thing altogether.

Yes. One of the difficulties here is that in such a case the term "molecule" may be a sort of statistical term. You see, the organic chemist has always worked on the basis that if you say, "Here is alizarin," there is one and only one molecule concerned. Now if you get up to a thing where you determine that the molecular weight is about 15 million, it may in fact be a mixture of huge molecules with slightly varying sizes—maybe running from 13 million up to 17 million, all there in a bunch. It seems to me you need here a sort of statistical approach foreign to traditional chemistry.

You lose the sense of structure?

No. But the properties of these big molecules—or aggregates of molecules—the functions they perform, probably are determined to a considerable extent by their physical nature as well as their chemical structure. What the biophysicist calls structure is not what I would call structure. It's what I would call conformation—the way these things are oriented, the way the whole complex lies in space and is stuck together. In many cases the big molecules are held in these conformations by hydrogen bonding.

Hydrogen bonding?

Bonding between molecules—not within molecules but between the molecules—as a result of the loose links through hydrogen atoms; it's almost like a partial valence bonding between molecules. Now organic chemistry in general ignores hydrogen bonding. Of course, we recognize that it exists; but in all our degradative methods we begin after the hydrogen bonds are broken. They break apart whenever you put chemical reagents on them.

Amino acids are the small molecules from which nucleic acids and proteins are built. If they are present in adequate amounts in our food supplies, our bodies flourish.

Molecular weight is just a relative term a chemist uses to tell how much heavier his molecule is than one atom of hydrogen. Carbon is 12 times as heavy, oxygen 16, uranium 238, etc. Plastics may be 10,000 to 100,000.

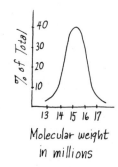

There are many kinds of "bonds" in chemistry. Some hold individual atoms together very tightly and are hard to break, others are much weaker, but still affect the properties of the bound atoms or molecules. Hydrogen bonds are the weakest of all, and since they occur in almost every compound, they are often ignored.

But that doesn't work with a molecule with a 15 million molecular weight?

Exactly. How are you going to know what you're finding? You probably know that the nucleic acids are made up, roughly, of four different monomers. The difference between individual nucleic acids is simply in the sequence in which these monomers are found in them. Add to this that you may have a statistical molecule; it may not be one molecule in the stuff you are looking at; your techniques may only be able to get you a mixture of closely related molecules. When you start your chemical degradation, with classical organic methods, what kind of an answer are you going to get? You are not going to get any answer at all.

Is it a hopeless problem to attack chemically?

Certainly not! But the big molecules are so similar that they are beyond the precision of our present techniques. So we must look for new techniques. This doesn't depress me. This has been happening all along in our science, though it may be that this is a bigger jump than we have ever had to make before. There's no doubt that we are moving into a new phase.

Will this new phase affect the industrial side of the science, too?

It has implications, of course. In the field of plastics and polymers one is coming up against the same problem. The demand is for the chemist in industry to produce materials that will have certain precise properties. And of course these will depend on subtle structural differences between the molecules of these big polymers. In a way the ultimate solution of the industrial problem and the ultimate solution of things like the nucleic acids are overlapping each other.

This suggests to me that one of the things you will have to do is gather a lot more data, take more measurements, like a physicist.

This is true. One of the striking features of chemistry during the last fifteen or twenty years has been the vast and rapid increase in the use of physical methods. We now look for data on a compound that we would never have dreamed of looking for twenty years ago. We'll have more and more of these physical tools, more and more data to collect, much more analysis.

So now the chemists, like the physicists, will be using big machines and hooking up experiments to computers and . . .

Oh yes, computers and things like that. But I don't know that they are likely to get to anything like the nuclear physicists and the enormously expensive machines they have. If a physicist sets out to examine the structure of matter and has to deal with processes that have no terrestrial analogues, he has to have energy—and energy is expensive. Now the chemist, perhaps particularly the organic chemist, is a somewhat earthbound creature. Things that are not terrestrial are not very significant, from his point of view. I don't mean the problems are not interesting, but in general I wouldn't expect the chemist to require very high energies. And if he doesn't require high energies, then I don't think it is going to cost an awful lot of money.

If you don't need energy, what do you need?

Clearly, we have got to develop a theoretical concept, one involving more and more statistical aspects. Just as physics had to go to statistical mechanics, we're going to have to start dealing with statistical molecules.

Living systems handle these problems remarkably well. What's going on inside us that you are not yet able to do?

I think people are inclined to attribute almost magical properties to things like enzymes in living cells, when the real truth of the matter is that we just do not fully understand what I am sure will ultimately prove to be the quite simple chemical mechanism of the systems involved. In almost all cases that I know, when one has really got down to it and really understands what is going on, nature is doing things that are quite simple. Of course, what we don't understand at the moment is the system of control in living matter. But I think we may get at that a bit more easily when we know in detail what is going on in the individual reactions.

Enzymes are the catalysts that allow the body cell to perform chemical reactions that chemical engineers can't do without strong chemicals and high temperatures and pressures.

This is a sort of faith on your part?

In our laboratory here, because of our interest in nucleic acid, we got interested in pushing ahead the organic chemistry of the phosphates and other derivatives of phosphoric acid. We found out things about the chemistry of phosphoric acid which make clear a number of things in nature that were quite mysterious before. Certain derivatives of phosphoric acid do quite simply, in the laboratory, things that seemed so mysterious in the living system. We were inclined to think that it was more complicated than it is. Nature, you know, is fundamentally a rather simple old lady. She doesn't do things in a complicated way when it is possible to do them in a simple way.

I gather you feel that when we understand these living systems we'll be able to use some of the chemical techniques in industrial processes; and then we'll have to transcend them.

In the few years since this interview, chemists have gotten closer to synthesizing life of some sort in a test tube, and to being able to modify the genetic material that determines inheritance. Lord Todd is worrying about the problems of who exercises this control, and to what purpose.

Oh yes. But of course if we get to the point where we understand living matter, there are a lot of serious problems that are going to face human beings. As a matter of fact, some of the major problems are not all that far around the corner. We use a lot of ink on the dangers of nuclear energy and nuclear weapons, but you must realize that the time may not be far off when we may be able deliberately to alter living systems. Now when you get to that point I'm afraid the problems for humanity may be very large indeed.

The scientists were not able to reach the politicians on the first use of the atom bomb. Do you think you will be able to . . . ?

I think there is a possibility. We talk about politicians who don't understand science, but there is no doubt at all that, in the last ten years or so, the politicians have been becoming much more aware of the implications of scientific advance. I think they are aware. They are certainly paying more attention to science than ever before.

Albert Szent-Gyorgyi

*A*fter the summer tourists depart, Woods Hole, Massachusetts, is a quiet place, populated by a few hundred year-
round residents and a few thousand sea gulls. A similar
exodus takes place from Woods Hole's two great scientific
institutions—the Marine Biological Laboratory and the
Oceanographic Institution. The 300-odd scientists who flood
MBL in June return to their full-time jobs, the college boys
who man the specimen-collecting boats go back to their
classrooms, the few secretaries and staff people lucky enough
to have summered there go back to the big city. The ram-
bling facility is left to Nobel-laureate Albert Szent-Gyorgyi
and his half-dozen or so full-time associates. Tucked away
in a rented group of rooms at MBL, these scientists comprise

the Institute for Muscle Research; its mainspring and director is the seventy-three-year-old Szent-Gyorgyi.

It's not a lonely life. Szent-Gyorgyi has research programs going all the time, takes short trips to make speeches and deliver papers at professional meetings, gets in an annual ten-day cruise in the Caribbean, and, of course, watches his beloved ocean and the sea gulls.

His concerns are not wholly scientific either; recently he has been writing letters far and wide on the subject of the propriety of our military actions in Vietnam. He has also recorded a disk called "Psalmus Humanus and Six Prayers" (Pax label), which deplores man's inhumanity to man, in free verse, against a background of appropriately discordant piano chords.

Szent-Gyorgyi has moved through several scientific careers; in fact, he describes himself as "a poacher in science," and his relationship with science as "promiscuous, very promiscuous." His training has been largely informal and self-directed, although he does hold an MD degree from the University of Budapest and a PhD from Cambridge University. He came to the U.S. from Hungary in 1947 to set up his institute at Woods Hole and has now become firmly wedded to that location, as well as to a beautiful young wife, his first wife having died of cancer some years ago.

One of the first experimental animals he introduced to the Woods Hole lab was the goat, but it soon became apparent to everyone within five miles that goats were not marine animals, and the colony was banished to a more landlocked facility. The biology done there now is chiefly on marine creatures, not because they are inherently more interesting, but because they are so diverse and available. He also has a big mouse colony for studies of growth and cancer.

When someone works as long and as widely in science as Szent-Gyorgyi has, and has been as outspoken as he concerning the interfaces between science and politics, and between both of these and morality, you can assume that he has come to some basic conclusions. These were what we tried to capture.

Dr. Szent-Gyorgyi, you've spent fifty years in various branches of science. Can you detect any unifying thread through it all?

Only in retrospect. Naturally, like all other scientists, when I publish or speak about my work, I like to make it appear as though it has been one straight line, one preconceived logical unit. But while I work I usually do not know where I am going. I just follow hunches. I dream up all sorts of theories at night and then disprove them in the laboratory the next day. Checking a hunch, sometimes I see some discrepancy, something unexpected—then I follow it up. Success depends on whether the hunch was good or bad.

You've had some good ones, to judge from your Nobel prize.

Yes, I was more lucky than many of my colleagues and this surprises me sometimes. So many scientists that I meet here during the summer know much more than I. They can put down their ideas much more clearly, more mathematically, and can describe exactly what they are after. I'm often ashamed to attend our Saturday morning seminars, because I can't do this. I just wander about, without especially clear ideas or preconceived notions so far as I know, and now and then something pops up—boom!—something that is entirely new, that leads to new lines of research.

Many of the most productive scientists seem to have worked in this apparently unprogramed way.

Claude Bernard, the greatest of physiologists and one of my idols, worked in this way, too. I like the distinction he made between the two kinds of knowledge—that which has been achieved already and that which has yet to be wrung from the unknown. The great scientists were those who were at home in the unknown and left their footsteps there, the dreamy fellows moving about with hands in pockets, who suddenly came up with something new. In the domain of knowledge already achieved these hazy fellows—the intuitive types—are often easily topped by others who know much more, who have read much more, who are more logical and clear in their presentations. I read very little; I talk intelligently about science very little.

Does this automatically put you in the ranks of the greats?

I don't know. Surely this is for others to judge. But I count myself among those who are driven mostly by some unknown instinct.

When did you first become aware of this drive in yourself?

My people have been scientists for four generations. I had an uncle who was a famous anatomist; he had great mysterious books and I had to know what was in those books. So I became an anatomist and made a reputation in histology, but it was all dead materials, not very interesting. So I turned to living things. At that time, you know, there were three life sciences. One that was done with rabbits—that was physiology; one that was done on man—that was medicine; and one that was done on protozoa or spiders—that was zoology. And they were sharply divided, and had nothing to do with each other. So when I left anatomy for something livelier I started with rabbits, but very soon I found that the rabbit was too complicated for my simple mind. Not only that, it kicks and bites.

So I thought, I'll go into pharmacology. That must be much simpler, because the drug is so simple. But the problem was that while the drug was simple, it acted on the rabbit, and without knowing the rabbit, I couldn't understand the drug.

We still have that problem today, don't we?

Yes, we still don't know why most drugs act. By the way, my friend Loewy had a good definition of a drug: "A drug is a substance which, if injected into an animal, produces a paper."

Finding the rabbit too complex, I said to myself, "To hell with it all," and I turned to bacteria and became a bacteriologist. Bacteria are so small they must be very simple, I thought. So I worked for a time in bacteriology, but soon found that the bacterium is also a whole universe.

Then I said, "What is simpler than a microbe? A molecule." So I became a chemist, by studying in my spare time, because I thought that there I would be able to put things together. Then much later I decided that this was still too complicated and that I didn't understand things because I hadn't gotten down deep enough, so I started muddling with electrons and quantum mechanics in my middle age. By doing this, at least I managed to call the attention of the good physicists to the entirely new field of biophysics—I was so successful that so many people came in who really knew what they were doing that I had to clear out myself.

What, in particular, were you looking for in each of these fields that made you feel that things were too complicated?

Looking back, I was really looking for simplicity, though I've often said I was looking for the secret of life. I have a very simple mind, I can take in only simple things. New knowledge should lead to generalization, simplification. When I started as a student, I was just flabbergasted at the enormous complexity. There seemed to be no order in nature. The first generalization I was led to—one that has guided my work—is based on the simple fact that there are two ways you can put things together: randomly or in a meaningful way, a way that makes sense.

Randomness is an "extensive property"; it doesn't matter how many toothpicks you put together at random—they're still just toothpicks. But if you put together six toothpicks and two corks in an orderly way, you can get a figure that looks something like a horse—something entirely new. Order is an "intensive property." This holds throughout science. If you put together protons and neutrons, you get a nucleus—something entirely new. It has new qualities, qualities you can't describe in terms of the constituents. If you then put electrons around this nucleus, you have an atom—again something entirely new, something more than just a nucleus and electrons. Then you can put atoms together into molecules, molecules into macromolecules, macromolecules into organelles, organelles into cells, cells into whole individuals, and individuals into societies. Each time something new.

Macromolecules are "giant molecules," like proteins. Organelles are loose groupings of macromolecules, not yet organized into a living cell.

So that each level is qualitatively different from the others, not just quantitatively. The whole is more than the sum of its parts.

Yes, each level is qualitatively different, each level is exciting. But you must know where you are; you mustn't draw conclusions from one level and apply them to the next. As soon as you mix them up, you are lost, and your conclusions have no meaning. Each level has its own meaning.

It gets dangerous to extrapolate from the quantum mechanical level to the individual rabbit.

Yes. All the same, as a biologist you must have an idea of all levels, so that you know where you are, and what you are talking about. If there was a creator, he was not a quantum mechanician, nor was he a macromolecular chemist or physiologist—he was all of these, and knew all of it. In the same way, we must know a little bit about all of it. This concept of levels of organization in nature cleared my mind a great deal. In inanimate nature this organization stops at a fairly low level. Life drives it much further. That's why in living nature you find qualities you can't find outside of it. But there is one danger in this situation. You understand any level best by studying the next lower level. So if you want to understand your car, you must pull it to pieces, down to the "nuts and bolts" level. But in studying life, you keep diving from higher levels to lower ones until somewhere along the way life fades out, leaving you empty-handed. Molecules and electrons have no life.

Life itself trickled through my fingers as I descended to the quantum-electron level. I found that I had to go back up the ladder again.

Can you identify at what point life "fades out"?

Life is a very complex business. I don't know what life is, but I know when my dog is dead. Life is essentially connected with the transduction of energy. I know the dog is dead if he doesn't move—if he doesn't transduce chemical energy into mechanical energy, if he has no reflexes—doesn't transduce chemical energy into electrical energy. Also, my carpet stays clean—he doesn't transduce chemical energy into osmotic work.

As I said, there are two ways you can study a machine—the first is by looking at its structure, its nuts and bolts, or you can look at the energy which drives it. The second approach was the one I settled on to study life. I said, "Let's study the oxidation process, that which supplies most of the energy which drives the living machine." In tackling oxidation I suppose I was led by my fascination by colors. I still like colors, they give me a childish pleasure. I started with the question "Why does a banana turn brown when I hurt it?" There were many complicated oxidation theories around at that time, but I soon found out that there was nothing but an enzyme that was kept in an inactive condition until you damaged the plant. Then this very active enzyme oxidized the colorless polyphenols in the banana into colored quinones. The quinone then combined with protein (tannins, the same sort of chemicals that are used to tan leather), closing the wound, and at the same time killing the bacteria. So the whole sequence started by this simple oxidation has an important survival value to the plant.

Where were you when you did this work?

In Holland. Just before this I had gone to Hamburg, the Institute for Technical Medicine, as a bacteriologist, after being "excommunicated" from Europe after World War I. Being a Hungarian, I had to fight on the "wrong side." I was thus an enemy alien in England and America—so I was limited to Germany. But then the Dutch Physiological Society met in Hamburg, and a friend of mine introduced me to a Dutch professor who invited me to Holland. That was where I began to muddle in chemistry. In the daytime I worked at pharmacology, which proved useless, but at night I could do chemistry—there were very good chemists there in Leiden. But after a short time I had to leave Leiden for personal reasons. My wife was young and beautiful, and the good professor who had invited me to Holland was young too—and he admired her very much.

Where did you go?

We went to Groningen, where I thought I'd get a Dutch medical diploma and go to the Dutch Indies. I didn't realize how little I knew, and I flunked the test. So there I was with no diploma and no money. But one of the physiology professors, a Professor Hamburger, gave me a chance to perform a complicated operation on a dog. No one could do this as well as I did it; my dog survived—so he gave me a job.

And it was here you did the chemical work on the bananas and the apples?

Yes, after working-hours, but after I had written my paper on my first "baby work," Professor Hamburger died, and my new professor thought animal psychology was the only important thing. This was no more a fit place for a biochemist. So I quit my job and sent my wife and child back to her parents, with the idea of giving up both life and science, which meant the same to me. But for one last time I wanted to have a good time. I went to Stockholm for the International Physiological Congress, presided over by the great biochemist Sir F. G. Hopkins. In his presidential address he mentioned my name four times. So I picked up my courage and went up to him after his lecture. "Why don't you come to Cambridge?" he asked. "I'll see that you get a fellowship." So I went to Cambridge and stayed alive and in science.

What sort of work did you do there?

Well, I continued my work with plants.

This was the work that led you to the isolation of ascorbic acid—vitamin C? And the Nobel prize?

Yes, I got half of the Nobel prize for that. There are two categories of plants, you see—those that turn black on being damaged and those in which there is no color change. Now, Sir Francis Bacon said that research is like going for a walk with your bird dog. You just keep walking until something flies up, then you go after it. The plants that turned black were clearly being oxidized as a result of the damage and the plant's attempt to survive it. But why didn't all plants do this? Why no color in some damaged plants?

To find out, I did one reaction that every student does in his first-year biochemistry course, the peroxidase reaction. You take the plant juice, add benzedine and then peroxide, and it turns blue immediately—poof! I tried it with several plants, and in many, especially in the citrus plants, after I had added the peroxide I also got a color reaction—but with a very important difference. In these plants, some substance (which proved to be ascorbic acid) caused a significant delay of a half-second—no color, no blue—before the added peroxide had its usual effect.

How did you run the substance down? This was in the 1930's wasn't it? No infrared spectroscopy then?

I knew that the compound I had was a carbohydrate derivative, but I didn't know what it was, so I sent samples of the crystals all over the world, to clear up the constitution. This part was easy, but naming the compound proved stickier.

How was that?

When you name a carbohydrate, a sugar, you add the suffix "ose" to its name, and I called this one "ignose" because I didn't know what it was. I sent my paper to the editor of *Biochemical Journal,* who was a very serious gentleman. He reprimanded me very sternly and said there was to be no joking about science. So I asked him, "What about Godnose?" but he didn't like that either. He said, "You call it hexuronic acid." It was the wrong name; and later we called it ascorbic acid. That was my second shot at oxidation.

Glucose, sucrose, etc.

"Ig" stands for ignosco.
Ignosco = I don't know.

Then you switched out of the plant field entirely didn't you?

Yes, but not out of oxidation studies, at least not right away. I introduced a new material, pigeon breast muscle, which no one else had used before. This is a very beautiful, sappy, juicy sort of muscle, because a pigeon—unlike a chicken—is made to fly, and needs a powerful oxidation mechanism in his muscles to produce the energy he needs. I very quickly found that the four- and six-carbon straight chain dicarboxylic acids—succinic and citric acids—were fundamental catalysts in oxidation. I showed that if you "poisoned" these compounds, there wasn't any oxidation. These compounds are the basis of what's called now "the Krebs cycle," one of the most basic mechanisms of life. I got the other half of the Nobel prize partly for the discovery of this fundamental catalytic activity of succinic oxidase.

$$C \overset{\displaystyle O}{-} OH$$
$$\mid$$
$$CH_2$$
$$\mid$$
$$CH_2$$
$$\mid$$
$$C - OH$$
$$\diagdown O$$

Succinic acid

Then why did you switch from such successful research at the chemical level to research at the physiological level?

If one works for ten or twenty years on something, one needs a change of atmosphere. One gets stale, one doesn't see things. So I said, "Maybe now I have enough experience at lower levels on the ladder of life to tackle a more physiological problem, something at a higher level of organization." And since I was interested in energy transduction, I decided to try muscle, because muscle has the most violent energy transformation, and it's easy to work with—you can easily see what it does, and you get violent chemical changes which accompany its action. If science is the art of measuring, it is the more successful the more there is to measure. In muscle there is a lot to measure. But the question is, when you go into a new field, what do you do with yourself?

You must either make a big theory and then try to disprove it, or you just repeat what people did a hundred years earlier. And that can be very rewarding sometimes, because those people had very little hardware—they had to use their eyes and their brains, which we don't do today. Biochemists today, if they regard themselves as scientists, mince up their material, put it into a big machine, and look at the pointer.

What do you do?

I use my eyes, my fingers, my nose. So I did what W. Kühne did a hundred years earlier. He just minced up muscle and put it in a strong salt solution. Then he diluted the solution and out came a large amount of protein which he called "myosin." Now, myosin is the main protein in muscle, hence it is evidently a contractile protein, and a contractile protein should contract wherever it is. But the extracted myosin wouldn't do anything, no matter what you did with it. So I repeated the work very carefully, and this time I didn't cut a muscle out of the rabbit, but cut the rabbit away from the muscle—there's quite a difference you know.

What is the difference?

The muscle must not notice. You must disturb nothing, handle it very gently, as gently as you can. So I repeated Kühne's experiments very carefully, keeping my eyes open— like Bacon on his walk—and I found that if I made the extraction slowly the extract was much more viscous. Now I don't mean intrinsic viscosity as measured by some involved instrument. I just put my finger into it and said, "Oh golly, that's sticky."

But why was it so sticky? There must be something new in it, I thought, and there *was* a new protein in it. My pupil Straub isolated it, and we called it "actin." We found that it made a complex with myosin, which we called "actomyosin." From it we could make little artificial muscles. To make them feel at home we extracted the small molecules of another muscle by boiling water and suspended one little artificial muscle in this juice and we got a contraction—boom! For the first time, motion, the great sign of life whose absence signifies death was produced outside the body. This was the most exciting moment of my scientific life.

You had, in a sense, created life in the laboratory?

Yes.

When was this?

In 1939, at the University of Szeged, Hungary.

Once you'd made the muscle contract, where did you go from there?

Well, then it was easy to find out next what was in our boiled muscle juice which made actomyosin contract. It was ATP—adenosine triphosphate and ions derived from it that gave the muscle its energy. At that point I was convinced that in a few weeks' time I would understand muscle completely. But I worked on it for the next twenty years and didn't learn a damned thing more—I had just happened to do a crucial experiment.

Was your muscle work, then, a dead end?

It was not completely a dead end, for we made one or another small observations—like finding the cause of rigor mortis, the stiffness of death. And major discoveries in

121

muscle physiology have been made since—like the "sliding filament" theory of muscle contraction, made in England. But I did not make these discoveries. I failed. If you are too long in a line, you don't see things. If you come in fresh, you see them, and I couldn't. So after twenty years, I decided I'd better clear out. Muscle did not lead me to a generalization, as my oxidation theory had. That had led to a very important generalization about nature for me: Nature is organized like a "horizontal trust" in business, in contrast to a "vertical trust."

I don't quite follow this "trust" analogy.

Nature has a horizontal trust. By that I mean it uses a similar chain of reactions everywhere to achieve similar ends. Oh, here and there it puts out one member for a special role, as when it uses quinones to protect plants against damage. But in citrus fruits, it shoves ascorbic acid to the fore, and in animals, succinic or citric acid—three oxidation systems which look quite different. You have phenol in your body also which you could oxidize to quinones, and you have ascorbic acid, while even bacteria use C_4 and C_6 dicarboxylic acids as basic catalysts. So basically all living systems apply similar long chains of reaction for oxidation. They only look different—that's what I mean by nature's "horizontal trust."

The most classical example of this—I haven't worked on it—is the torpedo electric fish, which kills its prey by electric shock. Has he discovered something new? Not at all. It's just that every muscle action has an electric potential, and the torpedo puts those membrane potentials together so they add up to a shock. It's nothing new, just another expression of the same horizontal trust organization. Life is based on an amazingly small number of principles, which nature discovered one at a time and uses cleverly for the most varied ends.

What would you say was the basic such discovery of nature?

I think it was the discovery that you can get free energy out of a foodstuff molecule by twisting it or splitting it and can preserve this energy—store it—in the form of certain high-energy chemical links. This is fermentation, the oldest and most basic process of life.

What was the next new discovery of nature?

Photosynthesis—the discovery of a method to use the energy of the sun, the energy of light. Plants use this energy to reduce CO_2 and separate water into elemental hydrogen and oxygen.

Was this the end of the line?

No, but when nature discovers a new principle, it doesn't throw away the old one—it keeps the old one and adds the new things into it. There were several next steps leading up the ladder. Next came the reversion of the photosynthesis process—the coupling of C to O, and the coupling of H to O, the process of biological oxidation. The next step was to put these processes into little machines, into boxes with a membrane around them, and make "chloroplasts" for photosynthesis and "mitochondria" for oxidation. The genetic material was also surrounded by a membrane and closed into a little box 've call the cell nucleus. When all this was done you had a cell, the greatest wonder of nature, which could be perfected no more.

These structures are details within the living cell—essential in its function, but incomplete in themselves.

The cell, then, is the top rung of the ladder?

Not yet. Nowhere near it. Once there was order at the cell level of organization, you could go to a next higher level, put two cells together, then three and four. Now you can do more than you can with one cell, because the cells can specialize. But in order to live in a community of cells, each cell had to give up certain qualities and develop new ones. Cells had to develop a new surface, for instance. The old surface only had to keep the rough world outside of the cell; the new surface had to allow subtle reactions between the cells.

One of the basic principles in nature is unlimited proliferation. As long as the cells lived alone they wanted to proliferate as fast as they could. You could populate the whole continent in one year if all the sperm and egg cells of two humans became mature, right? But if you live in a community you have to subjugate this drive in the interests of the whole.

That meant that a new principle had to be developed by nature—a principle of regulation, to stop proliferation, but not to stop it irreversibly, because then you couldn't regenerate—you wouldn't heal your wounds when you cut yourself shaving, for instance. When you cut yourself, the cells have to return briefly to the old way of living of single cells; they have to begin to divide as they did in their original state. Then, when the wound is closed, they stop multiplying. In a sense, they switch back and forth between evolutionary states.

Where will this "switching process" be important?

I'm sure that this line of thinking will be of importance in the eventual understanding of cancer. You see, the "newer" a process, in the evolutionary sense, the easier it is to throw off. You can never shake off fermentation, or oxidation, but you can shake off regulation—that is very new. And when regulation is shaken off, if new cell growth doesn't stop when cell touches cell, you have cancer. So my theory now is that cancer is a shift between the present and past state of evolution, and that could be very important as a new avenue of investigation. At least it clears up my ideas on cancer enormously, because while cancer is an obscure, mysterious disease, it seems to involve simply a shift in the last evolutionary state. The question, as I see it, is not what makes the cancer cell grow, but where the brake, the regulator, has gone wrong.

How are you going about this work?

I use a cancer tissue which grows fast enough so I can measure it, and use the growth as an indicator. I found many years ago, as others found before and after, that tissues contain substances which promote or retard growth. My first simple, perhaps even childish, idea was to isolate these substances, produce them in pure condition, find out what they are and what they are good for. Now it is clear to me that the problem is not so simple. It isn't one substance that stops cell division or makes cell division go—bang. It must be a very complex system of regulators within our genetic material, with complex equilibria, which cannot be shifted easily. Very recently, we have found that there is a certain probability that the active component is an activated ketone, possibly a ketone-aldehyde, with two CO groups, probably a derivative of methyl glyoxal, which is known to react specifically with —SH—sulphur and hydrogen. These are known to be essential for cell division.

$$
\begin{array}{c}
CH_3 \\
| \\
C=0 \\
| \\
C=0 \\
| \\
H
\end{array}
$$

Methyl
glyoxal

Which of the two elements is the important one in this —SH complex? Or are they equally essential for cell division?

They are both essential, but sulphur is the important one. The sulphur atom is a most fascinating, versatile atom—it plays an important role in many enzyme processes and, possibly, dominates the structure, the "conformation," of these important catalysts. But we find that glyoxal does stop all cell division in a low concentration, completely, by arresting protein synthesis. We also find an enzymatic system that inactivates glyoxal, transforming it into lactic acid, an inactive substance which is very widely spread throughout the cells. Hopkins in England and Dakin and Racker in the U.S. have worked on this, and feel that it is so widely spread it must have some fundamental importance. It's a complex system, composed of two enzymes and a soluble compound called "glutathiole." This inactivation effect makes it difficult to test glyoxals in the animal, because if you inject a glyoxal derivative into an animal, it is destroyed before it reaches the cell, but it may be formed right there, where it acts. You must understand that I am speculating here—I have my doubts about this theory.

How has this theory been received by your colleagues?

One of the greatest compliments of my life came when George Wald said, introducing me to an audience, that any of his undergraduates could get his PhD by showing that Szent-Gyorgyi's latest work was wrong, and then twenty years later he could get a degree for showing that I was right after all! So, as far as this theory is concerned I am at the first stage. Some people have even laughed at me and said the old man has cracked up. But that's OK with me because I am left alone. I can work quietly. And I can take comfort, not that I think I need it, from what Keilin, the discoverer of the cytochromes, told a visitor who said I was no good because I made so many mistakes: "I like his mistakes better than your correct stuff."

Where do you get your ideas for research?

In my bed, when waking between three and four A.M., or while sleeping. The brain does a great deal of unconscious work, without our knowing it, and that is how most of our great problems are solved. We must think very hard, but that is just "priming." It mostly will not get you anywhere, because we are misled by so many false statements and pictures. You must leave the brain alone—go fishing, or to sleep—and the brain will begin to clean up all that, and in the end, out come results. That's my experience. The brain is like a laxative which was advertised back in Hungary with the slogan, "It works while you sleep."

But the brain needs something to work on . . .

Of course, but I'm seventy-three and have had plenty of time to prime it, giving all of it to my research. I read very little, but I hear what is important—my associates tell me. You see, the bottleneck of research is up here, in the head. And that's the wonderful thing about Woods Hole—three hundred active associates to prime you during the summer —but it doesn't narrow the bottleneck by noise and hustle-bustle all the time. There's time to think; a lost art. Look out over the ocean. I love the ocean. It's all spread out and you're ashamed to work on little things. If I lived in a house where I had to look out to see another concrete wall, I think I would just be a blank.

What do you expect to do in the future?

Well, my plans for my next fifty years of research are to find out how living systems are generated. I don't mean in the ordinary evolutionary sense—random mutations, natural selection, and all that. What Darwin and his followers said was all right, but I'm profoundly convinced that it is not the whole truth. I'm convinced that there is a drive in things to improve, to get complicated, and that the chemical wisdom of the body, its foreknowledge, or something that looks very much like foreknowledge, is incredible. If you cut the optic nerve and turn the eyeball around, the severed nerve endings will find their corresponding nerve endings, and you will still see. There is a drive in life to improve life.

That's a pretty dangerous thing to say nowadays . . .

Yes, they say this is mysticism, but it is not. The drive must find its physical expression in time, but I don't know if present-day physics has the data we need. Physics itself is looking for something entirely new, which would open the door to some entirely new knowledge, consisting perhaps of quantized space or time—I don't know what it will be.

Neither do the physicists. Weisskopf talked about it in your interview with him (see page 87).

So some physical picture of this drive may come in time, but for now it's just "chemical wisdom," and the intelligence of the living nature as it exists. When I say that, some say, "Oh, he doesn't know anything."

It does sound like a new vitalism, which is an anathema to many hard-nosed scientists . . .

Well, twenty years ago we didn't know anything about the things we know today either, and twenty years hence we may know things we don't even dream of today.

Life is not like physical things. Life itself keeps life going —if you use your car a lot, the car wears out and your legs get weak, but if you walk a lot, your legs get strong. The non-living wears itself out by work; but the living builds itself up. That's one of the great differences between life and non-life. The heart works the same way. If it is rested for a minute between beats, the next beat is weaker, rather than stronger. The living machine goes to pieces if it doesn't work.

And all these reactions are fitted into a long chain of incredibly involved reactions. For instance, there is a sea gull out there with a red spot on its beak. When the mama sea gull comes back to her nest after fishing, the baby pecks at that spot and mama regurgitates her food to feed him. Why should they develop a red spot? Just a random mutation? And if mama develops a red spot and the baby does not have its correct reflex machinery, what good is it? Even the baby itself is part of an enormously complex reflex machinery. I can't see how such a very complex system can be built by random mutation alone—there must be something pushing it all.

When I was a student, we knew only that there were twenty amino acids and twelve sugars, and we felt obliged to explain life. Anybody who didn't explain life was an obscurantist and a metaphysician.

Today we know more. But what do we know about what we don't know? Forty years ago there was no quantum mechanics; somewhat over half a century ago there was no atomic nucleus, no electron. At the end of the last century Wien advised Planck to become a pianist, rather than a physicist, because physics was a closed subject. How many

Plancks are there now who are playing the piano rather than doing physics? And how much new physics is there to be discovered? What does small mean? We still don't know why most molecules act biologically as they do, why andosterone makes you a man rather than a woman and why estrogen and progesterone produce "Mother love." We must try everything we can. There is still lots and lots to explore.

Guy Ourisson

*O*ne day in 1963 Professor Guy Ourisson gave a seminar
at his alma mater, the École Normale Supérieure in Paris.
Instead of choosing a topic from his field of organic chemistry, he spoke—and with some misgivings—about the ethical
choices confronting the scientist in his workaday world. To
his astonishment, the discussion dragged on and on; when he
returned to Paris later, he found his seminar being discussed
in laboratories all over the city.

Ourisson first began thinking about these problems when
they came before him as a graduate student at Harvard
University some fifteen years ago. As you will see in the
interview that follows, the "deadly sins of research" that he
talks about are really moral problems with which all of us
are quite familiar. By relating them to the world of science,
however, Ourisson gives the scientist a wholly new way of
looking at his efforts.

Professor Ourisson would be the first to deny being the
creator of any systematic code of laboratory behavior. As a
staff member at the Institut de Chimie at the University of
Strasbourg, he is a working scientist himself, and he supervises the work of many others. The Institut de Chimie is a
large organic-chemistry laboratory, at the graduate-student
level, supported by the French government. In the last ten
years, he has been in charge of some fifty collaborators from

twenty different countries. It is precisely this involvement which has intensified his concern with the moral aspects of science.

At the outset of a thoughtful discussion with Professor Ourisson in Paris, we asked him:

You have been concerned for some time, I know, about the problem of "ethics in research." Just what do you mean by this?

There has been much public discussion, since the war, on the ethics of science, but I think it has been nearly always from one point of view: the moral responsibility of a scientist toward the consequences of his discoveries. It seems to me that one other aspect has been largely ignored, and this is the moral impact of his work on the scientist himself. When you live in the laboratory, you face problems every day which can either be completely ignored, or which can be viewed as moral choices. These choices are important, for scientists constitute an increasingly influential segment of our population.

Isn't the scientist's task simply to search for the truth?

To be sure; but to accomplish this he has to be truthful. You see, the search for truth is not entirely free; it has limitations and, in particular, it is very much influenced by one's idea, in a given problem, of what the truth must be.

Let me take an example from my own field, chemistry. Very often we have to compare two substances, but we always have a preconception: Either we think they must be identical, or that they must be different. Suppose we measure the melting points. They will never be *exactly* the same; there is always a difference of one or two degrees. Now, depending on our preconception, we tend to overemphasize the difference or the identity. The same is true when we compare them by other means—let's say by infrared absorption. The complex spectroscopic curves are never quite superimposable; there are differences in peak intensity and so on. There is room for doubt. We may be influenced to dismiss small differences if our inclination is toward identity. Or, if we wanted really to prove that the two substances were different, we might tend to conclude that the peak intensities *are* different.

In infrared spectroscopy, materials are analyzed and often identified by the amount of energy they absorb at different frequencies when subjected to electromagnetic radiation in the band just below that of visible light.

Now this type of pitfall cannot be fully avoided. But the moment you realize that you have an inner tendency to be influenced by what you think you must find, I believe you are already halfway to salvation in the laboratory.

To go the rest of the way, there must be other pitfalls to avoid?

Yes, I believe so. How to win paradise (or hell) in a lab coat, you might say. Searching out the deadly sins in research is seldom done, but doing so can give valuable insights to the way good science can be achieved.

Let's take the sin of "envy" as an example.

The green-eyed monster is very much in evidence in the laboratory. I am not thinking of the envy one researcher has for another's position or laboratory. These are trivial and common to many walks of life. I am thinking of the way you—if I may personalize here for sake of emphasis—tend to view your neighbor's problem at the next bench. His problem is *always* easier than yours, and *you* would be better able to handle it. You will tend to underestimate the difficulties he faces and, at the same time, underestimate the importance of what he is after. If, then, there arises a question of using the same piece of equipment, you may find yourself instinctively reaching to take it first on the grounds that your problem is the more difficult and important. This is a very complex attitude that I find very few people escape from. It is a curious mixture of envy, pride, and even covetousness.

Can such an attitude seriously affect the performance of researchers in a laboratory?

Indeed it can. Covetousness can lead to many small actions which, in the aggregate, may seriously compromise a laboratory's effectiveness. A research leader may develop a collector's lust for equipment, for laboratory space, or for personnel even though his imagination for new problems is at a low point. Another researcher may "borrow" equipment or monopolize the time of technicians by having them prepare or analyze needless quantities of samples.

It seems to me that the race a scientist runs to publish his results is at the bottom of a lot of this.

Publication is at once his greatest need and his greatest temptation. Pride can lead a scientist to try to hide his mistakes, but this seldom occurs, because discovery is all too certain. More important, I think, is the tendency toward gluttony that the need for publication creates in many of us working in the laboratory. The problem is the demand for large numbers of publications attached to one's name. This raises the whole specter of authorship and, when there are many researchers involved, whose name comes first. Some maintain that the man who has done the most important part of the work should have his name first; others say that the name of the head of the laboratory should precede the rest. British chemists use the alphabetical order—a clever way to avoid trouble. However, the point I want to stress here is that every act in the laboratory, even the simplest, has its moral side.

The ethical problem of authorship, it seems to me, can be handled pretty easily so long as it is recognized as a problem. But how about the ethics of discovery?

Here, we are on very dangerous ground indeed. I am not

so concerned with how you assign credit for a discovery after the event, as I am with the thought habits of the "discoverer" in the first place. This is a particular moral problem I first heard discussed by Professor Bartlett of Harvard, the "grandfather" of American organic chemistry and one of the truly wise men.

Here is the problem. You meet many people and you discuss many problems with them. You participate in discussions on their problems and yours, and you then forget who told you what. You forget it and then you rediscover it. And then you put someone to work on it because you think it's a good problem—and you come out first.

This can be something as simple as a suggestion of an avenue of possible research?

Yes. Exactly. Now, this looks completely crazy—the idea that you may be told about an idea or some results by a good friend or colleague, and then forget the incident to the point where you think, honestly, that you discover them when you think of the matter later. But, believe me, I have already seen this happen three times. In all three cases I knew the people and the circumstances intimately enough to be absolutely sure that there was no trace of dishonesty, but only a lack of awareness.

How does one cope with this problem—the scientist's need to discover and also to communicate, which seem to be in potential conflict ethically?

It's a matter of awareness, really. Our first reaction to having a "discovery" is to be proud of having had a good idea. This is good so long as we remember that most of our ideas are the consequences of what we have read about, been told, or confronted with in the lab. To become too bedeviled with the problem would be to stifle creativity altogether.

Science is, in many senses, a group activity. Could you explore some of the problems you see, from the ethical viewpoint, of researchers working together?

Well, the scientific community is still a small community, but it is a very tight one. So, as a society, it has very special problems. These will probably warrant the study, someday, of good sociologists. I would like to focus, as an amateur and an insider, on the smaller community that is the research laboratory. More specifically, I think we should look at the researcher and the man directly above him—the group leader or research director.

The way I like to discuss this with my people is to explain to them when they start (and repeat to them later) that there is, in fact, an implicit contract between a group leader and his research collaborators. The leader's responsibilities within this contract are to open the field to his new people, to show them any special techniques they may need, and then to encourage them toward independent research by all possible means.

And the researchers' responsibilities under this unwritten contract . . . ?

They, of course, must be ready to accept the director's leadership and learn from him. But as they gain proficiency and begin to work on their own, complications creep in. After a while, the individual researcher knows more about his problem than the man who gave it to him in the first place. He has a responsibility, then, to help his boss to increase his own knowledge of the original problem. Both must realize that they are not involved in a master-slave relationship; rather, that it is as partners that the best results will be achieved . . . discoveries, promotions, awards, and all the rest.

Where, aside from meeting these responsibilities honorably, do some of the ethical problems lie?

Both director and researcher face moral problems in their relations with each other. They relate to the sin of pride and ought to, in my view, be understood but left completely *out* of the unwritten contract. Let's look again at the researcher who is mastering his problem and fast approaching independence. As he overtakes his boss in knowledge of *this particular problem,* he must resist the temptation to show his superior how much smarter he is in this area. He must be ready to perceive and to accept new and valid reasons for respecting his director. He must appreciate, for example, that the boss has knowledge of and insight into many different problems going on at once, and that he can see rela-

tionships that the individual researcher, working in his own restricted domain, may not see.

How about on the boss's side?

Here, too, there are subtle dangers relating to our quite human tendency to dominate. For example, many a research manager assumes that his researchers have special merit by virtue of the fact that they came to work for *him,* and that they are thus better than his colleagues' researchers and so deserve special pushing. This is a kind of imperialism that is found everywhere in every country. Perhaps by looking at the problem in this light, the research manager may become aware of the immorality of feeling he has to make special efforts to place his men, whatever their real merits, in key positions.

There is another difficulty on the boss's side that I want to mention. This is that in the small world of the laboratory it is very hard to avoid sentimental complications. The manager will always have researchers with whom it is easier to discuss matters than it is with others. These people respond to his interest in them as persons, and become nearer to him; a series of father-son relationships can easily arise, and the laboratory can split into a group of loved researchers and those who are unloved. This can pose an extremely dangerous ethical problem because, as research manager, you may give more of yourself to the people who are closer to you. The unloved researchers must receive as much of your attention as the others, or else they might go astray in their work and it would be your fault. To favor the one over the other would be utterly wrong, but is very difficult to escape.

I should think that such problems could lead to strained relations among research scientists themselves.

This is true. You have this even in labs where the researchers have become effective partners with their group leader. You see, they share his time and his brain power, and often they feel they are competing with one another. So there is a built-in tendency for researchers working side by side to become competitors, even enemies in a way. The scientific life is, in many ways, a very cloistered life; consequently, many researchers fail to reflect upon the fact that when they enter this tightly knit world they have to think out a new type of behavior.

The few specific cases we have discussed are only a sampling; every practitioner of the art will see countless others. I have found, though, that as soon as the research manager warns the new researcher about some of the moral choices he will have to make in his new environment, or just tells him that he *will* face such choices, the problems cease to be crucial. To be aware of the moral and social aspects of scientific life is, in itself, a way to improve the quality of one's involvement in science.

A WAY OF ACTING

What it is like to put scientific knowledge to work in the world—
or to train and lead men to do it

Philip Sporn

*A*nyone who set out to draw up a list of the great engineers
in American industry would be pretty certain to include
Philip Sporn among the men at the top. For many years
Sporn held the highest engineering post in the country's biggest aggregation of electric power companies, then he went
on to become the company's chief executive.

Born in Austria in 1896, Sporn came to the United States
with his parents and became a U.S. citizen at the age of
eleven. His speech still has a trace of an accent. He learned
his electrical engineering at Columbia University, where he
earned a degree in 1917. In 1920 he joined the company
that is known today as American Electric Power and pro-
gressed upward from protection engineer, then communication engineer, then transmission and distribution engineer,
to the position of chief engineer, which he attained at age
thirty-seven. In 1947 he became president of American Electric Power, serving in that office until 1961. When we talked
with him in 1963, Sporn was still a director of the company,
member of its executive committee, and chairman of its system development committee.

Sporn has been a leader in the steady drive of the electric
utility industry toward higher voltages, higher steam pressures, and greater fuel efficiencies. For the past twenty years,
he has been among the most active pioneers in the development of the technology and the economic application of

nuclear energy in the electric power supply industry. In recent years, especially, he has been much concerned with questions of engineering education. This concern has put him on advisory councils of Columbia and Cornell and visiting committees on electrical engineering at Princeton and MIT. It was to this concern that we addressed our questions.

In all the ferment going on now about engineering education, how much voice do you think people from industry should have? Or do they have much?

You need to make up your mind what industry you are talking about. It's one thing if you are talking about the part of industry that today dominates research and development —basically government-sponsored, not entirely involved with defense, but largely. It is another thing if you are talking about the great enterprises that produce the things that make a society like ours what it is.

Another thing?

I am fearful that we have been gradually slipping into a situation in which the former segment has become the all-dominant segment, as far as our programs of education are concerned. In that process we have almost forgotten the term "engineer," as if it were a term of reproach. Great schools of engineering have discovered that engineering is really not what they wanted to teach at all; they have almost forgotten what an engineer is and how you educate an engineer.

Well, what is an engineer—in the eyes of a basic industry such as your own utility industry, say? What sort of man do you want?

The essential thing that we want him to be able to do is to become the inheritor of a great historic development, of the tradition, the know-how, of past ages—a lot of which goes back to the days before the word "science" was more than a word. In addition, he must be able to conceive, to design, to synthesize, be able to build and operate systems representing great aggregations of capital and energy and human abilities. He's got to be vastly concerned with efficiency and costs and economics—things that the scientist in many cases doesn't know anything about; or if he does, he thinks they are almost Philistine.

Is this ability to synthesize, this understanding of economics, the sort of thing that can be taught in school?

I do not know if synthesis can be taught on a base of zero. But it can be developed. And economics can be taught. No engineering is engineering if it doesn't include the element of economics. When anyone in industry says that his engineer doesn't understand money, he is saying that he is no engineer.

And the engineering schools don't understand this?

I think we have underemphasized economics to an amazing degree. Not only among the students sent out of our engineering schools—we've underemphasized it in the faculties; we've underemphasized it in the curricula.

You feel the schools should de-emphasize science?

No. If I would de-emphasize anything I would de-emphasize detailed technological knowledge. I would want a student to be broadly trained scientifically but also broadly trained in humanities and also trained in social economics— so that he would know what kind of a world he is going to live and work in.

A moment ago you said you thought this viewpoint was underemphasized in most faculties nowadays. And you have said that students should be exposed to great engineers as well as to academic people. How could this be accomplished?

We have a long job ahead of us, but I think it is not an impossible job. Certainly the first thing to do would be to bring into full-time teaching engineers who have demonstrated that they can be successful and have perhaps acquired a certain amount of financial security at the age of forty or forty-five, long before the age considered normal for retirement. Men who can say, "I'm perfectly willing to quit here and now, not because the company doesn't want me, not because I'm tired of it, but because I think teaching has in it elements of satisfaction I couldn't get any other way. What are these elements? They come from passing on to the new generation ideas that I, perhaps, have done reasonably well in developing and that I want to see perpetuated." It is the old time-binding operation of the human race.

When you were forty, did you feel any temptation to teach?

Yes, I did, and if someone had tempted me strongly enough, I might have done something about it. But I think you must also consider another sort of teacher. You have them today in medicine—great medical practitioners who both teach and practice their profession. I think it would be possible to find engineers to do a limited amount of teaching. They might give one course a year, maybe only one course every two years. But they could be a great influence on scores of people who would have contact with engineers who engineer, who have standing and reputation. Students would get a feel of how they think—how they tackle a problem—what are the essentials and what are the non-essentials. And this is almost entirely absent in our schools of engineering.

Is it up to industry or up to the schools to get such a thing started?

It is a mutual responsibility.

Suppose today one of the good engineers in one of your utility systems should say, "I'd like to devote a quarter of my time to teaching." What would American Power do?

Although it is almost two years since I relinquished the responsibility of chief executive, I am conversant with the principles that underlie policies of the AEP system today. So today, too, I would hope that if we found a man who wanted to do that, and who we thought was well equipped to do that, and if the net effect of this would be to broaden him, we would try to do two things: We would try to keep him in our engineering and not to break the connection between the company and him. And we would let him go out and do a job of teaching where he might be of influence.

Has this happened at all?

It hasn't happened to any of our younger people. But when I was sixty-six or thereabouts—I had reached the decision earlier—I accepted a professorship at Cornell. And this past spring I was visiting professor of engineering at Cornell; I lectured and gave a seminar on what I call the foundations of engineering. This is now appearing as a book.

Isn't that a more likely way for it to happen, more likely than when a man is in his forties?

Perhaps. But I think not enough has happened even of this. I haven't heard of more than one or two cases. Have you? So this too is exceptional, and it shouldn't be exceptional. But there is nothing automatically otiose about sixty-five; a man of sixty-five might be as occupied as a man of fifty-three. And I don't see why a way couldn't be found to induce a man of fifty-three, holding a responsible post in engineering—for the self-expression it would offer him, for the opportunity to develop ideas, for the benefit of future generations in a profession he has been happy with. . . .

A way? What sort of way might be found?

These men could be challenged. If I telescope time backward two decades, which would find me at the age of forty-seven, I could have been challenged then to go into a university, because I had these ideas then. I might have had to work very hard and with considerable sacrifice of such little spare time as I had to pick up that responsibility—even for a year or two. You don't have to do it for more than a year or two. I think we need to make a beginning on that; I think we really have gone pretty far in kicking the engineer out of engineering training.

Will the initiative come from the colleges?

I have a hunch that there has been a sort of closed shop on that. I know that some years ago I was on a committee to find a new department head in the college of engineering of one of our great universities. The most striking thing to me in all of this rather interesting chore was when we sat down with the staff of the department. Their attitude was, and these were their words: "We don't see why we need any outsiders. We don't see why we shouldn't close ranks." They used that phrase. They wanted to close ranks. An outsider—in a great institution of learning, mind you—was the enemy. He might bring in some ideas that would upset them. I think, in a sense, we've had this kind of barrier put up against the engineers. They might propagate ideas that are not popular—possibly the idea that engineering is more than just advanced mathematics and physics and chemistry.

If you yourself were twenty today, would you still want to be an engineer?

I really think that if I could see even half the excitement and half the satisfactions I have had in engineering and in my parallel career in business, I would choose engineering. I think the great disservice we do the new generation of youth, the great wrong we do them, is that we have failed to show them the vistas for great and exciting careers. I'm not talking about remuneration, because that takes care of itself. I mean engineering in its broadest sense: developing everything that really makes the modern world—bridges and highways and great factories, systems and institutions that provide for a more productive and richer life; providing human satisfactions—human wants—these things that engineering and industry can do. The young have no concept of what it is they are giving up; they give that up, and they enter a narrow segment of specialization at an early age. This is putting blinders on them and sending them to make their way in the modern world without having a chance to see what this world is. It isn't fair. It isn't fair to the world. It isn't fair to the youth.

When you went into engineering as a young man, into electric power engineering, was it because your best teacher was in that field?

No. Well . . . I went into power engineering because I had wanted to and also because one of my teachers found an opportunity for me.

What was the opportunity?

To go out to Michigan—this was in early 1919—and join an organization that was developing a 140,000-volt transmission system. This was the highest voltage that we had at that time, and this was very exciting to me. I went out there in 1919, and I've never been in anything but electric power ever since.

And in high-voltage power.

High voltage fascinated me then and hasn't stopped fascinating me now. Two of my younger colleagues and I are preparing a paper now on some of the possibilities of going to 1,100,000 volts—and some of the difficult problems this will bring up. The need for it isn't apparent right now, but it will be there. I would say by somewhere at the end of this century—which is only a third of the century away, you see. If anyone had proposed 1,100-kv in 1919, as a practical transmission voltage, the technical world of that time would have said he was crazy. And within thirty years from now, I would say roughly, we will be building lines of over a million volts. We have to do a lot of work on it, and I find it a very exciting thing to contemplate.

Myron Tribus

*T*he name Myron Tribus has popped up in a variety of places during the past few years.

In the early fifties there was a Myron Tribus at the University of Michigan who directed research on problems of deicing of aircraft. Or, if you happen to have a professional interest in water resources, you may have heard the name in connection with water conservation and desalinization. If you are an engineer, you may have run across Thermostatics and Thermodynamics, *an introduction to energy, information, and states of matter, with engineering applications; the work was published in the early sixties and its author was one Myron Tribus. If you are an educator, you may have read a paper on engineering education that caused quite a stir a few years back, written by three men at UCLA—D. Rosenthal, A. B. Rosenstein, and M. Tribus.*

The Tribus in each of these instances is the same Myron Tribus, the man who today is dean of the Thayer School of Engineering at Dartmouth College in Hanover, New Hampshire.

Tribus came to Dartmouth in 1961. In a way, it was a curious event. Tribus, a Californian, is a product of the big California schools—Berkeley '42 and UCLA '49. The Thayer School, on the other hand, exemplifies a tradition of smallness, with some thirty engineers per graduating class, and a strong flavoring of the liberal arts. Yet, Tribus and Thayer provide an excellent mix, for each is striving to pro-

duce engineers who understand: *"The product of engineering activity must be functional, economic, and desired by human beings. The engineer must be strongly conscious of the legal and ethical obligations and constraints of his profession."*

It may be that the Tribus of Thayer will have a significant role in shaping the character of the engineering profession of the future. A pilot program in engineering education at Dartmouth College has attracted the attention of engineering educators throughout the nation—indeed, throughout the world.

Thayer offers two advanced-degree programs. In one, leading to the master of science and the PhD, the candidate must display his ability to contribute to knowledge. In the other, leading to the master and doctor of engineering, the emphasis is on the professional side of engineering. The candidate must show that he can do creative design in a time limit and within a budget. He must show that he can contribute to the state of the art.

Only time will tell whether Dartmouth's approach is the right one, but there is no question concerning the commitment of Tribus and his young faculty, nor is there any question that industry and the philanthropic foundations are watching the pilot program closely. The Sloan Foundation has provided a million dollars to help launch it and the Ford Foundation has given $150,000, with the understanding that the bulk of the money will be used in helping other schools to make similar experiments. If the program catches on, the practice of engineering will certainly be greatly modified—as we shall see with Tribus' remarks. Our discussion began with a question dealing with his definition of engineering:

Would it be correct to say that what you are really attempting to do at Thayer is to define engineering, to make a distinction between engineering and science?

That's really the distinguishing feature of our program. We're trying to bring out a distinction, because we think it's been lost. I don't want to sound dramatic, but I believe that the trend toward engineering science, without really emphasizing the engineering, is a very dangerous one in this country.

You feel that the drift in engineering over the past couple of decades has been toward science.

Let's say there are more people who have been interested in science who call themselves engineers. It's always been true that men coming out of college with an engineering degree were not prepared to practice. They're not yet prepared to practice. This we've always known. But what we see now are men who have a stronger bias *against* the essence of engineering. The economic side of engineering and the design side of engineering have been de-emphasized more and more. More emphasis is put on the analysis and the analytical procedures to analyze what has been *done* and not very much on the creation of *new things*.

We've forgotten about costs. Is that what you mean?

We don't turn out really a large number of engineers who think that making something cheaper than it's been made before is an important thing. . . . Where do you go to find a PhD who is really an expert on minimum-cost production? Now we feel that we have to emphasize this. It doesn't mean throwing science out. It means instituting a different kind of balance. And the way we propose to go is to differentiate very strongly between an engineering contribution and a contribution to science. We don't say that one is inferior to the other. We do say that unless you distinguish, they tend to wash one another out.

In what way, do you feel, has engineering education contributed to this washing out?

Because so many professors of engineering are men who themselves have not done engineering. Or if they have participated in engineering, they've participated on the level of a research consultant in metallurgy, or a research consultant in a scientific specialty. The student has practically no exposure to men who have carried products from conception to consumer.

You want your engineers to worry about finances as well as fields. Will they be more maestros than engineers?

Our degrees, the ones that have the word "engineering" in them, have some minimum requirements which require the candidate to demonstrate, at successively higher levels, his

ability to synthesize optimally, to use his resources economically. Once he has learned this, once he appreciates that this
is the nature of his contribution, then we think he will master
all the science he needs and put it to work. But if he wants
only to master the science and contribute to it—but not use
it—then we think he ought not to call himself an engineer.
He is really an applied scientist. Otherwise, the word "engineer" will lose its meaning. People will hire men, thinking
they are engineers but they will not get what I think they
should be getting, namely, men who will use their resources
prudently.

*When you talk to students about engineering, who are some
of the great men you can cite, the great engineers of the day?*
    This is a problem. There are very few names. You ask
people to name the great engineers . . . and maybe they
know Nervi or Steinman. But then they stop. But take such
a company as General Electric. They do not have a title of
chief engineer. This is deliberate. A deliberate act to develop
the team. There are men who are really top notch. But they
are not famous, because they work in teams. And this is
one of the difficulties of engineering.

*It has always seemed to me that most boys of nineteen or
twenty don't really know what they want to be. How can you
tell that this boy might make it, but that the other one might
be better in science, or in economics?*
    You're asking how can we predict. I don't think we can.
We try to keep the choices open as long as we can for the
student. If he thinks he might like to be an economist, or an
engineer, or a physicist—if he knows that much—we can
work out a program for him that will enable him to delay
his choice up until his junior year. Then, if he says, "I still
don't know if I'm going to be an economist or an engineer,"
we can delay his choice until the fifth year.
    Most boys don't want to say, "I don't know," because
they're afraid people will think they're not very able fellows.
But in their hearts they may not know what they want to do.
What we must do is give them additional information to help
make up their minds.
    Now, the potential engineer must have a strong interest
in math and science, or he isn't going to get anywhere in

engineering, with us or any other first class school. It may be that his major interests lie in science and math for their own sakes—then we think he should go in that direction. But if he is interested in doing things where he will *need* math and science (I'm in this class myself: I'm interested in math but I can't get interested in math for its own sake) then he may do best in engineering. And finally, he's got to have an interest in synthesis. In the undergraduate college, he's learning about science, math, the liberal arts. Our job at Thayer is to teach him about synthesis. When he begins to enjoy it, we can use that as a means of showing him how important it is to learn more science and math, more liberal arts.

Let's talk about the engineer as the world sometimes sees him: the good, old, reliable, dull fellow. There's some truth to this. Is there something in the curriculum that makes it happen?

I remember a study of several years ago. A Chicago group of psychologists conducted "depth" interviews with senior students of engineering at Ohio State, MIT, UCLA, and several other places. They would give a man a photograph and ask him what it inspired him to think about, and what he wanted to be, and how many kids he wanted to have, and what his wife should be like. Now the thing that happened was that all of the interviewers wrote identical reports. The interviewers were not engineers: they were attorneys, sociologists, psychologists . . . different backgrounds. But they all came to one conclusion: If they could avoid hiring one of these fellows, they certainly would. They were described by the interviewers as men whose images of themselves were identical, narrow, and—as one fellow put it—"young men begging to be exploited."

Martin Loeb is a social anthropologist and psychologist; Lawrence Kubie is a psychiatrist.

Martin Loeb, Larry Kubie, and I want to do some research on this. We want to find, one, is it really so?—and I'm pretty sure it is. And, two, if it is, why is it so? Is it something we're doing in the colleges? Is it the whole attitude we have toward the curriculum?

Maybe it's an innate conservatism that somehow leads a fellow into a conservative area.

I feel in my heart that it is a combination of self-selection and the fact that the people who teach engineering are the people who came through the system. They perpetuate it.

The creative youngster who wants to come into engineering may be repelled by what he has to go through before he can exercise his originality and the only one who perseveres is the fellow who has a certain attitude toward life . . . representative of the Puritan ethic, work is good for you. I don't quarrel with "work is good for you," but I do think now and then there ought to be a fellow who feels that it's not so smart to work so hard. But the guy who says, "To hell with it. I'm not going to submit to this kind of nonsense,"— he disappears, becomes something else.

A scientist can get away with a "to hell with it" attitude, but an engineer can't.

Well, there's a little of this in science. But a physicist, for example, is a lot more tolerant of the boy who says, "That's chemistry. To hell with it. I refuse to learn it." Provided the boy does something else very well. There are many men— particularly in theoretical physics—who are proud of the fact that they can't do something practical. This marks them somehow as part of the intellectual elite. But this is never acceptable in engineering. The boy who is proud of the fact that he doesn't know how an automobile engine works is considered simply not fit to be an engineer.

Then you think that engineering training has been too full of "make-work" drudgery.

We're trying to break away from that. Not that we relax the notion that you ought to be prepared to do anything. I think you ought to be prepared to do many things, and the more, the better. It is true that the broader your education, the more likely you are to be able to contribute in a fresh way to an engineering problem, because engineering means pulling facts from other fields . . . and you've got to know how to connect them.

But what we'll have to try to do is have the students learn to live with uncertainty, because that's something the engineer has to live with all the time. We're trying to make them understand the generalized processes of engineering design, and how they fit. And we think when we do that, the students will conceive of themselves in less narrow terms.

Then how does your more worldly engineer fit into the still quite-narrow world of engineering? The acre-sized offices full of engineers?

Well, you have to have acres of engineers if the engineers are too narrow. If the engineer's training is too narrow, you need five or six to do what two might do. And then you have to have three or four more on top of that to supervise the five or six. If you don't really have enough competent guys to supervise them, then there is no limit to the number of people you need.

But if you find four or five broadly trained men, and put them together, they can really do a job. They can run circles around an organization of three hundred or four hundred.

You talk about engineering in much the way the dean of a good school of architecture would talk about architecture.

They are as close as any two professions could be. The architects have always had a professional image of themselves. But remember that the architect has been used to practicing as an individual. The engineer had to function on the team. But I do see that we are coming close together, and it's not an accident that,we do. You see more than just a similarity. It's something real.

Will the great engineers of the future function more like architects, more like individuals? Will there be more engineers like Nervi and fewer anonymous "greats"?

I don't know. This is going to be answered soon, by some of the developments in computers. I make this prediction: Very soon, if it isn't already happening, you will find that an engineer sits in his office in Manhattan, with a small "computer" on one side of his desk. Only it isn't really a computer at all; it's a remote station, connected to a giant computer that occupies maybe one whole floor of the building. And in that computer are standardized routines for an enormous number of engineering jobs. A person comes to the engineer and wants a product. The engineer instructs his assistants —they are not engineers—to "synthesize the standard things on the computer."

For example, you need some sort of machine tool. The engineer visualizes the functions to be fulfilled and the sequence of operations that need to be done. His knowledge of materials tells him what he wants; he doesn't look things up in a handbook, but works out a few equations and the computer then selects the materials and costs for that element, and he starts to pull this information together. He gets from his computer and his subroutine the answers he is looking for. Maybe one-half of his fee goes into the rental of the computer and the services of the specialist agencies—who do nothing but keep those subroutines up to date.

So it becomes The Maestro and His Computer.

I can conceive of an enormous change in the practice of engineering due to the computer, and due to a complete reorganization of the way we do things.

How will the maestro tackle a field so full of qualitative features—such as "reliability engineering"?

My contention is that the only thing unique about reliability engineering is that it is the first time the customer and the designer discuss openly how they handle the things that they don't mutually understand.

But the customer will find another designer who does understand—or who claims that he understands.

Yes. He won't stand for bluffing. The risks are too high. But the fact is we don't know *everything*. The customer wants to know why the designer believes something to be so. He wants him to document his belief. He wants him to document it in such a way that he—the customer—can get into the designer's position and agree that this is the reasonable and rational thing to do.

This is the major stumbling block of the reliability program. And I believe we're on the threshold of learning how to program inductive logic. We don't do it today, but we're going to do it. One of these days, we will learn to program computers for this kind of reasoning. And when we do, we will then begin to pull a lot of intuition out of engineering. This won't take the creativity out. It will mean that whole classes of questions that we thought required creativity turn out not to.

Give me an example of inductive logic in engineering.

Say we're going to put a fresh water plant into a small town in Idaho. The town has poor water. How does it decide the kind of plant to put in? The size? You can get a lot of scientific facts, but then you must put together the costs of various alternatives. Then you must put together what the town's demands for water will be, and how the town will grow in twenty years. You have to put together such factors as the possibility of passing a bond issue, which is related to the size of the bond issue, which is determined by the size of the plant. And so forth. This puts the engineer knee-deep in politics.

Now I think we will be able to program the logic of this kind of decision in such a way that an engineer will be able to try out the interaction between the parameters of the plant and the probability of the bond issue's going through. The engineer can concentrate on getting the data—the computer will handle the inductive logic. . . . We don't program our computers for it today. But we almost can—we don't have enough people working on it yet to demonstrate it.

So your engineer will take on problems other than the routine ones of the designer of a water plant. He would come into the town a couple of steps before the traditional engineer would come in.

You take a little town of six thousand people that has to mortgage itself for twenty years. Who's to help the town make this decision? The local city engineer? The city fathers? Ha! This is not the way to do things. We want to turn out men who will be capable of doing these professional jobs. There will be others capable of doing engineering jobs of a more routine nature. And there will always be a need for such men.

And we will have engineers and Engineers.

Either that or we're going to change the name of the engineer to something else, or emphasize the word "technician." I suspect we'll find another name for engineer. Somebody said that there's a "very important mother-in-law problem" in this country—if a man says he's a technician rather than an engineer, half the would-be mothers-in-law decide their daughters should not marry him. So we'll just have to let him be called an engineer and invent a new word. Gresham's law at work.

I don't think we need tremendous numbers of these new Engineers. But we do need them desperately. That's our mission here.

F. C. Williams

*I*nvent used to mean "come upon." Our interview with one
of Britain's great inventors demonstrates that there is still
pertinence to that archaic definition. The way F. C. Williams
sees it, invention implies a forward step that doesn't proceed
logically from those that preceded it. One has to "come
upon" a connection that effort alone will not reveal.

By the same token invention can't be taught. In fact, Williams is suspicious of too much learning, suspicious even of
formal teaching.

It comes as a surprise then to learn that Williams is a
teacher. He is professor of electrical engineering and head of
that department at Manchester University, England. However, his teaching is more in the nature of a master-apprentice
relationship. If one is born with a talent for invention, it will
prosper in such surroundings, Williams claims.

He's a man worth listening to, for he has many inventions
to his credit. The most famous of these is the Williams storage
tube. That's a device, very similar to a television picture tube,
for storing computer information; it's one form of computer
memory. In essence, the electron beam that draws the picture in a TV tube is used to deposit a pattern of charges that
can serve as the ones and zeros of the computer's binary
arithmetic. The charges can be "read" to find out what's in
the memory, altered when something new needs to be
remembered.

157

The Williams storage tube is little used today; it's been largely superseded by magnetic memory systems, which have proved more economical. But it was a serious invention in its time, and, as you will see when he talks, it neatly illustrates the illogical elements in invention.

Williams' reputation as an inventor caused us to seek him out on a trip to Europe in the fall of 1963. Our interview began in his university office and concluded in his laboratory, amidst his latest inventions—new sorts of electric motors. In both locations he was very much in command—opinionated, yes, but sure of those opinions, a man of conviction. His sharp features match the mind within.

I've been reading a book about inventions. Its author does not seem to recognize a difference between those developments that come as a result of steady application and those which have in them the sudden moment of illumination. It is that which I would like to talk about, Professor Williams.

Yes. You can make progress by steady application, but you can't make invention by steady application. You can sit down and work very, very hard indeed, and you will never make an invention in your life, unless you're the sort of chap who can do it.

What is an invention? It's a particular kind of a departure, you're implying.

Well, it is something that does not logically follow from the data. You can't really define it, but I would say the im-

portant thing about it is that it is a forward step which cannot be logically taken—correction!—which *in fact* is not logically taken as a result of the available data. Very often when you've made this step, then you can see how you should have got there by logical processes—what we call the "bright light of hindsight."

I think part of the trouble with the word is that so often descriptions of inventions are cast in terms of the careful light of hindsight.

Most inventions—most of them that I've made anyway—if they are described in strict historical terms, are, in the light of the final answer, rather stupid. They seem like the wanderings of rather stupid people, who ought to have been able to see the goal over there; but instead they went here, and they went right around there, and they got back to there.

Invention is a semilogical process. It's logical to the extent that you exclude what you can't use. But it's illogical in the sense that logic doesn't tell you what you should do. It tells you only what you can't do. Now, when I say, "what you can't do," I mean literally what the individual inventor can't do. It is essentially a personal statement.

Can you give me some examples of inventions of your own career? The storage tube, for example. Was that an invention?

That was an invention, yes. It must have been, because all the information and all the apparatus that led to the invention of the storage system were available and had been available for years, but they just hadn't been put into the right

159

configuration to do the trick. It was in 1945. At that time, there was really just the mercury delay line as a storage method for computers, and its application was limited.

A mercury delay line, as I recall, is a system in which you store information in the form of acoustic pulses.

Exactly. You merely load impulses at the end of a delay line and you collect them at the other end and stick them back at the beginning. The whole thing is sort of a telephone line talking to itself.

Cathode-ray tube is a species of television tube; it was the starting point for Williams' work on his storage tube.

The thing that attracted us most about the cathode-ray tube was that you would not have to wait the whole delay time to get your information. In principle, you would be able to go quickly to a particular point on the cathode-ray tube and get the information stored there.

Suggestion: Follow the anecdote without worrying too much about what is happening on the tube. Williams' thought process is the point here.

Random, rather than serial, access.

Yes. The particular experiment we were doing was to discover what signal you got when you put an ordinary repetitive trace on the cathode-ray tube, modified only by the fact that in the middle of it, you momentarily turn the brilliance off, so that you've got a black gap in the trace. We took our signals from a pickup plate that was mounted against the viewing face of the tube.

We'd been looking at this particular thing, trying to understand the mechanism, for a long time when we suddenly realized that, as the spot approached the gap, there was a signal coming out of the amplifier before the spot actually reached the gap. So we immediately called this pulse the anticipation pulse—it was the pulse anticipating the fact that it was going to be turned off. Now, because this happened *before* the spot got to the hole, this gave us time as the spot approached to say, "Ha! There is going to be a hole in the trace."

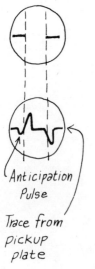

Anticipation
Pulse

Trace from
pickup
plate

Can you draw what it looks like?

Yes. On the cathode-ray tube that is used for storage, the trace is just like this. Now, if we look on another oscilloscope at the signals that we get from the amplifier just using the same time base, then the signal is one that comes along roughly like this. Now, you see, the spot is moving from left to right, and as it approaches the hole, you get this anticipation pulse. Now then, we use that to operate a circuit to put the hole in again. So, you can store holes (and no-holes) indefinitely.

So you saw a possibility of preserving the hole and of storing a bit of information.

Indeed. The inventive activity was precisely that—to realize that you could use this anticipation pulse. This occurred before we understood what was going on on the face of the cathode-ray tube. Before we knew why this pulse existed, we decided to use it. The essential fact that one had determined was that a principle of regeneration could be applied. The spot could be prevented from fading by the process of giving it a fresh start. That's the first thing that is important.

The second very important thing is that once we had seen this, it stuck up like a sore thumb. Anybody who wasn't an idiot should have seen this three months ago and said, "I can use this." Nothing had changed. The apparatus hadn't changed. The display hadn't changed. The only thing that had changed was an attitude of mind.

What came after that?

We got three or four spots, sufficient to establish that there was no doubt that this was the basis of a memory system. But clearly the next thing to do was to improve it. This is always true. First you have the sort of thing that I would call "key invention" in the sense that there is a discontinuity. Now you know you can do it, so let's make it really work!

So then we set about. We put a couple of spots in adjacent areas of our cathode-ray tube face and determined how one area was influenced by the fact that there was a spot in the other. This was intended to be quite simply a scientific experiment, to find out a bit more data. Now, as soon as we did that, we realized that if you put two spots on a cathode-ray tube, side by side alternately, what you're going to see when you hit one spot is going to be determined by whether or not the other spot is present. That is to say, if you illuminate a spot, you can tell whether the last time there was a spot next to it, or not. You therefore have an alternative method of storage—what we call "the double-spot system."

Now, you see, the whole question of anticipation, which is absolutely the key to the previous system, has vanished.

There is no sense of anticipation here because you are not actually doing things in progression. You're just going to a spot, looking at it, determining its state, and replacing it in that state. So that the first invention of improvement is to eliminate the real "Aha!" Innumerable other configurations become possible.

They're all inventive in the sense that you have to decide what configuration is going to give you a working store. But they are less inventive; they are improvements.

There are an awful lot of patents, but there are very few inventions.

And therefore, the textbooks don't talk about the anticipation pulse. But, in fact, that's why I'm here; we want to get some of these actual routes. The problem in science is to define the problem.

Let's be quite clear about this. In my humble opinion, the scientist is on an easy wicket compared with the engineer. I think that scientific research is much more open to a sort of method approach. We hear a lot about the boundaries of knowledge, and so forth. Well, at least they know which boundary they're on, and they do know the step that they want to make.

Now, the real inventive engineer—he merely knows that he is in a sort of sea of half-knowledge, and he wants to make something better and he really doesn't care what it is— whether it's a better zip fastener or radio or whatnot. Just as long as it is better. This is what matters to him. He flits about more than the scientist.

How do you think this is for scientists?

I don't know what their life is like really. But one gets the impression that they start off with a mission in life—they become extremely specialized. If you're a radio astronomer —particularly in this university—the thing that matters above all else is knowing what goes on in the stars.

Now, engineers aren't like that. They can't be like that because their life is not; the things they have to do are not so logical and orderly. Most of the steps that an engineer takes he takes on half-knowledge. You don't design a bridge by the process of knowing precisely what goes on at every point in that bridge. You design a bridge by the process of knowing a few general principles and exercising your judgment and saying, "Well, this is going to be all right." And if you're right, you're right, and if you're wrong, it falls down. And if it falls down, you can't just write another paper and say you're sorry.

I disagree with you in part; I think there is more similarity than perhaps your description suggests.

I think there is a big difference in general motivation . . . the things that make a man rise in the morning singing.

There is, I think, one big difference between the scientific advance and the engineering advance. In a way, a scientific advance can't be superseded. It can only be added to . . . until, of course, somebody finds out that the whole lot of them were absolutely wrong. The engineering advance tends to be more transient. It tends to be more transient in the mind of the man who does it; because he is an engineer, he expects things to work every time. If it works once, you get a terrific kick, and if it doesn't work every time after that, you get rapidly depressed. I mean depressed in the sense that you're no longer walking on air. I myself get very tired, and very frustrated, but I don't get low, because I'm too interested. The great thing is not to wake up in the morning and say, "Oh God! I've got to go to work!"

Do you think there is a correlation between inventiveness and this ability to come back again and again?

I don't know of any characteristic at all. Of the few people that I know, whom I recognize as being inventors, they are just about as different people as, say, the ones who have the initial *F* for their Christian name. You get the same variety of people, except of course, you would find a fair number of morons among the people with the initial *F,* and you wouldn't expect them to invent. I'm talking about the class of intellects where you would expect it to happen. You don't have to be an academic, and you don't have to be a mathematician. You don't have to be really terribly good. It's something quite 'additional to this. I think really good inventors are about as rare as good painters or good musicians.

What things encourage inventiveness?

Well, if you want to encourage inventiveness in a particular individual—first you find him. I defy you to do this on any basis that's tried anywhere at the moment—school examinations and things of this kind. All the people I know who are inventive got good results in school examinations, but then so did a hell of a lot of other chaps as well. So it might be a method of elimination, but it is not a method of selection.

If you really want to do it, I think the only way is to go right back to the Middle Ages and get back to the apprenticeship—the man and the master, you know. Somebody who really lives and works with somebody who can do it. You eliminate the man who can't do it. And if it's there, this is one way to bring it out. You will not bring it out by postgraduate courses. You will not bring it out by any amount of formal teaching. You know, if you could find some form of engineering course to help people invent, and you kept this secret within any one nation, you would be able to mop up the world in about twelve months flat.

Do you really mean to organize university teaching on apprenticeship lines?

I am firmly of the opinion that we must stick in this country to having advanced engineering degrees be research degrees in the broad sense. Scientific research answers for itself; but in the engineering field, there's a great danger that one might say, "We should give the graduate student more information over a wider field. . . . More mathematics, more physics, more detailed technological information." This I resist most strongly . . . because it will not help a man to invent.

You don't have to *know* about things to invent; you have to *think* about them yourself. You don't have to be taught. You don't have to be told. Nobody can tell you. You've got to do it yourself. And the sooner you get a chap put into an atmosphere where he's expected to do things himself, the better.

You spoke of the apprentice living with his master. Man doesn't live by engineering alone. What about the rest of his life? Do you feel other interests—art, literature—contribute to the spirit of inventiveness?

No, I do not.

Are there contraindications? I think it was Hadamard the mathematician who once counseled his students to get themselves a peasant wife; then they would have their home life in order and simple so that, in the study, they could do complicated mathematics.

Well, I think you need a quite stimulating home life.

See Jacques Hadamard, The Psychology of Invention in the Mathematical Field (*Dover, 1945*).

Stimulating how?

Well, you've got to be interested in something else, children, golf. . . .

Do you get ideas on the golf course?

Oh no. This is the great thing about a golf course. You don't think.

But you did say earlier that many ideas come at home, away from the lab. How does that go? Maybe you can mention another invention, and one that did have the "Aha!" while you were at home.

Well, one case is the subsequent methods of storage for the cathode-ray storage system. These subsequent inventions were all made at home in one afternoon. About five or six of them just sort of flowed, one after the other. I had nothing to do. I was at home. Probably a Sunday morning. . . . Now, when I say that you must have other interests—don't misunderstand me. I'm not suggesting invention is a nine-to-five activity or anything like that. But if I had a peasant wife, who wouldn't distract me at home, I think I should go mad. Because one must have something else. It becomes obsessive otherwise. It's obsessive enough as it is.

You spoke of masters and apprentices. I presume electrical engineering is taught that way here in Manchester. Then what do your students do to get abreast of all the advanced mathematics and suchlike?

What do they want to bother with that rubbish for? The time to learn about that class of things is—never. What you do is: You get a grasp of what they can do, and you find somebody else who knows how to handle them. This is the way I proceed, anyway. I don't know any mathematics at all. I have some vague ideas about this and that and what they can be used for, but, believe me, it never mattered to me. I could crank the handle on somebody who does know about it, and make sure he produced the answer.

The danger I see is that you say, "Having reached your graduation, there is an awful lot you don't know. Therefore, we will teach you about these sophisticated things." But suppose you do that for three years. There's still a hell of a lot more to know. So you see, you've just made a little scratch on the surface of what the chap doesn't know. The thing to do is not to teach him more, but make him able to use what he's got, and able to use other people, too.

I think it's a great mistake to learn too much, to be taught too much, to be too good at anything, because this tends to become important in itself. It's just no good knowing about these things if you're not going to do anything about them. You might just as well study Shakespeare and know all about that, because you're not going to do anything with that either. There's a great danger, you know, that scientific education will go that way. That it will become a virtue within itself to be able to do things that can already be done —whereas the true virtue is to be able to do things that have not already been done.

And so this feeling that one must learn what has been done . . .

People sometimes ask me why I left the computer business. Well, I have two answers to that. One is that I say simply that a score of one out of one can't be bettered; and the other is that it is now too difficult. You know, it's too sophisticated. There are too many people in it. I would suggest, if you're trying to make progress nowadays in the computer business, you can do one of two things: You can either work on your own and try and make some progress, or you can keep abreast of what other people are doing. But you damned certainly can't do both. . . .

There's only one easy place to be in science and in engineering, and that's in the front. If you're there first, you have nothing to read. You've got all your time to think.

Frank Nixon

*I*t is paradoxical, in an age when manned space capsules
are lofted into precise orbit regularly, almost flawlessly, that
we still find ourselves thumping recalcitrant washing machines, kicking tires, and sadly concluding, "They don't make
'em the way they used to." But quality is not simply a hall-
mark of space-age engineering. For some engineers, it has
always been a quiet tradition. At Rolls Royce, for instance,
the loudest noise is the clicking of engineering minds, and the
company turns out automobiles bearing a name synonymous
with quality the world over. What is the secret of making
superb consumer products? We wondered. And so we sought
out the chief consulting engineer (quality) for Rolls Royce.

We first met Frank Nixon on a raw, gray, slushy day in
New York. He was waiting for us in front of the British
Consulate, standing before an incredibly clean Rolls Royce
of a lustrous pewter color. Nixon looked for all the world

like a suave salesman of automobiles, which, of course, he is not. Mr. Nixon is an engineer's engineer, responsible for getting that nebulous ingredient called quality into an output of products of which only 8 per cent are automobiles, the rest being aircraft engines (80 per cent) and other gasoline and diesel engines and nuclear reactors.

What is there about a Rolls Royce power plant that makes it so good, we wanted to know, and looked in vain for a way to open the bonnet. Which gave Nixon the chance to get the first word in:

There's no need to bother looking under there. We've taken care of the engine design so there never will be any trouble.

You're saying the Rolls Royce trick is not just quality control in production but fine design and engineering from the beginning!

Precisely. We worry about the capabilities of materials— the strength, and duty, which is the stress on them imposed by the way they're used. When they first built this model of car they really whaled the daylights out of it. They tested, tested, tested it . . . all the time. Every little defect was examined and scrutinized by the designer and was rectified so that trouble wouldn't happen again. They went in for races sixty years ago. If they were going for a 1,000-mile race, they would send a car 2,000 miles over the same course before they entered for the race. So the trick, really, is to discover the maximum variability of capabilities and duties.

But don't all engineers try to stay within limits of fatigue curves?

That's one of the popular beliefs that makes me quite angry. You hardly ever see any indication of the *scatter* of fatigue strength or fatigue life. You just get a thick black line showing the relationship of stress and life. Many researchers in fatigue of metals refuse to acknowledge the existence of scatter in their end results, and if they do acknowledge it, they pay no heed to it whatsoever in their reporting. All but a small minority have dismissed the deviations from "normal" as rogues and mavericks. Now this is quite crazy, for unless the design engineer knows the extent of this scatter and knows the shortest life and lowest strength he's likely to encounter, he can't produce a refined design.

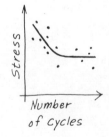

When he lacks this information, he has to make an instinctive allowance based on past experience. This is laughingly called The Factor of Safety. This isn't fine design at all.

Then electronics or rocket designers who hedge their bets on reliability with statistics of probability aren't producing fine . . .

. . . well, a rather narrow statistical approach was begun about twelve years ago partly in an attempt to account for the early failures at Cape Canaveral. Say you had a system with 100 components in it, each with a reliability of 99 per cent. The reliability of the whole would be 0.99 raised to the 100th power, meaning that only about one system in three would perform correctly. If any designer produced an automobile engine, a tank, an aircraft in which more than a very small number of components were unreliable, he'd be fired.

Now Cape Kennedy.

But this philosophy of the statistical approach is spreading?

Unfortunately yes, because much of it is misapplied, and many wonderful opportunities of using statistical methods where they could be of real value are neglected. This seems to me to be one symptom of the present rather frightening trend—for science, or what passes for science, to oust basic engineering thinking. You might say that it is creating an Era of Non-Management, of Non-Engineering. Take what happens with jet airplane engines. The various government agencies—the FAA, the military—tell us that we must carry out a Type Approval Test of 150 hours' duration. Having passed it, experience tells us that we are safe to start flying that gas turbine with a life to first overhaul of, say, 1,000 hours. In other words, we are given a license to start flying. But passing that test merely establishes the viability of the design. The test bears little relationship to the reliability which will eventually be achieved. But the purpose of development testing is to try to find the weak components. If you fix them effectively, you have a product with a good reliability potential. You then build up its actual reliability by a service experience, a feedback, and remedial action.

Feedback of trouble data?

It's more than just data collecting. Many manufacturers do not study their service failures at all. Some of those who have set up an effective system are content to leave it at that.

171

While a study of service troubles is a prime requirement, it is not enough. We ourselves make a detailed collection of service experience, sent in by our hundreds of service engineers from stations all over the world. Their reports are submitted on cards which are punched and fed into a computer to give a running analysis. This gives our engineers a rapid indication of any developing trend which needs attention, but engineers *must* see the hardware.

You say engineers; where does the scientist come into the reliability picture?

In recent years, science has come to dominate activities in most areas of industrial enterprise. The fantastic developments in aerospace, in electronics and nucleonics, have introduced a wide range of problems of extreme novelty and difficulty. It seems wrong to me.

So you think the automotive industry has sounder practices than the space industry because it's more engineering-minded?

In production the same problems exist. But there seems to be too much of the scientific control of reliability in aerospace production. These are science-based industries, so the scientists were there first, and perhaps they didn't stop to bring the engineers in. But their jargon of reliability is not reliability but a *demonstration* of reliability to meet government specifications, which is often an estimate of the *probability* of reliability.

Your wife wouldn't be happy with a probably reliable dishwasher?

She certainly wouldn't. Women have a fundamentally sound approach—which turns out to be equally applicable to the products we make at Royce's. She expects something to work when she presses a switch. She expects it to work every time—for as long as she feels it ought to for the money she paid.

The cost accountant tends to be oriented rather statistically to quality in engineering.

Well, I think the accountant has to realize that it is economic to spend more money on development testing. You will be able to reduce the cost of warranty claims, though the investment may not show a benefit for two or three years. Though this is a little contrary to the annual budget idea, manufacturers ought to think more about total product costs and the full life of those products.

If you play it that way, you can afford to let the consumer be the ultimate inspector?

Only when the level of product quality is built up to a high standard. Marks and Spencer does this profitably. Marks and Spencer is a big organization in the U.K.—I don't think there is quite their equivalent in the States—they have a line of both clothing and food products. They have appreciated, more than anybody I know, the importance of evolving specifications of customer requirements—design requirements in absolute detail. Everything they sell is made for them by subcontractors who know precisely what must be produced for a particular market. Marks and Spencer sends in its own engineers to train the vendors' production people. Once a vendor has produced the goods to the desired design quality—they say, "Now you are on your own—this is the product you are going to continue to deliver to us." They build up mutual trust—they check the first few to be sure they are built up to a high standard of quality. It is now cheaper for them to depend on the customer to act as the inspector and to give immediate satisfaction upon customer complaint.

So a car with a 5-year and 50,000-mile warranty is not a sales gimmick?

I don't think it is a sales gimmick. It's obviously a good selling point, but it's also going to put great pressure on Chrysler to do its best job, to back the warranty by solid improvement in product. This is the kind of self-challenge we've applied ourselves at Royce's.

But reliability, I assume, is nothing new at Royce's?

This is the extraordinary thing. We've always had to have it. And in the aircraft business, always under compulsion of safety of life. So we had to evolve basically sound engineering attitudes. The great pity is much of the newer part of aerospace industry has grown up without this background of experience—many exceptionally brilliant new people coming into it, basically science-oriented, but with no background of experience of aircraft and engines.

Then, how do you get a good reliable engine, right from the beginning? What's the trick?

Well, we do a great deal of component testing . . . in parallel. As soon as one section of an engine is designed, we start testing that section of the engine. Repeated testing, on detail components, and on the whole section.

But ultimately the whole engine?

Without question—for thousands of hours before and after production. For example, take that Japanese camera you're using. By Japanese law, it had to be tested before it was allowed to be exported. The Japanese Camera Inspection Institute tests every camera for apertures, speed of shutter, and so forth, *after* a 5-minute vibration test—2,000 cycles a minute at 2 mm amplitude of vibration. Now this really is *proving,* though it bears no relationship to an "environmental test."

Is there any parallel in Great Britain?

Not as a government activity. But we've realized that the easiest way to build up productivity and to gain and keep markets is to assure product quality. Perhaps it's too little known that Britain is still the world's biggest exporter of woolens, of agricultural machinery, of commercial vehicles. Dacron was a British invention, under the name terylene. The first gas turbine patent was taken out by John Barber, in 1791. He lived eight miles from where the Rolls Royce works now stands. From time to time, we export Beatles, and occasionally a few Wilkinson razor blades. And Rolls Royce powers half the world's civil aircraft.

Richard C. Raymond

Richard C. Raymond is as difficult to define as the organization he once headed, a California "think factory." The output of such a factory is the deep, different, "what-would-happen-if?" kind of thinking which can be done by teams of scientists, engineers, economists, psychologists, etc., who interact with one another in trying to identify future problems and what may be needed to solve them. The government has always sponsored a number of such captive organizations, but a privately owned one like TEMPO is unique. By education, Raymond might be called a physicist, yet he calls himself a manager, a dreamer. His organization, TEMPO, is a component of General Electric's Defense Systems Department, yet its activities range to questions of world politics and food supply, to cold-war strategy and Chinese technology.

Perhaps the most interesting point about this man and his organization is the parallel they establish, a parallel so often witnessed in this fluid world: Raymond is a scientist whose interests have stretched far beyond the traditional bounds of science. His employer is a giant corporation whose concerns must now extend far beyond the electric generators, light bulbs, and pop-up toasters from which it grew.

Raymond, now consultant in information to GE's Advanced Technology Services, has been a physics professor, a research associate at the MIT Radiation Laboratory, a de-

partment head at RAND Corporation (a government captive think tank). When we talked to him in 1962 he was actively in charge of GE's private "think factory." How does a scientist get along in such an environment? We began our conversation with a rather difficult question:

How do you think ahead even a few years in an age when things are going so fast anyway?

Well, when I first started out to try to do this on a systematic basis, I decided there were really three parts to the process. The first part is to gain the best picture you can of all the things which are going to bear on your decisions in five to fifteen years. I picked the five- to fifteen-year interval because anything that we do cannot really have much operational significance in less than five years and the crystal ball gets very cloudy as you go farther out, so I say, "Well, let's pick a decade and we'll look five to fifteen years in the future." I group everything that bears on the success or failure of particular enterprises in this period under the heading of environmental factors.

What are these environmental factors?

Demography is the statistical study of population. People are the most important environmental factors. This is under the heading of demography, political science, sociology, ideology, psychology—the broad-scale problem of where do the people live, what is their condition, and what are the wants which are going to drive them to take various kinds of actions?

And the people who work with you are sociologists, psychologists . . .

Yes, and physicists—you have to include the technology because it's one of the driving forces in the culture. I asked them to write me a book about the year 1970. I wanted it to cover the size and distribution of human population in 1970, the nature of world economies, the ideologies, the politics. Then they were to try and draw whatever conclusions they could from this book as to company strategies and U.S. strategies, for the upcoming year or two. The following year, we expanded this work and projected it out to 1975. . . .

What did you find?

Well, we found, for example, that it was very unlikely that the Russian-Chinese love feast would last till 1970 . . . that there were just too many potential sources of conflict between the Soviet Union and the Communist Chinese to allow them to hang together that long.

How does a physicist feel about the believability of an extrapolation of that type as compared with an extrapolation of how well we'll be able to separate uranium in 1970?

It's more believable than technological extrapolations in general. The fundamental things which propel nations to do things are more readable in the long run than the kinds of things you have to look for in a technical surprise.

Can you give us a sample of what you see ahead?

It's impossible to go back to a food-finding culture or even a simple agrarian culture. We have to have an industrial culture. Before many years are out, we're going to have to have a chemical process food industry. We see some signs of this developing right now, but the investment in such an industry is going to be hundreds of billions of dollars and we are going to need it in a lot of areas of the earth within ten years. And we're going to need it perhaps for the whole earth in fifty years.

How are your ideas communicated to the world leaders?

Well, this I'll never know, but I'll tell you a cute story. *Real butch = very crude.* Back in early 1957, we conducted a real butch broad-scale analysis of the Middle Eastern limited-war situation. We concluded that the Soviet Union would have a great deal to gain and very little to lose by the "let's-you-and-him-fight" kind of war in Syria, Lebanon, Iran, Iraq. This was based upon an analysis of strategic deterrent force balance and on an analysis of the Soviet Union's primary objective at that time, which was to secure control over Western Europe. It looked as though Middle East oil was a good way to get control over Western Europe. And it looked as though the balance of current military forces was such that a limited war could be provoked in late 1958 or the middle of 1959, so as to give the Soviet Union the opportunity to send volunteers and seize control of the Middle East oil fields. We wrote this in a very short document. I briefed our company officials on it, and also several people in the government who I knew were in positions to pass this information on.

The study was done with your own funds?

Our own funds and initiative. I will never know whether our report had any effect or not, but I was very pleased to see the Marines landing in Lebanon, I'll tell you.

You must be handicapped by not having access to the information that the CIA has.

Well, I'd prefer not to discuss this in any great detail because we do get a lot of that kind of information from many sources. We do cooperate with a number of government agencies on both a formal and an informal basis. I'm a member of the Air Force Scientific Advisory Board and the National Security Agency Scientific Advisory Board. Some of our other people are consultants in various ways to government agencies, so that a great deal of this important kind of information does get around on an informal basis. We don't normally try to formalize a great deal of this, not that there's anything improper or dishonest about it. But a lot of it is connected with sensitive security areas and could be misunderstood by your hostile Congressmen for example. But we have been like Caesar's wife in this respect, trying not only to avoid evil but also the appearance of evil. And I think we've been successful. Everybody who goes into this is highly motivated.

What motivates you?

I mean by a highly motivated person one who is honest, objective, and who works on things which seem to him to matter the most. We all have our individual ideas as to what those are and one of our most interesting management challenges in a planning organization of this kind is to rub these ideas together until we can get a sense of direction for the whole organization.

How do your studies make their effect in the government? Who are the people you talk to?

The government has many decision points in it. Generally speaking, the achievement of a major decision in the government is a process which involves many people, many inputs, much discussion. We try to contribute to the knowledge and understanding of all of these people as much as their time will allow. We're going to go down to Washington on Friday to spend some time with the people in the Pentagon.

Can you tell us, to make that more specific, some of the people you are going to see?

The people I'm going to see on Friday are the next echelon below Harold Brown. I know a lot of these people from working with them for many years in a variety of ways. Dr. Fubini, for example, who is his deputy for research. Gene and I were together in Italy during the war. Art Robinson, who is the Deputy for International Programs, and Bert Brown, who is his deputy for Air Defense, and Bruno Augenstein, his deputy for special programs. These are the kinds of people with whom we work most effectively, because the subjects we want to discuss are generally at about their level of authority, competence, and understanding. There is a broad, genuine community of understanding among many of us in industry, government, and the other institutions in our field.

Harold Brown was then head of research and development for the Defense Department.

But you are concerned with the very largest aspects of a problem, often the non-military.

These people are, too. These are deep thinkers and broad-gauge people. They are faced with the problems of making management-type decisions that concern the future of the nation and the human race.

Non-military decisions, in other words . . .

If we wish to provide what seems to me to be the best chance for human security in the next fifteen years, we are going to have to learn to substitute political power for military power. I realize I'm saying just what Spengler said would happen many years ago. But military power which has for many years been the final arbiter in international relations has now become so powerful that it is not really useful in a lot of kinds of disputes which can arise. We're going to have to find ways of adjudicating international disputes without recourse to military power, because military power is not as useful as it used to be.

When you say military power, are you thinking of atomic military power or the whole spectrum?

The broad spectrum. But there is an excluded middle in military engagements these days where you say, "Sure, we can have a few people throw hand grenades and shoot across the Berlin wall. Or we can have a nuclear war." But the realm in the middle here tends to go either one way or the other. If something bigger starts, we must jump on it real quick and quiet it down to the level of a police action or it will escalate to the level of nuclear war. The kinds of wars which nations used to fight lie in this middle region, so that you can't fight a big enough war these days to accomplish any real solution to an international problem without risking the whole world. This is the problem. There are three kinds of power . . . military power, political power, economic power. Right now, for example, we're trying to solve the Cuban problem by economic power and it appears to be working very well.

The Cuban missile crisis came a few months later. Today, Raymond still feels that the necessity to prop a faltering Cuban economy puts a hole in the Communist economic bucket.

One doesn't think of the average technical man giving much concern to these problems. Do you see a growing sense of concern?

Well, I don't honestly know, but this brings me to one other point. I once put together a proposal for a university program in which you take a scientist through the university as rapidly as possible, cast him out into research; after he's been there until the age of, say, thirty-five, you bring him back to the university for a couple of years and teach him politics, ideology, sociology, and literature. I think too much of this is thrown at young scientists and engineers in the universities these days. It is beyond their capacity, particularly as it deals with human problems. You don't understand a lot of these things until you've lived a while.

I tried this out on a friend of mine who is a retired dean of engineering and he said it's impossible. He said you'd never be able to find a faculty that could deal with these people, because they'd know so much more than the faculty.

Does your own career parallel this? Did you appliqué your own understanding of world problems and cultural problems on top of a purely scientific education or were you from the beginning a reader?

No, no, I was a physicist who knew how to build and operate cyclotrons. . . . I'm not a scientist any more. I'm a manager. I was a scientist ten years ago, but since then most of my problems have been with people rather than things. So I'm no longer a scientist. Oh, I can still read some of the papers, but I'd have a terrible time trying to write one. Young scientists and young engineers eat up old scientists and engineers.

You say "eat up." . . . ?

Well, they beat them down . . . you don't remain a scientist in the active, progressive sense of the word for a great many years any more.

In 1945, when you were a young scientist, you didn't think very much about the power struggle.

No, in fact didn't even begin to. I'm still learning. I'm amazed every New Year's Day at how much I learned in the last year.

Do you feel a certain cockiness about what a physicist can do in these areas?

Oh, I am arrogant, but unjustifiably so. I think the scientist can offer to world political problems the values which are derived from work in science and these are values on truth. They are values on objectivity. They are values on experiment. Scientists all over the world, regardless of the race, color, nation of origin, can talk to each other, because they have generally a common set of values associated with truth. It may be that this is the best basis for world understanding if we add the real basic values of food, sex, shelter, and so on.

Oppenheimer said that the physical scientist can bring something to politics that the political scientist cannot, and that is the experience he's had in finding his world can change completely overnight. The scientist looks to the future know-

*ing that the future is not going to be quite the way he thinks
it's going to be.*

Well, more than that, it's essentially a reverence for truth
and objectivity. He can get the results of an experiment.
We'll always accept these in preference to a theory that
merely says what *should* happen. And you can always find a
point on which you can agree—"Yes, this did happen. No,
it didn't happen," rather than "Yes, it should happen," or
"No, it shouldn't happen." You can't agree on "should" or
"shouldn't" very often, but you can always agree on "did"
or "didn't"—if you can get enough data.

Have you thought of running for Congress?
Occasionally, but I don't think I can afford it.

*Maybe the physicists ought to chip in and run a physics can-
didate from California. Lots of good wealthy physicists out
there.*

I do think that scientists can bring something to politics;
willingness to examine all the possible alternatives without
becoming emotionally attached to any one of them. A scientist can compare them and use perhaps different value
criteria to find out which has the best chance of doing something, or which one has the least worst chance.

There's a very interesting book by Heilbroner, *The Future
as History,* in which he points out rather dramatically that
the U.S. over the last couple of hundred years is the only
place and the only time on earth when optimism was at all
justified. But as we look at the developing future course of
history, optimism seems less and less justifiable. But I go
with Edward Teller on this. He says a pessimist is a man
who knows what's going to happen and an optimist is one
who thinks he might be able to do something about it.

And you're an optimist.
I'm an optimist.

*You called yourself a manager, but that's too broad a defini-
tion. How do you think of yourself?*

Well, I'm a dreamer. I'm a guy who does the best he can
in every situation he gets involved in, where the best may not

be very good in many respects. I'm impatient. I see what in my mind are courses of action which ought to be taken right now, but they won't be taken for several years simply because the idea hasn't got around. Now this doesn't mean that I'm way ahead of everybody. There are many people who are way ahead of me in lots of things. I just can't know enough about enough subjects to be the leader in lots of fields, but I do the best I can within the environment in which I operate. In TEMPO, I've had financial problems, I've had personnel problems, I've had organizational problems, I've had information-flow problems, I've had the real basic problem of taking two guys who don't get along very well, but each has his own skill to apply to something and helped them to create the situation in which they at least will get along well enough to get the job done. That's what a manager is.

Augustus B. Kinzel

*D*espite *the predominance of engineers among technically trained Americans, it is the scientists to whom the government has most often turned for technical advice. Most of the armed services have chief scientists; the President has a science adviser; the top technical man in DoD is a physicist. Yet it does seem the engineers have a contribution to make. Many of the problems with which the government wrestles nowadays have a strong engineering flavor; their solution will demand more of sound engineering practice than of breakthrough science. In 1964, with the formation of a National Academy of Engineering alongside and connected with the National Academy of Sciences, the engineers gained their chance—to serve, to deploy their technical skill, and to take a respected place in the councils of government.*

Gus Kinzel, one of the prime movers in the creation of the new Academy, is also its first president. In a way, this makes Kinzel first among the nation's engineers. Yet he has been for many years vice president for research at Union Carbide Corporation. The reason for this seeming paradox is that Kinzel, by virtue of his metallurgical engineering training and his breadth of interests, proved to be one of those technical folk equally at home in applied science and in engineering years before this flexibility became the fashion. Indeed, since his retirement from Carbide several months after this interview, he has turned to the biological field, once one of his minor interests at Carbide. Dr. Kinzel is now president and chief operating officer of the Salk Institute for Biological Studies in San Diego, California.

Catching this energetic, bouncy, and ubiquitous man took some doing, but once we pinned him down in his office high above midtown Manhattan we asked him this question:

Why is it, Dr. Kinzel, that engineers apparently haven't played a larger role in the government's decisions with respect to science and technology—at least thus far?

I think engineers play a larger role than meets the eye. You must remember that the National Academy of Sciences —one of the main advisory adjuncts to our government— has within its associated National Research Council an engineering division. Advice on matters having a large engineering content flows from this division to the agencies asking for it by way of the Council and the Academy. By the time the advice gets to the agency involved, the engineering participation often becomes lost, so the engineer as adviser has not been as visible as he might otherwise have been. Then too, of course, we have had the continuing problem of lack of differentiation between the words "science" and "engineering," but this is an old story.

There's more to it, though, isn't there? We've been struck by the fact that the Defense Department, which has an enormous commitment to engineering, has had mostly physicists as head of developmental work.

Defense Department Research and Engineering.

It seems to me that in these jobs they want people who are looking more to the future than to the practical present; the engineer is always thinking about what he can really do now, or at most two to five years hence, as distinct from what might be done twenty years from now. So the imagination needed for these jobs is scientific rather than engineering in nature.

It was not always thus.

Right. Engineering led science through most of the ages; things only began to go the other way about the middle of the last century. The scientist used to try to understand what the engineer had done and give reasons for it. With this

better understanding, the engineer then further improved on what he had done. Now the basic finding usually comes first; the engineer climbs on board and turns it into something useful that can, if necessary, be manufactured in quantity.

Are you saying, then, that because our technical society is radically different, the government needs a different type of technical advice—from scientists rather than engineers?

No, no. I think the government needs both and in equal measure. And this is why we have set up the National Academy of Engineering in the way we have. It could have been a separate organization, by an act of Congress, as much as four years ago. But this would have created a rift, a rivalry, a lack of unity. It would have driven scientists and engineers apart instead of bringing them together. Now, with the NAE an autonomous parallel body to the NAS, we will have a situation in which the engineer will have the quality status he needs in order that his advice to the government have weight.

Why do engineers seem to hunger for status?

I don't believe they do, by and large. You need it in the government-advice game, though. Unless you have the kind of status you get by having unbiased quality people, men who have reached the stage where they can afford not to have self-interests in these matters, engineering advice to the government will not carry the weight that it should. This is the reason engineers need status, not because they want to throw out their chests at home.

Engineers, more often than scientists, work for profit-making organizations. Do you think the new National Academy of Engineers will lift engineering advice above the normal business milieu?

I don't like the implication in your question, but my answer is that I would certainly hope so. Many of the men now organizing the Academy—and probably some of those to be elected to it—are men eminent in the business-technical world, presidents or board chairmen of very large organizations. But each of these men has a personal, specific engineering achievement to his credit. Each has gotten far enough in the business world that he doesn't have to worry about anything but the giving of himself to the government. As a vice president of Carbide, I administer research. Obviously I am in a position where profits to Carbide are important. But in all my work with the government, I've never had the slightest conflict-of-interest problem.

Could we explore a bit the kind of problems on which you would like to see a larger component of engineering advice?

Well, let me take the example of highway and transportation research. Presently, the National Research Council—which is the implementing arm, you might say, of the Academy of Sciences—initiates and coordinates research projects of various sorts in this field. The actual work here, which is 90 per cent engineering, is done by *ad hoc* committees appointed by the NRC, whose policies, in turn, are approved by the National Academy of Sciences. Under the new setup, the highway-research program will get its guidance directly from the Academy of Engineering.

How would the advice that is rendered, or the research that is done, differ from that presently achieved?

As we have been presently operating, those involved with highway research within NRC have had to do their own thinking, imagining, and planning without, really, very much help from topside. That is, the engineers within the Academy of Sciences itself weren't too involved because, in the nature of things, scientific matters have played a predominant role. Now with this work coming under the new Academy of Engineering, it will be guided by men who understand things from the engineering viewpoint.

As in industry nowadays?

Precisely. In any large industrial concern you have smaller groups—akin to these committees—that think certain tasks seem worth tackling and present them as projects to be done. Then topside looks such a project over and says, "Look, if this is successful, thus and so will be the result. But if you follow a somewhat different route, then broader and more significant goals can be reached than those originally outlined." It's this sort of broadly based experienced guidance that we hope will be brought to bear on essentially engineering matters, more than has been the case in the past.

What other fruitful fields have you in mind?

I would say the growing field of ocean engineering is a good example. As a result of a request directly to the Academy of Engineering from one government agency, supported by others, we are setting up a working committee to carefully examine the engineering side of ocean exploration. The Academy of Sciences will continue to advise on what needs doing so that we understand the oceans more fully. The Academy of Engineering, on the other hand, will advise on just how better tools for doing this work might be developed and, equally important, what the economic-engineering problems are with respect to exploiting the resources of the oceans.

Would the members of this panel on ocean engineering be very different from those on the NAS panel on oceanography?

Oh quite different. It will probably have one individual, probably the chairman, who could serve either place—with the oceanographers or with the engineers. He will thus have to be a very broad-gauged person. But the others would be, for the most part, people that the oceanographers would never think of.

Here you have the classic position of the engineer engaged in the business world. You, for example, have a certain concern for a new Carbide venture—Ocean Systems, Incorporated—and at the same time you'll be involved in advising the government on its program for ocean exploration. Surely, this is a tough one?

It shouldn't be any tougher than for, say, a professor of physics trying to honestly advise the government on its program in high-energy physics, particularly if he has just set up his own little company. You see, as president of the new Academy, I will be deeply involved in seeing that the best committee is organized, but once this is done the committee will handle the details. I have resolved the thorny conflict-of-interest question this way: If you want the best advice, you *must* get it from people in the field who have done the best work. Naturally, these experienced people have biases of one sort or another, but this should not rule them out. I have found over long years of experience that, on a committee, the subconscious bias of one offsets that of another, and so on. So you almost always get a good result if you pick good people and assume they are basically honest and willing to do a fine job. I get mad as the devil when someone assumes that industry people aren't basically honest until proven so!

In your job, you are a research administrator. Yet you speak of yourself as an engineer and you head the new Academy of Engineering.

As it happens, I have qualified as a scientist through my work in metallurgy, but because of the way the industrial world works, you don't see as well what I have done in engineering. My first job in Carbide, back in 1926, began as a problem in metallurgy and wound up as an engineering job. There was a failure problem in a welded flat-spherical pressure-vessel head, and it was thought there was something wrong in either the steel or the welding. I turned to my mathematical training, a graduate school specialty, and showed that it was really a geometrical problem, and satisfied myself that an elliptical head with an axis ratio of 2:1 would result in much lower stresses all around. This was shown simultaneously in Switzerland, and the pressure-vessel code adopted the new shape at once. The point is that the boundary between "science" and "engineering" is very uncertain, and you never know in advance which will be most exciting.

Apparently you get satisfaction from both?

I get major satisfaction out of anything I do that I feel is a real contribution; this can be either a new theory or a new product.

Perhaps this is the kind of person you are looking for to serve on the various panels within the Academy of Engineering?

To serve as chairmen, certainly. However, you must keep in mind that although engineers are being trained much more broadly these days, with a deeper appreciation of science, there are still few who can work equally effectively in both worlds.

Will there be any of these young science-oriented engineers in the initial membership?

Probably not, in view of the fact that we shall need people of proven quality. You see, in science you can prove yourself shortly after graduation, or even before, if you can do one piece of imaginative and skillful laboratory work. You know the saying that most physicists do their best work before age thirty-five. Now in engineering you do your best work much later in life, for you must build up a reservoir of experience. Adding science to the curriculum doesn't change this basic fact.

How do you view the "experienced" engineer?

I like to think of him as a bridge between science and man. Now, when you make something useful to man you have to take man into account. Any time you design a machine or a structure, man's interaction with it must be taken into account. For example, before we engineers can tackle urban transportation we must first know why people come into cities, what they do when they get there, what services they expect, how often they come.

This seems to imply that the experienced engineer must be one who somehow has become more comfortable with people problems.

Let me sum it up by saying that we'll always need the kind of engineer who has successfully turned materials and ideas into useful products. But we need, more than ever, engineers who think of these things not as ends in themselves but as the components of larger systems we humans can use.

A
PUBLIC CONCERN

On the interplay between science and government

George B. Kistiakowsky

*I*t is a new job. Since its creation, in 1957, only four men
have served as the science adviser to the President of the
United States.

*During those few years, the importance of the job has
increased tremendously. In part, we can attribute the job's
growing importance simply to the fact that science and technology are becoming more important activities in the affairs
of the national government. In the early fifties, for example,
science and technology accounted for only about one billion
dollars of the total federal budget, but by 1965 this figure
had grown to fifteen billion. During those years, spanning the
administrations of three Presidents, nothing was growing as
rapidly and as pervasively as science and technology.*

*But there is more to the story than this budgetary side. The
office of the science adviser has been stretched in its influence
by the four men who have occupied the office. The first was
James R. Killian, Jr., the chairman of Massachusetts Institute of Technology. Killian arrived in Washington in late
1957, just a few weeks after the Russians had astonished the
world with the launching of Sputnik. Indeed, the creation of
the office of Presidential science adviser must be attributed,
in large measure, to that great event in outer space—and to
the turmoil and fear it created in the national government.
During his two years as the Presidential science adviser,
Killian's principal role was that of the military adviser.*

195

In 1959 Killian returned to MIT, to the post he had vacated when he came to Washington. He was succeeded as Presidential science adviser by George B. Kistiakowsky, a Russian-born chemist and Harvard professor, who was to serve out the last months of the Eisenhower administration.

Kistiakowsky served from mid-1959 until January of 1961, but one senses that these were not the most rewarding years of his life. The job was still mostly that of military adviser and, though Kistiakowsky is one of the world's foremost authorities on the chemistry of explosions, his real interests tend away from military science and toward such problems as how to strengthen American education and how to increase the support of basic science. It was during his service that the adviser's office began to be involved in nonmilitary activities. We see the beginnings of this new involvement in our conversation.

We visited Kistiakowsky in the Gibbs Chemical Laboratory at Harvard. It was the summer of 1964. You weave through his outer office, which is filled with books, periodicals, and conversing young chemists. The air is spiced with those familiar smells of college chemistry. It is as though you were a youth again, going in to see the prof. But then you enter his office and it is different. It is a large, comfortable room, decorated with mementos of the White House days.

Kistiakowsky is a tall, bony man with a great air of calm about him and, one senses, a rather strong urge to amuse. The purpose of our visit was to talk with him about his role as the science adviser to Eisenhower. He was perhaps a little impatient with the topic, though he accepted it with grace and talked easily as the conversation moved along.

More than most scientists we have encountered, Kistiakowsky thinks politically, knows how to accommodate divergent opinions, how to smooth the way for his own projects. The end of the Eisenhower era signaled no end of his political involvement. When we talked with him, he was in the midst of one of the most important roles of his life. As chairman of a special panel of the National Academy of Sciences, he was preparing a report that had been requested by the Congress of the United States on "Basic Research and Na-

tional Goals." The report would recommend, for example, that the National Science Foundation's role, as a source of support for basic science, be significantly increased during the coming years. In the weeks following its publication, early in 1965, one began to hear that same recommendation being echoed by the Congressmen themselves.

But Kistiakowsky is not always successful in the political world. This fact emerged as we got along in our interview.

Professor Kistiakowsky, how did the scientists get into the White House?

If you trace the history of the executive branch of the government, you'll discover that before the Second World War, scientists were really extraordinarily ineffective in advising Presidents. There was some attempt at the Academy under President Roosevelt, but the attempt collapsed. During the war there was a great deal of advice, but strictly on matters of military necessity. After the war, however, the executive decided that it was advantageous to get technically competent people into higher levels of government, but they weren't very much listened to.

Then came Sputnik.

I think the President became aware that the advice he was getting from his statutory advisers—the Cabinet members, the heads of the agencies like AEC, and the Bureau of the Budget and his national security organization in the White House—that their advice was somewhat inadequate in matters of technology. There was another aspect to it: President Eisenhower felt himself being sort of crowded by the military demands for ever-increasing R and D money and new weapons systems. He might have felt that the channel of command wasn't screening the proposals effectively enough and that therefore he was forced to approve actions which he wasn't agreeable to for lack of technically meaningful advice.

R and D = research and development.

This concern was explicit, was it not, in his famous farewell address?

President Eisenhower was very much concerned. You see, he was under tremendous pressure: this acute public alarm, partially politically inspired, partially quite sincere, that there was this terrible missile gap. Then the Sputnik went up, and there was also a technological gap. People were saying left and right that there was a hell of a lag in key areas of technology. On the other hand, President Eisenhower deeply believed that the budget must be balanced, that the federal government must stay sound financially.

So you have to bear in mind that when the science advisers moved into the White House, and a special assistantship was set up with Jim Killian as the first incumbent, it was mainly for national security reasons—military technology, strategy, intelligence, and space and missiles, all of these things tied together. During the Eisenhower administration, except for one instance, really all of our activities outside of the area of national security were pretty much on our initiative. The one case on which the President specifically called me in and said, "George, look into this!" was the cranberry episode, because he found himself in an impossible situation in which his two statutory advisers in this area— the Secretary of Agriculture, and the Secretary of Health, Education, and Welfare—were giving him diametrically opposite recommendations.

That was back in the fall of 1959, wasn't it?

The Secretary of Agriculture was getting advice from people who were close to the agricultural community. Hence, as far as he was concerned, the important thing was that actually there wasn't any significant danger from the insecticide. (I forget what the name of the compound was.) His people were saying that you would have to eat, as I recall, a thousand pounds of cranberries a day for a month before you ingested enough of the material to get the kind of effects that had been observed experimentally in rats —degeneration of the liver followed by carcinogenic symptoms.

The Secretary of Health, Education, and Welfare was giving completely opposite advice: that this is a toxic substance which in principle has carcinogenic effects, and that we can't allow this sort of thing to go into foodstuffs . . . if we allow it here, what will be next? . . . a very dangerous precedent even if it actually doesn't kill anybody.

Well, what do you do in a case like this? You've got to find a group of people who have no vested interests—who have no ax to grind. You need staff people who don't spend any money . . . who have no authority over budgets . . . who don't have to worry about hungry mouths in the federal establishment . . . and who are shielded politically because they are in the White House and therefore can give their advice on a privileged basis. Presumably such people will be able to give you more objective advice if, intrinsically, they are as intelligent as other people. Of course, the President, like any policy-level official, has to make up his mind on the basis of many influences other than the technical one. I've never seen President Eisenhower make up his mind exclusively on technical advice.

What did happen in the cranberry case? What kind of advice did you give? And how did you give it?

I brought in a group of people. Since this was such an emotionally loaded issue, I even kept the membership of the panel secret. We had some very lengthy deliberations which lasted four to five months, did some very intensive work. We had plenty of occasion to explore conflicts of opinion within the panel, because it was deliberately a mixed panel, all the way from people from agricultural experiment stations to people working in cancer research hospitals. But we finally arrived at a common point of view: It is technically nonsense, unrealistic, to make categorical assertions. We kept saying, "Let's use some common sense about it." The question of harmful additives and toxic substances present in food had to be judged not on the abstract principle —yes or no—black or white, but had to be judged on the basis of whether there was actual danger in its actual mode of use. There was quite an argument within the government as to whether to make this report public or not; eventually the President, after some advice, made it public. And that quieted things somewhat.

It's doubtful science, isn't it? A lot of these experiments depend on the use of unrealistically large concentrations of additive . . .

Yes, and in many cases, you see, the animal experiments employ a very different form of administration than that to which a human would be exposed. The stuff would be applied to the skin, or even injected intravenously—that sort of thing. Of course, this was done to accelerate the tests.

I'd like to pursue that just a bit, because I presume one of the consequences was that you became aware that science as applied in this sector of the federal government was not as good science as you could picture. Did you then feed correctives into the system?

Well, we recommended a number of steps which were proposed but not actually put through, although the President approved them. For instance, we discovered that within the Health, Education, and Welfare Department there was a good technical advisory service, but not highly enough placed. What we recommended was the establishment of a scientific or technical advisory board on the secretary's level —one which would give advice to the secretary, or his assistant secretaries. This was opposed, I recall, by the Food and Drug Administration and, naturally, by the Surgeon General—both parts of HEW—because that meant that they might be by-passed. Since HEW in those days was just a loose collection of essentially independent government operations, it was not hard for somebody in the HEW to refuse, in effect, to appoint this committee. They didn't refuse, but they delayed so long that nothing happened, although the President had concluded in April, or so, of '60, this was a good thing to do. Came June and July, and eventually we became lame ducks, so . . .

It was one thing then to advise and another thing to see your advice implemented.

Oh yes. It's funny, because on the surface of things, the secretary of HEW, Fleming, had asked for our advice.

But in the end, Fleming didn't want—or couldn't follow— your advice.

Well, somehow the whole case died down. There was no longer any excitement about it in the spring of 1960, and because of that, I think, Secretary Fleming was able not to take any steps to implement our recommendations. Of course, since then, the Food and Drug Administration has been criticized for different reasons. It ran into the opposite kind of problem, namely the thalidomide case and a few others like that. Here it was charged that they were very lax in a few instances.

The interesting thing here, of course, is that there is a technical question—the hazard of the limited amount of poison in the cranberries. It should be discussed on straight scientific grounds, but still cannot be because it involves people and their health.

In these matters, I may be accused of being somewhat callous, because as I see it there are situations where a minute amount of individual hazard may be justified for the common good. I differ somewhat from let's say somebody like Pauling, who has said, in a different context, that regardless of other considerations there mustn't be any nuclear tests in the atmosphere because every addition of fallout will harm somebody. To him it makes no difference if the estimated damage is very nominal statistically compared with other sources of illness and death. I've never been quite able to see it that way, because if you are really logical about it, then you clearly should not permit automobiles to travel on the highways. They kill forty thousand people a year and maim seriously several hundred thousand. You can go right through almost the entire modern technology: It hurts somebody. The important issue is the balance between good and bad.

If there be a science adviser in the White House, it means that a President can be influenced by a man of science. Just how much of this took place between Eisenhower and yourself . . .

Well, I was a White House staff member for a relatively short time. As a staff member I gave advice influenced by technical considerations. My relations with the President were professional. Matter of fact, I made it a practice, when an issue came up which involved one of the executive agencies, not to talk to him alone, but always to notify the head of the agency and so to give him a chance to participate in the discussion.

But my other function—the one which took an enormous amount of time—was dealing with the various executive agencies, the special assistants, and others on a sub-Cabinet level. We sought to resolve differences, to try to reach a unanimity of opinion which could then be reported to the President. Eisenhower usually accepted these unanimous recommendations.

So the staff in the White House could bring your function into play without the President himself calling on you for this advice. You did this automatically.

Yes, I was helping the President, trying to save him the time and the effort, so long as problems didn't develop in a way which required Presidential decision. If it turned out that we saw the situation in a different light from some executive agency, then the matter was brought up before the President.

Nowadays the science adviser is up on the Hill and testifies; something you were not required to do. How has this changed the role of his advising?

Well, a special assistant, and I think Killian and Wiesner behaved the same way, has many different functions. First off, he is a staff assistant. He has to make snap judgments, or give advice or information. The President may turn to him during a National Security Council meeting, as he has done to me, and say, "George, what do you think about it?" And you try to do the best you can. You learn that even though you don't know much about it—if it's a technical matter, you probably know more than anybody else in the room. At most, you can postpone this kind of advice, say for twenty-four hours, and then you rely on backup information that is in possession of your regular full-time staff . . . ten or so people who were first class in my time.

A very different function is one in which the special assistant is chairman of the President's Science Advisory Committee. This is indeed advisory—a deliberative, thoughtful, slow-moving operation. It operates mainly through advisory panels of experts, called for a particular job, that may involve sometimes as much as twelve months of work. Their advice was in turn filtered through the Committee, which acted as the first non-specialist audience, because typically only one or two members of our eighteen-man group thought themselves experts in the field. But all were versed in problems of science and technology in the government and so they judged the work of the experts. This usually took the form of a report . . . sometimes a few pages . . . in special cases, only a memorandum to the President . . . but usually a report. Most of these, of course, never have seen the light of day as public papers. But once in a while, one

Seaborg was chancellor of the University of California at the time of the report. In 1961, with the advent of the Kennedy administration, he became chairman of the Atomic Energy Commission—the highest post ever held in the Federal government by a Nobel laureate. See the interview with him.

prepared public documents to create a greater impact on the nation. In my case, I think the most important one, from that point of view, was the report called "Scientific Research, the Universities, and the Federal Government," produced under the chairmanship of Glenn Seaborg. I took a very active interest in that enterprise, and the report very much expresses my general philosophy.

Would you say that working on that report was the point at which the role of the adviser began to broaden, or did it happen before?

Well, a little before. There were two earlier reports of a fairly general nature. One of them dealt with education. There were rather sweeping statements about the need for excellence, and so forth. In a way, the report I just mentioned was our attempt to translate generalities into explicit recommendations. The other, earlier report, dealt with the structure of scientific advice within the government, to some extent, and led to the establishment of the Federal Council for Science and Technology.

Since 1957 we have had sort of a second wave of technically trained people throughout the executive part of the government.

When you look now at the picture, it's a completely different one from what it was in '57. The prestige and the influence of these people is much greater than it was six or seven years ago. To some extent this has reduced the urgency of the need for the White House special assistant and his organization, because there are now more people wholly competent to judge these matters in the executive agencies. The best example, perhaps, is the DDR and E, Director of Defense Research and Engineering in the Defense Department, who took over much of the work that the President's advisers did in the first few years of their existence.

At the same time, and this is something that became very clear to me, we need the creation of something similar on the legislative side of the government. In 1959 and '60 I already felt very keenly my inability to establish effective channels of communication with Congress. At the time, that was especially difficult, because the opposite political party was in control of Congress. The ability to testify before

Congress, I think, is exceedingly important for the special assistant in his capacity as the director of OST since 1962.

What about the Congress? I understand your National Academy Committee on Science and Public Policy is seeking to advise the Congress?

I feel very keenly that the time has come for some group to assist Congress in its search for the same kind of technical advice that the President is getting—advice given on a "take it or leave it" basis. This is one of the things about which I have been thinking since I left the White House office. I once gave a speech that I entitled "Science for Policy and Policy for Science"—which are very different matters although both concern a special assistant. But since leaving the government, I became mainly interested in "policy for science" rather than the other part. Here, clearly, the Congressional role is of paramount importance and is very difficult. We on the Academy Committee hope that we can be of some service to Congress in this area, as an independent source of information.

Compare Senator Clinton Anderson's contrary view.

Jerome Wiesner

*W*hen *President Kennedy took office in 1961, the White House apparatus for keeping an eye on science was hardly more than three years old. The President's Science Advisory Committee, PSAC, had been created in 1957, when the Russians orbited Sputnik. The interdepartmental Federal Council for Science and Technology was two years younger still. Yet already the apparatus had acquired great political importance —along with a peculiar aura of being outside politics. It seemed to signify something non-political that Kennedy kept the same advisory committee which had served his predecessor, and even selected as his personal science adviser a committee member whom Eisenhower had put on PSAC.*

At the same time, the selection of Jerome Wiesner for the job told something of the political importance it had taken on. For Wiesner is no conventionally academic member of the science community. His technical credentials are sound,

*of course. He is an electrical engineer whose work has been
at that very high-brow level where engineering and science
are hardly distinguishable. Like most such men, he was active
in the development of radar during World War II. In those
same years Norbert Wiener was generalizing automatic-
gunnery techniques into a theory of cybernetic control and
automation; and Claude Shannon was demonstrating that
something he called "information" could be treated as a
mathematical quantity in analyzing communication systems.
Wiesner was one of those who seized on these insights and
helped develop them into working tools for electronic engineers. Nevertheless, it is probably more by his personal than
his intellectual influence that Wiesner has made his mark on
the world. He was influential in leading many investigators
into the new field of statistical information theory. He took
the leadership of the Electronics Laboratory at Massachusetts Institute of Technology and guided it through a manyfold expansion. Through two decades he served on one or
another of the Defense Department's advisory committees.
And late in the fifties, as the election of 1960 approached, he
became part of what was later known as the Cambridge*

Group: Harvard and MIT professors mostly, historians such as Schlesinger and economists such as Galbraith, men who had been devoted to Adlai Stevenson but who were becoming convinced that John F. Kennedy could win where Stevenson couldn't. The group worked on the position papers and speeches that helped win Kennedy the Democratic nomination and the presidency, and, after November 1960, Wiesner was a thoroughly political figure—and a thoroughly logical candidate to move into the science adviser's office in the ancient and high-ceilinged State-War-and-Navy Building next door to the White House.

At the time we interviewed him, Wiesner had been in his job less than a year. Afterward he served through the Kennedy years and the transition to the Johnson administration. It was he who brought together Johnson and Donald Hornig, who became Johnson's science adviser and who appears in the interview after this one. After his hitch in Washington, Wiesner returned to MIT as dean of science and then provost.

Wiesner was forty-six when this interview was recorded. He has a youthful face with big mussy features. He sits in a slouch, talks in a casual mutter which has the effect of putting a ring of passion into the slightest raising of his voice. His response to a question is quick and orderly, with no false starts or pauses to collect his thoughts. Our first question to him harked back to a speech he had made earlier.

Some months ago you remarked that you hoped to organize your work to concentrate more on long-range plans, the long-range problems of government and science; we would like to explore a bit what you mean by that.

These are the problems that relate to the development of basic science, the educational aspects of science and technology, the improvement of the status and quality of governmental research establishments, the creation of new industries based upon science, furthering international scientific collaboration and cooperation, and increasing the technical component of our development program, the things that are important in the longer term.

*Things that are likely to get crushed in the more imme-
diate . . . ?*

Yes, the more important problems get most of our attention. Take oceanography as an example. We have a large
amount of work in this field in the country . . .

Much of it of military origin?

Yes, but a lot of it not. Until recently the individual agencies interested in oceanography were working quite independently. The Federal Council for Science and Technology
established an interagency committee on oceanography to
integrate the work in this field.

Some oceanographic projects: deep-diving submarines, sound transmission in sea water, ocean currents, underwater oil and minerals, fish and plankton.

Did you yourself take the initiative in that?

Actually, that was set up before I came in, but this administration used the information made available by the interagency committee to create the beginning of a good national
program in oceanography. We'd like to go considerably further than we have so far. Last year when we planned the
first supplementary budget, President Kennedy encouraged
us to augment greatly the work in oceanography. We are
planning to increase our research activities on other natural
resources.

*In a program like that, is coordination done essentially in
budget preparation?*

It ends up in the budget. First we ask an independent
group of scientists to study a field for us. We normally depend on the National Academy of Sciences for this. For
example, in the broad field of natural resources.

Hornig tells about later Academy studies in the next interview.

Did you do this on oceanography?

In the case of oceanography the Academy took the initiative before the government was organized to handle the
planning of natural science programs. However, in the case
of atmospheric sciences, we suggested to the Academy that
they tell us what the scientific problems in the field were—
quite independently of whether the government is in a position to finance all the worthwhile research that it identifies.
What we would like to have in many fields are estimates
from the scientists themselves of what a very vigorous program in their field would be.

How specific does this get?

In oceanography, for example, the problem of the many special disciplines that make up this field, marine biology, physical oceanography, hydrology, the atmospheric aspects of oceanography, instrumentation, and many others, were examined in detail. Research in oceanography is also handicapped because we have never developed adequate instruments for this work; because most of the research ships are obsolete; and, because of space limitations, the institutes that work in this field cannot absorb any more scientists.

So a report like this comes to you?

It comes to my office, and perhaps we first attempt to get an independent review of the scientific aspects of the problem. Then it normally will go to an interagency committee representing the various groups in government that have responsibilities in the specific field.

This is a special committee?

Yes, this is usually a panel of the Federal Council for Science and Technology, which is the in-house organization for coordinating government scientific efforts. Then the interagency committee will try to identify what departments are able to do or want to do.

Now, here we get into an area that interests and puzzles me very much. Does it get to a question of deciding that if we spend this much for oceanography, we can't spend as much for water desalting, say? Is it ever looked at in those terms?

High-energy physics: breaking up atoms by hitting them with very high-speed particles— and studying the fragments.

Plans were just starting for a 200-billion-electron-volt accelerator, ten times the energy of existing machines. In 1966 a site is being selected.

It never gets to be that specific a question. But we are always aware of the fact that funds for research are limited. For example, when we fund money for a large new accelerator in high-energy physics we realize that this will have an impact on the total program, so we try to assess the importance of the device to the field. It is hard to make a decision between general support of basic research, where the individual projects may require relatively small amounts of money, and the need for a large tool like an accelerator that might cost a hundred million or two hundred million dollars.

Does such a choice get made?

The attitude we take—in the end it will always be tempered by physical considerations—is that each field should be considered independently. There is very great promise in high-energy physics—and it attracts some of our brightest scientists. Even though it is expensive, we must try to support the field adequately. We try to understand the impact of each proposal in its own field. High-energy physics, which is a very important intellectual pursuit, may come up against a dead end unless we can extend the energy range or the beam intensity of machines.

Do you, or anyone, at any point decide that there is a certain amount of money available for non-military research as a whole?

No, so far we have not done that. In fact, we have always been reluctant to do so, though we may be forced to as research expenditures grow. Up to now, as I have already indicated, fields have been treated separately—I suppose this has been possible because the research budget has not been a large part of the total federal budget.

If there is more money for high-energy physics, that does not necessarily mean less money for cancer research . . . ?

Not in the least. However, I do believe that there has been some lack of balance in our research and development program for other than fiscal reasons. At the moment, I am actually more concerned about the effect of too rapid program growth on manpower resources.

Thinking that you are using too many people?

So far we have taken a different point of view—that the country needs to increase its manpower, scientific manpower, and that basic research is important in this respect.

We've been discussing areas where research is needed and not being done. Do you still feel that the problem of disarmament involves a need for research as well as for political negotiations?

Yes I do. We are trying very hard to create an effective disarmament research organization within the government. This administration proposed to Congress the organization of a special agency for disarmament with a responsibility for studies including technical studies.

Arms Control and Disarmament Agency was created a few months later.

What kinds of research ought we to be doing in order to make it easier to work toward disarmament? How can research help?

You are probably thinking about the physical sciences, so I'll talk about that first. We need to understand inspection systems and we need to understand the interaction of them with military systems. We need to study the components of inspection systems. We need to study sampling techniques —what sampling techniques are adequate under different circumstances, the application of mathematical sampling techniques to inspection.

Such things as how many counties you would have to inspect to be sure that . . . ?

Yes. For example, can you estimate from physical examinations and from records and from waste stock piles what the total output of nuclear material might have been? Is it possible to inspect an industrial complex and discover clandestine production mixed in with legitimate production? Would you be able to tell whether the American electronics industry had buried in it the production of a hundred auto pilots a year for missiles? Or that someone was making clandestine rocket engines? Or are any of these questions relevant to a particular disarmament plan? These are all poorly understood.

Does lack of knowledge like this present a serious practical barrier . . . ?

Yes—a combination of that lack, plus lack of the kind of operational studies which would indicate what is safe and what isn't.

In the crudest terms, how many missiles would be relatively harmless and non-decisive?

Yes, what we can live with. To do a perfect surveillance job would be extremely costly—but a system providing a tolerable degree of certainty might be easy to create. Depending on how one plans a disarmament system and on what assumptions, it might require very intense inspection or very little.

Should research leading to disarmament be actively on the

docket now? Or do prospects of any kind of arms control look so remote that it is hardly worth while to carry on preparatory research?

At the moment, I think most people feel it necessary that we continue our studies—discouraged or not—if we want to create a rational world. Many of us feel that had we been better prepared, had we understood the technical problems during the previous period, things might have gone a lot better.

Mr. Libby said in a speech recently that six months after the Geneva test-ban negotiations started, U.S. scientists knew that test-ban detection was impossible because one could muffle underground tests—that facing up to that at that time would have caused the government to decide on the impossibility of a test ban.

Of course, or it might have led the government to set more modest requirements. I think we can follow a will-o'-the-wisp in the search for a perfect system. Part of the problem at Geneva was that we didn't have an understanding of what we could tolerate. Inspection systems will always be less than perfect, but if one has a good understanding of the risks, one might be willing to take them. What we are contending with is not whether there will be disarmament—because there will be someday—but whether it will be before or after World War III. Incidentally, though little has been said about it, recent U.S. experience has shown that it is much more difficult to conduct underground tests than opponents of the test ban claimed, even when one is not trying to carry them out clandestinely.

Present test ban excludes underground tests.

Just as this interview was being published, in February 1962, observations of a Siberian explosion started studies which now indicate that a few very elaborate detection stations can identify most underground explosions even at very long range.

Does it enter as a factor in your thinking at all that we are in some sense in scientific competition with the Russians?

I suppose it does unconsciously, though we ordinarily regard science as something we do for its own sake and for our own sake and not because of competition with Russia. I never defend any expenditure in science on the grounds that the Russians are doing something. If the Russians were expending a good deal of effort on a field, say oceanography, it would make me look at it more seriously, but I would not support a big program blindly just because the Russians were doing so.

*Are there any areas other than rockets where the Russians
are disturbingly ahead?*

I don't know of any. There are some where they are quite
good. Astronomy, applied mathematics. But I think we can
hold our own even in these. On the whole, I think American
science is much stronger than Soviet science. Sometimes I
think this is the reason for the seeming aloofness of Soviet
scientists. They are proud and not too anxious to look poor
by comparison.

*Of course, on this man-on-the-moon business, we are in
competition.*

Well, it is a factor. But I regard space exploration as one
of the really great adventures of this century. This is enough
of a human motivation to want to do it—just because it is
challenging. I think that scientific curiosity is also involved,
and a form of defense insurance.

Defense insurance?

First of all, there is a great deal of technology being developed in the outer space program which could be important
to defense. Although most people say that they see no military use for space, not to have a space capability is a risk
that I don't want to take. Of course, you might buy just
this insurance at a somewhat lower cost. But having decided
that space exploration is important, that it is one of the
great human adventures of the century, you must then decide upon the rate of effort. There are people who think
we are trying to do too much too fast. There are others who
think the effort is still too slow. But it won't cost any more
to meet a given objective, like landing a man on the moon,
rapidly than to do it slowly. And it might have less impact
if we did it slowly . . .

*How impressed are you by the widespread feeling in the
scientific community that a high-speed program is stealing
from other sciences?*

In my own view, the space program will augment the
whole science program, because there is a great deal of related science that will be supported by the space program
—astronomy of certain kinds will get a big lift, cosmology,
many supporting sciences. Furthermore, the climate will be

such that it will be generally easier to get support for science. So that on the whole it is not unhealthy. It does create some serious distortions in the use of technical manpower—in engineering worse than in science. To fulfill our objectives, we will have to learn how to use our manpower more effectively and we will have to educate more scientists and engineers.

There is a widespread feeling that the life sciences have a special importance now. Do you share this at all?

Yes, I think that they are among the most exciting areas of science today. A lot of questions that have puzzled people since man began to speculate about himself and the universe are, it seems to me, on the verge of being understood. We certainly are learning a great deal about the mysteries of life. The communication sciences, the field I used to work in, are concerned with understanding logical or thinking processes, and they are moving ahead at a surprising rate.

Is federal support for these sciences increasing relative to physical sciences? Would you feel that it is part of your business to see that it was?

My general impression is that various agencies supporting the life sciences are doing a pretty good job. Actually, I don't care if it is growing faster than the physical sciences or not. The important thing is that they receive adequate support. On the other hand, I believe that the behavioral sciences deserve more support. People in the behavior sciences have been somewhat timid about asking for support for their research projects.

A while ago there was a good bit of talk about a Cabinet department of science. Does the Federal Council do all that a department of science might do?

The Federal Council is an experiment. Just where it will come out, I really can't say. The other day someone asked me what my job was, and I said that I thought my responsibility was to keep a scientific anarchy working well enough so that people wouldn't try to change it and create a massive department of science. I think that a single department of science would not be a very sensible thing, because most of our research is done in support of the missions of government agencies. The agencies could not adequately carry out their responsibilities if they didn't have their own scientific activities. I was thinking about this problem last spring, and I asked myself, If I were designing a new country, would I design a single department of science? I decided that I would not, no more than I would have a single department of law. Though we are confronted with very serious management problems in the government, I believe that we should try very hard to operate within the existing framework. However, there is considerable merit in the proposal to create a somewhat limited department bringing together scientific activities not related to the mission of any single agency.

It is your feeling that the Federal Council can contribute to well-organized anarchy?

That is my hope, and we're trying to make it work. Our own view is that the best solution to many of the problems that we encounter is to attract a lot of good people into the government.

The uproar produced a Congressional investigation, an executive order setting some guidelines, no significant changes of the sort Wiesner feared.

This current uproar about conflict of interest doesn't help you operate, does it?

It could do a great deal of harm. It depends upon how it is handled. I think that there is actually a conflict-of-interest problem. One should be aware of it and try to operate so that there are no abuses. If one were to go very far in the direction of limiting the participation in the government of people with even a minor conflict-of-interest problem, the government's technical activity would suffer very seriously. The nature of much technical and scientific work is such that people come in temporarily. If they are legally judged to have a conflict of interest for some time afterward, when they go out, they may not be able to go back to the jobs they had previously. They might not have come, under such circumstances. The government also uses many technical consultants from universities and industry. Though the use of such consultants does pose conflict-of-interest problems, I believe that this practice works greatly to the advantage of the government.

Well, does some of this result from a failure on the part of the government to get its salary scales up to the standards of outside industry, and then using non-profit institutions to do things that are essentially governmental?

I don't believe the non-profit corporations present a very serious conflict-of-interest problem. The basic complaints about the non-profit corporations are two. One, that it's a device for circumventing civil service, and more importantly that it is an abdication of federal responsibilities. The problem, in my opinion, is not really the non-profit corporation, which I regard as only a symptom. The real problem is the one you mentioned earlier. In the postwar period the government has been spending increasing sums of money for research and development, but most of it is spent by contract with large corporations. Their salary scales are not supervised, and they create the environment in which the government must hire people. There are also many other factors about doing scientific work for the government which are not as attractive as working other places. So these non-profit corporations were devised to help meet that problem. The first non-profit corporations were on university campuses or run by universities, because the people whose help was wanted preferred to stay on their campuses. There has, of course, been an inflationary spiral and salary differentials have become a big factor. I think that the government is facing a serious crisis now and must do something to meet it. We've got to make working for the government as attractive as working elsewhere.

Congress has since raised the top pay available for government scientists from about $22,000 to nearly $30,000.

Donald F. Hornig

*I*t is startling to realize that the compact and powerful mechanism by which the President of the United States ties his office into the technical aspects of government has a history that dates back only eight years. It was in 1957, a month after the first Sputnik went into orbit, that Eisenhower created the President's Science Advisory Committee and made James Killian, its chairman, his special assistant for science. Two years later, establishment of the Federal Council for Science and Technology brought together representatives of *the federal departments under the chairmanship of the science adviser. And in 1962 the adviser was given a more formal role in the White House structure as director of the Office of Science and Technology, a role paralleling that of the director of the budget and the chairman of the Council of Economic Advisors.*

Each presidential adviser has brought his own style to the job. Donald F. Hornig, adviser for the last year and a half, had been less conspicuously a part than his predecessors were of Washington's science-military-political community. At forty-five, his career had been as a physical chemist, a teacher, and an administrator of teaching at Brown and Princeton. When you talk to him, his whole manner conveys the impression that, as adviser, he is exactly that, with no desire to be a behind-the-scenes manipulator of affairs. He seems to visualize himself as a sort of intellectual resource, available to anyone who needs help. Unlike most public officials we interview, he made no effort to control the direction of our discussion, responded wholeheartedly to each question we raised. When you ask Hornig a question, his face goes into an intent, listening stillness, his eyes remote. When you finish, the look of intense thought persists for several seconds. Then his face comes to life, his eyes engage yours, and he plunges into animated talk.

Any time you meet the science adviser to the most powerful political figure on earth, who administers by far the largest block of resources ever devoted to scientific purposes, one question is likely to loom large in your mind: How are all those resources allocated? Who decides what to use them for? On what principles? Our first question came at the problem from the educational side. We asked:

To what extent is the federal government planning and directing higher education in the sciences today?

That's a very hard question. Planning is involved to the extent that one provides the kind of support that makes it possible for people at the universities who understand what they want to do to do it, properly and well. But I've never conceived it to be the role of the federal government to plan in the sense of laying out the educational process, per se.

But, in fact, the government does have a tremendous influence on the way the process develops.

This is right. In the first place, a technological society has to have first rate research in progress—in some cases for immediate application and in other cases simply because we realize more and more that we have to depend on how much we know and understand in order to build a new society . . . everything from defense to water resources to health. So research, as research, is an important goal, and in accomplishing it we end up supporting two-thirds of all the research going on in the graduate schools of the country.

And in the second place?

We're supporting some 26,000 students a year, indirectly, through research grants. And now through direct federal grants and fellowships we're supporting a little more than that many again. So that even if we had no plan whatever, we already have a mighty effect on the higher educational system.

As an educator, do you find that worrisome?

Well, let me put on my other hat, as a former professor . . . still a professor for that matter. I have a deep conviction that the single most important ingredient of graduate education is the research a man does, using his own hands and his own brain. The rest is all background. And a second conviction I have is that the only good research apprenticeship is first class research on a meaningful and significant topic. To get that, a student has to be where that kind of research is going on—because you can't tell him how to pick meaningful topics; he's got to watch active minds doing it. Now, much of this sort of choice is made within the academic community, but the topics we in the government choose for the benefit of society are also meaningful and significant. These goals—the government's and the educators'—more or less coincide. Not perfectly, I agree.

So the critical question is the allocation of government funds. When you decide what directions the government will take, you are deciding the direction of science and education.

This whole question of allocation among fields is one I keep looking at, but I just haven't any idea how you solve

it. At the moment, we are putting two quite different ingredients into the mix. Not as a matter of deliberate planning . . . I think the country as a whole has done this.
One ingredient is the selection of social goals, as that reflects
back on science. This is why 40 per cent of all the money
we are spending in universities goes to medicine and health-
related research; this reflects a national conviction that these
things matter to us. Medicine also happens to be one of the
most exciting and fruitful fields of science, as science; this
has been a very happy coincidence during the postwar period.

And the second ingredient?

Since we have funded university science by the proposal
method, almost all academic science is selected on the basis
of proposals by faculty members. Thus the other ingredient
in the mix has been relevance and significance to knowledge
itself, in a broad sense.

*Can you feel any confidence that this sort of mix results in
an education program producing the people and specialties
the country needs?*

When you ask if we are producing the right ratio of chemists to physicists, I can only say I don't know. We are producing for a world that is ten or twenty years away. The
saving grace is that people do move fairly freely, if they are
well trained in science, from one field to another. I find it
hard to know if I am a chemist or a physicist . . . at one
time I lectured at Oxford in the mathematics department.

*If you look at this mix that determines allocation of science
effort, which ingredients are the important ones? Which have
the most influence?*

In the first place, there are several kinds of allocation.
For instance, there is the decision as to how much shall be
allocated to academic science . . . a matter of setting the
total effort of the National Science Foundation. That decision is made almost solely within the government, in the
executive and in Congress; we get advice, but it's a governmental decision. The balance shifts somewhat in the allocation within NSF—between, for example, the education
program and the basic research program. This is primarily
an administrative decision, with a strong ingredient from the

Congress and now an increasing ingredient of external advice. But the detailed allocation, the allocation within fields, is very largely dictated by the academic community, because this allocation is based largely on the volume of proposals received from different fields. This is also somewhat true of the National Institutes of Health.

How about Defense?

That situation is a little different. Again the decision as to total investment is administrative and Congressional; and, at that level, this office also has some influence. Moving down, the decision on how much military science is to be done in university and non-profit institutions is primarily administrative but reflects influence by industry and advisory mechanisms. Now if one talks about allocation among fields of effort in DoD, the criterion of relatedness to defense is important, so there is a much stronger ingredient of internal decision than at NSF. But in the end there is also an academic input, because the department does rely, though to a lesser extent, on proposals from universities. It adds up to a very complicated mesh of allocations.

Does it add up to good planning?

I really don't feel very kindly about detailed planning. Neither do I think we can live with anarchy. When decisions are made in this complicated maze, it is hard to believe that one can't do a little better by applying analysis and fact-finding and planning in broad outline. Getting back to academic science rather than the total picture, this is why for some years we have urged the National Academy of Sciences to undertake studies of each field . . . this is a beginning for better planning. Under Frank Westheimer, for instance, they've studied chemistry. They've really tried to make the people in the field focus on the questions: Where is the field going? What are the most important directions? What promises does it hold out? What are the internal priorities . . . if there were more money, how should it be spent? On equipment? On buildings? What would be the effect of 10 per cent more? It's the first time this has happened.

How is that program going?

Such studies have been carried out so far in chemistry,

physics, solid-earth geophysics, and ground-based astronomy. It's only a beginning. The hard question, of course, is how best to make use of these studies.

Do you think of them as having a direct influence on the allocation of government spending?

I don't think that someone will look at the Westheimer report and the Pake report on physics and conclude that the balance between physics and chemistry ought to be shifted. I do think one or the other may end up presenting a clearer case for evident need or evident promise—in which case those needs get satisfied at a higher priority. This becomes an indirect allocation.

Have you seen such effects?

I did a little exercise with the ground-based astronomy report; I circulated it to all the government departments and asked how the plans in it related to their own thinking and programs. What showed up immediately was that the report views astronomy as a rather abstract thing. Although there is a very direct relation between our space program and solar astronomy, the report emphasizes solar astronomy considerably less than does the NASA program. At this point one has to have a bit of discussion whether NASA itself has been disproportionate—and my own conclusion is they have not. This has also been discussed in the astronomical community. One of the interesting things that comes up after such a report is that the community itself begins to become self-conscious . . . and even to change its point of view.

Do you feel a personal responsibility for a decision about the proper direction for astronomy?

Perhaps I have a responsibility, but I have no capability of deciding between solar and galactic astronomy. I can be sure that we get the right people into the discussion, so that reasonable choices can be made. But when the issue gets onto a bigger scale, then I have to become involved. I can't avoid the debate on the balance between space and medical research.

What are the real criteria used on questions like this?

By and large, I think we have taken the right point of

view—that our real limiting commodity is talented and imaginative and creative people. In most of the "little sciences" —not little as science, but not requiring expensive tools— in the little sciences, I think the philosophy has been to make it possible for every really talented person to do his work at a reasonable level.

Do you feel we are achieving that?

It has been achieved in the little sciences. But it fails in the areas of science where you do big things and need expensive tools. You can't investigate space without building a rocket; the buy-in price is high. The next generation of accelerators to do fundamental particle physics will be very expensive indeed. The same thing in astronomy and radio astronomy.

You can't apply the same standard.

No. High-energy physics, for instance, probably meets all the tests for a very fruitful science. It draws some of the very brightest young men in our universities; it's been producing discoveries at a remarkable rate; it gathers a high density of Nobel prizes; there are great things on the horizon, and it teems with ideas in a way I wish other fields did. But among these ideas are ways to spend money—and if one tried even to approach the ideal of providing every talented man with the tools he thinks he needs . . . well, I have no idea where the budget would go, but it would be more astronomical than it is.

So what do you do?

In a field like that, we have to make a social decision— given the pressure from the scientists, which indicates there are great things to be done, how much are we willing to let them have? I know of no rational method of establishing the right amount. But I do think that in all of our planning, subconsciously, we have always used one criterion which is a check and balance on all the others—a determination that even if America isn't ahead in every field of science we'll at least be among the very first. This is a general public attitude, and it's an important factor.

You face still another kind of problem in the environmental sciences.

This is perfectly correct. Here we have found that the appropriate units for scientific investigation are the entire globe or the entire atmosphere or a whole ocean or continent; this has made them big sciences. In the atmosphere, the thing that looks most promising is the notion of automatic sensing stations with satellite collection of data. A very expensive system. Whether these things should be centralized in single agencies—I'd prefer to put that off for a bit. I think a reasonable diversity in sources of support and in decision-making contributes to the quality of the science, but there has to be some leadership too.

There's a regional aspect to that. How do you think we are doing in spreading science around through the country?

We're doing well, but not well enough. We're trying to achieve several things at once. We have to maintain those pinnacles of excellence which allow some people to be out at the very forefront. But it is quite clear to me that if every child in America is to have reasonably equal access to the best in education, some one of these centers must be located not too far from each place in the country. There's a high mobility in graduate education, but if the local intellectual tone is wrong, we may deprive a man of his opportunity before he ever applies to graduate school.

There's a matter of economics as well as education. For instance, the effect of research work on local industry, the sort of thing you see around Boston, along Route 128.

I think the Route 128 effect has been exaggerated; there are some first class universities which have not generated a Route 128. But the presence of a university is an economic asset to a community. We have to accelerate the growth of new enterprises.

I hear people saying that maybe in the past few years we have tried to spread too thin, regionally.

People always talk as if it were a question of abandoning the project system of distributing funds for research in favor of a regional formula system. It's not true. One is constantly asking whether each new program can do something to redress balances. My own thinking tends to rely on incremental planning; we have to make mistakes some of the time. This may be my background as an experimentalist, but I think absolute planning is almost hopeless.

This is something of the same philosophy the President has toward national growth. Will you talk a little about his attitudes toward science. How does he use science and technology?

So far as I can tell, the President has a deep conviction that great things are possible if we just don't think too small about what it is possible to utilize in science and technology. I don't think he would want to make choices in detail himself, on these things we have discussed, but he has pressed at all times for a flow of imaginative ideas. He is very concerned about education at all levels. His detailed interest in science is focused on certain broad areas in which he has had a special interest—space, health, desalting. . . .

How often do you see him?

This varies. I guess about once a week.

Kistiakowsky told us that when he was science adviser, the major part of the job was to help Eisenhower deal with the Defense Department.

This has changed very drastically. With the setting up of the office of the Director of Defense Research and Engineering, some of the things Kistiakowsky did are now done within the department. I suppose his people spent perhaps 90 per cent of their effort on the Department of Defense, and I suppose that would be more like a third now.

How about defense sponsorship of basic science; is the Defense Department doing as much as it should?

I think there is a very dangerous pressure to cut down on basic science in the Department of Defense. We've gone up and down again. The department was the first body in the country to see clearly that major new weapon systems would have to come out of a strong scientific base . . . so that by 1950, 90 per cent of federal support for university research was coming from Defense. I don't think that was a stable way for the country to run its business, and increasingly the pressure has been on the department to get out of support of basic science and to do things related to weapon systems.

You think this reaction is going too far?

That 90 per cent was excessive, but the original arguments really are sound. The department not only needs a sound basic science in existence, it needs to be aware of what's happening and have a feeling for it. You can invent all the information systems you want, but this really only works by contact of people. Moreover—and this relates to what we were discussing earlier—the defense priority on fields of science and their probable impact on defense problems is entirely different—and it should be—from the weight which would be assigned by scientists on the basis of scientific interest. The department must be able to promote those fields which are foreseeably going to have an impact.

Is this as true now as it was in the immediate postwar years?

We are in an interesting situation defensewise. There is a relative plateau, for the moment, in weapons development, and the existence of this plateau feeds the argument that we don't have to put so much into science. I think the reverse is true. We had such a plateau between the two world wars, but unbeknownst to most people the jet engine was coming along and wasn't foreseen; radar was coming along. The problem is to be sure that we anticipate the next big change when it comes. I think that's precisely the reason Defense has to be involved with basic science; when the day comes for another big breakthrough—and I don't doubt that there will be one—they've got to be in a position to assimilate it quickly.

Sir Harrie Massey

S*ir Harrie Massey is an Englishman from Australia with a spare frame and a dry, piercing manner. Yet when he speaks, it becomes apparent that his is an intellect of great keenness; the ideas come quickly, well expressed, always pertinent, and often entertaining. The quality of his thinking is familiar to many: to the physicists for whom he wrote such books as* Theory of Atomic Collisions, Negative Ions, *and* Space Physics; *to the German scientists with whom he played a deadly yet often humorous war game when he was chief scientist in the British Admiralty's Mine Design Department; and to the American colleagues whom he joined in 1943 in the Manhattan District group at Berkeley, California (this group had as its goal the electromagnetic separation of uranium-235 from its non-radioactive counterpart). The editors of* International Science and Technology *have also had a heavy exposure to his approach, since Sir Harrie was a member of our editorial board during the first three years of the magazine's existence. This interview took place during that period, in 1962.*

Perhaps his most important contribution to postwar science has been his work as chairman of the preparatory commission for the European Space Research Organization, which officially opened its eight-year research effort in January 1964. He is now its president, although he would deny that his role was anything more than organizational. Such

*activities are typical of those of many highly effective re-
search scientists who leave their laboratories for a period to
accomplish an important organizational or political goal, and
then return to their first love, the lab bench or teaching. The
interviews immediately preceding this one reflect the views
of three American scientists—Hornig, Wiesner, and Kistiakowsky—who have performed similar tasks.*

*Massey still hasn't been able to get back to his old post as
Quain professor and head of the department of physics at
University College, London. In December 1964 he was appointed chairman of then newly elected Prime Minister Wilson's Advisory Council for Scientific Policy. While this group
is not strictly comparable to the President's Science Advisory
Council, which Kistiakowsky, Wiesner, and Hornig described
above, it's the closest thing to it in the U.K. Also, he's still
chairman of the British National Committee for Space Research and a member of the National Institute for Research
in Nuclear Science. As such, he is deeply immersed in planning for large scientific projects, which is what we wanted to
talk to him about.*

Sir Harrie, we know you're concerned with the problems

presented by large-scale scientific efforts. What are the major problems?

Well, increasingly there are problems of finance—of paying for very expensive research projects. Then there is the problem of the scientist turned executive, who must handle the complex problems of team research without entirely losing touch with the science involved. And finally there is the problem of the individual scientist—keeping him motivated in an age of team research.

Is finance getting to be more of a problem than it used to be?

There is a definite trend to very expensive pure-research equipment. Perhaps we see this more clearly in Britain, because there are not so many projects and you can see the trend growing. This is acute at the moment in nuclear physics, but in other subjects it's coming. For instance, in radio astronomy we shall soon be facing the suggestion of a bigger radio telescope. And the same thing is likely to happen with big magnets for low-temperature research, gradually spreading to all branches of science.

In radio astronomy, you "listen" with antennas for radio noise from space, rather than looking for light with a telescope.

Why are things particularly acute in nuclear physics?

Well, this is the first pure science which is coming up against a financial ceiling—a really severe one. Penetrating

231

$10^9 = \$1,000,000,000.$
gigabuck = a billion dollars
megabuck = a million dollars

deeper and deeper into the microcosm is landing us in macroscopic difficulties. We may need gigabucks (10^9) before very long. This is a situation which is very obscure to most people outside of nuclear physics.

What are the problems?

As you seek to go to higher energies, accelerators get bigger and bigger and more costly. It's relativity that limits us. When you get up to a thousand million volts, relativity becomes important—it reduces the fraction of the energy you impart to the accelerated particle that is actually available for the reaction. This effect increases with the energy. It makes for tremendous technical complications and very great expense. At the same time, this is a field in which you really are up against the unknown and what you get out of it will be new in the full sense of the word. You cannot even be sure that the laws of physics as we know them remain valid. Indeed some of them will almost certainly be found wanting.

Einstein's theory of relativity enters here, because when you accelerate an electron nearer to the speed of light, more and more of the energy goes into increasing its mass and less into increasing its velocity.

How does one decide how much to spend in a field like this?

The whole problem arises out of what one has to compare the expenditure with. One has no absolute feeling for this. On the one hand, even in the very expensive fields of high-energy nuclear physics and space research, the actual sums involved are small compared with those spent in many other directions. But they are large compared with what we spend in other parts of pure science. My own rule, which is a very vague one, is that I judge the importance of a pure science on how fundamental it is in a certain sense. How far is it exploring in the unknown region where you don't understand the laws which govern the phenomenon studied? This is purely a standard of pure science from the point of view of a pure scientist.

High-energy physics is what is done on accelerators and cyclotrons.

How do you answer the taxpayer who insists he would get more benefit if the money were put into, say, medical research?

Here I think they've got to remember that you are limited in what you can get out of a particular scientific study by the number and quality of people that you can get to work on it; money on its own is not sufficient. You can starve a project and make it impossible to do any work. But if you don't have enough good people and there is not enough enthusiasm for working in a particular field, it is very hard to stimulate anyone by merely saying that, if he works in this field, he is going to have unlimited funds. The best scientific work comes from the enthusiastic person really eager to work in the field.

Are there real differences between the kind of man who can do truly original work in particle physics and the kind who can do truly original work in the cure of disease?

They aren't interchangeable, and it's a question again of the enthusiasm. Of course, there are many factors which have to be taken into account. I don't suggest that anything is ideal, by any means, in the distribution of funds. Clearly we must provide for any particular important branch where it is obvious that it is important to the whole of society, as in medical research.

How are the universities going to fare in an age when research equipment is getting so big and so expensive?

This is another very big issue. If you don't take steps to avoid it, the universities will be forced out of some fields of research before many years have gone by. They won't have a chance unless you give them opportunities to get these expensive equipments.

We are terribly anxious to preserve the universities, because if you go back into the past, you find out that most of the fundamental studies were made in the universities. The real reason is because you always have a stream of youth and enthusiasm coming through—the situation is never allowed to get stagnant—as it could in an isolated institution where more formal procedures apply and the freshness of youth is lacking.

In all these expensive, highly organized laboratories, what becomes of the little fellow in the ivory tower?

I think it safe to say that highly organized research is guaranteed to do one thing—produce nothing new. Because you organize on the basis of what you know, and you make sure that you find out what you organized to find.

What about the scientists who do the organizing—what problems do they face?

In my opinion, if we assume that at a certain age a scientist goes over completely to the executive side, then I think we are going to get into trouble. Because a few years after he goes, he will be out of scientific touch with those he administers. The only way you can be in touch with the others is by doing some of the scientific work yourself. Those in the organization who are doing the actual scientific work must have confidence in the person who has responsibility for directing the program as a whole. If he has gone off completely on the executive side, he soon is out of touch and can't make a balanced judgment.

At the moment it is not too serious, because in fact, a large number of executives are still living on their scientific fat—the experience they acquired. But it will get more difficult.

What do you personally do about this situation?

I still do some research—not enough, but some. One day a week is kept sacred to this end—I'm not to be disturbed for any reason. And I lunch in the lab with the young men; that helps me stay fresh. I don't consider I have done any work unless it includes real scientific study and research of some kind.

How do you spot the young fellow who can run a research team of specialists?

Again, it is very important that the executive people should be so closely in touch with the young people that they can pick out the future leaders from the team. If they are not in touch, such people are going to be lost in the mob.

Glenn Seaborg

As the government's annual expenditure on science and technology expands steadily past $15 billion—almost a fifth of the national budget—the business of science becomes increasingly mixed up with the business of government. Such circumstances demand capable administrators, men with the vision to see how science can best benefit mankind, and particularly, men who are able to articulate the capabilities and goals of science in terms the politician can understand. As he explained when we talked with him, Glenn Theodore Seaborg first came into that kind of administrative responsibility almost by accident. But is is a responsibility he has carried well. He now bears the title of chairman of the U.S. Atomic Energy Commission, from which position he directs the government's involvement in all matters pertaining to things atomic, from power plants to linear accelerators to hydrogen bombs. This enormous organization accounts for nearly $1.5 billion of that $15 billion the government spends on science. It's an awesome responsibility, perhaps the highest federal administrative position ever held by a top-ranking scientist.

That Seaborg deserves the title of "top-ranking scientist" is a statement beyond dispute. He is a chemist, and his special interest for more than a score of years has been the chemistry of the transuranium elements—those artificially created elements whose atoms are heavier than uranium

*(uranium being the heaviest atom generally found in nature).
To be studied, such elements have to be "created" in the
laboratory and therein lies the difficulty. The general pro-
cedure is to bombard the very heaviest atoms with the protons and neutrons of which atoms are composed, hoping that
some of the heavy atoms will capture the bombarding particles and be transformed into heavier elements. It's a tedious
business, not only because the yields are generally microscop-
ically small, but also because the elements produced are
generally unstable and must be detected and examined
quickly before they revert to their previous form. Seaborg has
been involved in the "discovery" of nine of the ten elements
thus far synthesized in this manner and is the author of two
books and numerous papers describing the chemistry of these
rare elements. It was for the early phases of this work that he
shared the 1951 Nobel prize in chemistry with his colleague,
E. M. McMillan.*

*Seaborg's transformation from a scientist to an adminis-
trator was not a sudden one and, indeed, is not yet complete.
He has been straddling the fence between the two worlds for
a number of years. Before his appointment to the AEC position by President Kennedy in 1961, he was chancellor of the
University of California and, before that, had been associate
director of Lawrence Radiation Laboratory. Through most
of his career he has maintained a lively interest in education,
an interest that is reflected in the influential Seaborg Report
that grew out of his membership on President Eisenhower's
Science Advisory Committee and was the genesis of much
of the present government's interest in scientific education.
When we interviewed him, in 1962, he was becoming interested in education at the elementary level.*

*Seaborg is a tall man who doesn't fit the clichés about sci-
entists any more easily than his 6' 3" frame fits federal office
furniture. He speaks quietly. Talking with him one has a great
sense of control, of precision in thought. That this is a life-
long habit emerged as we questioned him about his early
days in chemistry.*

How did you get into chemistry in the first place? I understand it goes back to a high school teacher.

Up until my entrance into high school I had almost no contact with science. I had been born and spent the first ten years of my life in a small mining town in upper Michigan, the son of a machinist and the grandson and great-grandson of machinists. When I was ten, my family moved to California, where I believe I was a good student, but I wouldn't say a student with any particular interests other than getting the regular education and again no special contact with science. When I entered high school I was faced with the problem of choosing a major. My choice basically was between a college preparatory major and a commercial major. My mother actually preferred that I choose the latter. It was just because she felt that it would be nice if I could have a white collar job—something respectable.

Like an accountant?

Bookkeeper is the way she referred to it. Somewhat to her disappointment, but never to her subsequent regret, I chose the other, less useful route, which was to take the college preparatory course—a literature major—with all the esoteric subjects that go along with it. This meant also that I had to take a laboratory science in the junior year. It being a small high school, there was alternation between chemistry and physics, and I hit chemistry in my junior year. I had a very enthusiastic teacher named Dwight Logan Reid who preached chemistry—whose eyes lighted up when he gave his lectures and who recounted many stories of his college days when he took chemistry. He had this quality of inspiring interest. It was early in Mr. Reid's course that I decided to go into science as a major, probably chemistry. Then when I went on in my senior year and took physics, this was reinforced. That's the whole story.

If you had come in the other phase and taken the physics course first, do you think you might be a physicist today?

I think not. Let me tell you my reasoning there. By the time I finished high school and had taken both chemistry and physics, I was ready to make my decision as to what my major would be as I went on to the university. I decided that, although I liked physics better, there was no way of

Glenn Seaborg

making a living in it other than teaching in a university. So I
decided that I would major in chemistry with the vague
objective of probably teaching in a university if I were
fortunate enough to obtain a position—but also having the
fall-back possibility of going into industry, which one could
do as a chemist. So with that objective I majored in chemistry but took the maximum amount of physics and since
then have been on the border line of physics.

*Is some of this hindsight, or did you have this perception of
subjects and such at that time? Often kids are confused.*

No, I had that perception. I had that view of the future—
I liked physics better, but it would be more practical to
major in chemistry. I did not have then or, I suppose I should
confess, later, any interest in biology or even organic
chemistry.

*Then it was physical chemistry that you studied at the Uni-
versity of California at Los Angeles?*

In my senior year at the university, I took a course in
modern physics from a Professor Adams, who told us all
about the recent work in nuclear physics. It was at that time
that I decided that I would specialize in the nuclear part of
chemistry. I resolved to go to the University of California
and work somewhere near Ernest Lawrence, although I knew
I couldn't work right with him because he was a physicist,
and I, of course, would enter the chemistry department. I
was also interested in working near the great physical chemist Gilbert Newton Lewis.

This was in what year?

From 1934 to 1937—three years.

*Very early then in the history of the neutron. This was just
a couple of years . . .*

Yes, just a year or two after Chadwick's discovery of the
neutron. In the fall of 1934 I remember reports from
Fermi's group in Italy on the bombardment of uranium with
neutrons producing what they *thought* were transuranium
elements. Later, when this work was taken up by Hahn and
Strassmann and Meitner in Germany, I recall presenting one
of their papers at a seminar in the chemistry department—

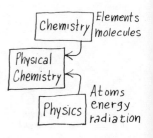

*Ernest O. Lawrence
invented the cyclotron
(1934), the first
high-energy particle
accelerator.*

*Chemists today often
speak of "Lewis acids"
meaning acids as first
defined by Lewis in
the mid-thirties.*

*A neutron is the uncharged
neutral particle which
is part of an atom. Its
discovery led to the
atom bomb a dozen
years later.*

239

a paper in which they attributed the many radioactivities that result from the bombardment of uranium with neutrons to transuranium elements. I went over this paper and went along presenting it as a description of the chemical properties of the transuranium elements. These particular radioisotopes, of course, were shown in the classic experiment of Hahn and Strassmann in December of 1938 to be products of the *fission* of uranium.

Discovered this was happening:

This paper of Hahn and Strassmann—that represents perhaps the first time that the transuranics came into your research life?

I would say that that was the time when I began to consider seriously the possibility of searching for the real transuranium elements—yes. And that became a major theme for my research within two years and has been ever since.

Not this...

Your researches in that field are well documented, so let me skip over that period into one that is equally intriguing, namely, your progress from a researcher to an administrator.

Well, I think the start came with the advent of the war. The group at Berkeley, which had already discovered plutonium and the fissionable isotope uranium-233, expanded right after Pearl Harbor. Most of the people with me were junior people, either graduate students or research assistants or, in one case, an instructor, so that I more or less naturally came into the position of leading an expanding research team. Then, with the formation of the Plutonium Project, we moved to the University of Chicago, at least several of us, in April of 1942 and immediately thereafter. There the group rapidly expanded because of the requirement that a chemical separation process for plutonium following its manufacture in a chain-reacting pile be developed in the shortest possible time so that the atomic bomb could be built.

The plutonium process:

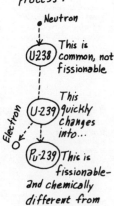

You spoke of "naturally" coming into the leadership of this group, and it certainly is natural from the standpoint of your eminence as a chemist, even then. I wonder how natural it was in terms of your own temperament? To what extent did you like the job of having to lead people?

Well, I don't think I ever gave that a thought. It just seemed the logical thing to do, under the circumstances.

Was it in a sense, though, a contrast to the Seaborg who had spent long, solitary nights working in the lab?

Yes, it was. It was a transition and a rather early one, because I would say it was during late 1941 and early 1942 when I was twenty-nine years old, going past my thirtieth birthday.

One would normally come rather slowly into the leadership just of graduate students, and here you were suddenly given rather major responsibility . . .

That's right. I think normally one wouldn't—well, I suppose without a war, it's doubtful that normally one would ever have found oneself in that sort of a position. I'm sure it would have been a matter of just advancing as a college faculty member through the ranks with graduate students.

Speaking of graduate students, do you think today's graduate students work as hard as you did then?

I do feel that there was a tradition in those days of working longer hours, almost around the clock. I can remember at one stage starting about noon and working the whole afternoon and early evening getting ready for experiments. A radium-beryllium neutron source for neutron-scattering experiments was available only at night. So we worked until daylight, had our breakfast, went home and slept till noon, and then started the next day. I do feel that there probably are not too many graduate students who are working that schedule today.

Certainly you worry about nine-to-five science.

Yes, I would say that nine-to-five science is almost impossible. When I find a graduate student with that attitude, I almost write him off unless he can be convinced that that is the wrong attitude.

Also you were under the close influence of inspiring teachers.

I do think that perhaps there is a problem here too. I don't know how to solve it, but it does seem to me that there isn't as much of that individual inspiration as there used to be when you had the professor working with his smaller group of graduate students. There perhaps are things that are taking its place that take care of this. I don't know. More equipment, better support, more intermediate people, post-doctorate scientists, and so forth, give students firsthand help. I don't know if this takes the place of the inspiration of the great men or not.

This lack of student-to-teacher contacts can perhaps be compensated in part by a far more explicit statement of what science seeks to do, of the scientific society.

I think that there is certainly a greater recognition of the role of science in society by our government, both in the organization of new departments as exemplified by the Office of Science and Technology and in the role that scientists are beginning to play in government and as members of government.

In one of your speeches you say that you can see scientists as lawmakers.

Yes, I think I can see scientists as lawmakers if we can find scientists who are willing to have a try at this mode of life and if we can find scientists who have the necessary combination of what I call scientific and political capabilities. I do not picture a scientist, just because he is a scientist, going into positions of governmental responsibility successfully.

But compare what Harrison Brown has to say about this.

Do you have some candidates here? I mean can we run somebody off the Berkeley campus or the radiation lab for Congress from California?

I think that I could think of some people, who obviously wouldn't want to be identified by name, who would be very satisfactory if they could be convinced to have a try at it.

Do you think it's important to convince them? Do you think the Congress should have more people with deep training in science?

I think it is. I think that it would be very helpful on the whole. However, I think that, if it isn't possible, the other approach is feasible and is being shown to be feasible, namely, the learning of science by the lawmakers who are now in Congress.

You have, of course, a magnificent illustration of that in the Joint Committee on Atomic Energy.

In the JCAE and in the Committees on Science and Astronautics in the House and Senate.

There's no question in my own view that the Joint Committee has been . . .

. . . probably the outstanding example. I think that this has been over a number of years a hard-working committee, a committee in which the membership has not changed very much, so that it has been possible through years of experience to acquire knowledge. This committee has had a number of members who have worked very hard, who have studied very hard, and who are about as knowledgeable about atomic energy as they need be. They strike a good balance between the scientific and political capabilities of which I speak. Oh, I would like to see a few people in Congress who tried it from the other way around—who started with the scientific background and who picked up the political capability.

Certainly there has been no lack of people from Berkeley who have come onto the executive side here in Washington. Yourself, Herbert York and Harold Brown in the Department of Defense—so that conceivably that kind of person could also enter the legislative branch.

Yes, and there's Roger Revelle who's become science adviser to the Secretary of the Interior from San Diego. And Jerry Johnson, who is chairman of DoD's Military Liaison Committee to AEC.

Herbert York is now president of the La Jolla campus of the University of California. Harold Brown is Secretary of the Air Force. See interview with him. Roger Revelle is now director of the Center for Population Studies at Harvard. Jerry Johnson is director of the program for peaceful uses of nuclear explosives at Lawrence Radiation Laboratory.

Is anything being done about this? I mean do people talk about this late in the night?

Well, I don't know that they do now. In my last semester or two as chancellor, I began to have late afternoon coffee hours in which we began to explore subjects like this. They were just getting started at the time I was called to Washington.

I understand that the Atomic Energy Commission has recommended changing from a five-man arrangement to a single administrator. If the Commission had a single administrator, such as NASA does, what's your feeling about whether he should be a scientist or non-scientist?

I couldn't answer your question on that basis. I think I would have to compare the people involved.

The idea is still being discussed.

FPC = Federal Power
Commission.

*Vested interests are always a problem where government and
big business interact—and science has gotten to be big business in recent years. Some people express concern as to
whether one shouldn't be as wary of having a scientist run
the AEC as one should be of having an oil man run the FPC.
Now that's an intentionally overstated viewpoint, but I
wonder whether you feel that scientists are immune from
vested interests?*

Oh, I don't think they're immune. I think it's a matter of
the man. I think, however, that the advantage that the com-
missioner has in having a background in science is very great,
because he is in a position to understand more completely
the scientific basis for the decisions. Now—I don't say that
that is the only basis. He has to also be in a position to understand the fiscal basis, the legal basis, the political basis, and so
forth. But there is a great advantage, in running an agency with
as much science involvement as the Atomic Energy Commission, in having this ability to understand the scientific background.

*You say "completely" understand. That's an interesting
problem. I'm sure people will be coming to you soon and
asking for various kinds of equipment in connection with the
new neutrino-interaction experiments they're trying to do.
Now, I know that you know the physics of these things . . .*

I don't mean "completely" in the sense of a specialist. I
mean completely in the sense of being able to evaluate the
one scientific aspect as against another.

*Is there a sense in which you can "smell" when a scientific
argument brought to you is wrong somehow, or incomplete?
Is that the kind of thing that guides you in choosing?*

Let's say that after you have studied it awhile, with a scientific background, you probably can. Yes . . . that's a
good way of putting it. I don't say that you know it immediately, but you can go back and study it and certainly understand it well enough to suit the purposes.

And also communicate with the scientific community.

And also communicate directly with the scientific community, rather than through the medium of the staff here at
the Commission.

I'd like to turn the conversation to another area, if I might, and ask you about the future of atomic energy. Could you just talk about some of the things in the atomic energy program that you feel that our readers ought to be aware of?

Well, of course there's the whole area of civilian nuclear power. The development of electricity from the heat energy developed by the fission reaction. We have the aim of developing this source of energy so that it will supplement—not supplant—energy from conventional sources. Because although the resources of coal, and oil to some extent also, are very large and will last a long time, they're not infinite. Someday we're going to need a supplemental source of energy. Also, the conventional fossil fuels have other uses—in the case of coal and oil, for the manufacture of chemicals, in the case of oil, for the propulsion of mobile vehicles—that nuclear energy cannot take care of. So eventually we're going to have to conserve them for these purposes. Therefore, it's only a question of when.

It is just a question of economics today, isn't it?

It is just a question of economics, yes. That's an important point. Nuclear power is a reality. We can build small, medium-sized, or large plants with nuclear energy today.

At that time (1962) there were about thirty nuclear power plants in operation in the world. In 1966, the number is closer to twice that.

Do you think if proper value were put on these uses of fossil fuels for mobile vehicles even today you would put a premium on nuclear energy?

I think if we had a national fuels policy, we would perhaps begin to place a greater premium on nuclear energy.

What about nuclear power in space?

Nuclear energy has a very definite role to play in space, a dual role. It can be used in the propulsion—direct propulsion—of space vehicles. A reactor can heat a propellant like hydrogen which is expelled out the back to propel the vehicle, giving it much longer ranges for heavy payloads than is possible with chemical fuel. The other use is to develop electrical power as auxiliary power in space vehicles and in satellites. This is the SNAP program—Systems for Nuclear Auxiliary Power—and here we have two approaches. One is the compact nuclear reactors for the higher-energy ranges, beginning down around kilowatts and up to tens of kilowatts and

An average home would need a power plant with a steady output of around 5 kilowatts.

eventually to megawatts and above. The other approach is
through the use of the isotope power sources, where, for
example, isotopes of some of the transuranium elements,
such as plutonium-238 and curium-242, are used to give
compact heat sources for development of this auxiliary power
in satellites.

You spoke of millions of watts. Just what are the Commission's programs for, let's say, the 1970's in the way of having a power package available?

We have programs which by the 1970's would give us
millions of watts as space-vehicle auxiliary power at weights
of about ten pounds per kilowatt.

How does that compare with chemical systems?

Well, in this case you can't do it with chemical systems at
all. For example, we have two satellites in orbit now, the
Navy navigational Transit satellites, the first of which was

launched on June 29 of 1961 and was the first demonstration of nuclear power in space in the history of the world—and the second of which was launched November 15 of 1961. There we have nuclear electrical power sources weighing just five pounds or so that are putting out a total amount of electrical energy equivalent to that which could be put out by thousands or tens of thousands of pounds of batteries.

At bottom, what is causing this link between nuclear things and space things?

The high power density and the long life of the power source. You see, you have in the case of an isotope like plutonium-238 in these Navy navigational satellites, an isotope that has a half-life of ninety years, so it is only diminished half in its heat intensity in ninety years. The auxiliary equipment, the electrical equipment will wear out much before that, say in five years, but even this exceeds the life of solar cells and of course cannot be duplicated at all by chemical batteries. In addition there are terrestrial applications—such as at the North Pole, Antarctica, in ocean buoys, and underwater.

Half-life is a measure of how fast an unstable material gives up its energy.

We've been hearing talk about reactors under the ocean.

I think eventually. Right now we have a reactor under the icecap up at Camp Century in Greenland. And we have a couple of reactors down near the South Pole.

Another one of your very forward-looking programs, thermonuclear power—how's that doing?

This is a long-range program. Progress is being made in our ability to confine these plasmas for increasingly long times, generating increasingly high temperatures, but we're a long way from having any practical source of thermonuclear energy—electrical power.

With thermonuclear power, as with fission power, there has been a phase of considerable optimism followed by the discouragement of reality. What are your observations generally about the problems that are faced in an age when science and technology can do an awful lot, but it doesn't all happen instantaneously?

Well, I would say that the scientists themselves have prob-

fusion

Thermonuclear Power

fission

Conventional Nuclear Power

247

ably not gone through these cycles to the extent that perhaps some others have. There was an unrealistically optimistic attitude toward nuclear power ten years ago. Then we've gone through a pessimistic period and perhaps are just emerging from that. But I know a number of scientists who through it all had never predicted a faster rate of attainment of economic nuclear power. I think I can quote from the written record predictions, including my own, that are just about consistent with the rate of progress toward economic power.

Harold Brown

H*arold Brown is an example of a new breed of military man that has evolved in this country since World War II. Those were the years when the military arts became highly technical, immensely complex. And they have drawn a group of men who, by training and cast of mind, would once have headed inevitably toward science or scholarship.*

At thirty-seven, Brown is an accredited physicist, with a doctorate from Columbia based on low-energy nuclear research. He is also a man with a decade of military work behind him, in weapons research and the direction of weapons research. He joined the Livermore Laboratory in 1952 to work on nuclear explosives; he was a division head three years later, associate director of the laboratory three years after that, and became director in 1960. Meanwhile he had served on the Polaris Steering Committee, the Air Force Scientific Advisory Board, the Defense Department's Scientific Advisory Committee on Ballistic Missiles. He was an adviser on weapons-testing at the 1958 Geneva Conference and a frequent consultant to subcommittees of the President's Science Advisory Committee. He became Secretary of the Air Force under the Johnson administration.

Before that, in 1961, Brown became director of Defense Research and Engineering. Like his boss, Defense Secretary McNamara, he brought a hardheaded and analytic approach to defense matters, which some people admire and some resent—depending on where they sit, perhaps, and how they feel about central direction of large enterprises. At the time

of this interview, in 1963, he was still heading Research and Engineering.

When we interviewed him, it was evident that Brown has the administrator's knack of turning his attention on and off like a light. We walked into his office as an impressive parade of brass walked out. For the hour or more we talked we had the full use of a keen, eager intellect, focused in a relaxed yet intent way on each subject we brought up. As we walked out he was already on the phone in passionate discussion of something unrelated; we had disappeared from his consciousness.

The first subject we brought up was the current state of military technology.

A few months ago, Dr. Brown, you made a speech in which you talked about strategic weapons and their development and their deterrent effect. One thing you said was that "deterrence could be unbalanced by further technological advance—although I do not consider this likely." Is military technology having a stabilizing effect on the situation in the world now?

It certainly has tended to stabilize things over the past few years—by changing the strategic significance of the first strike. Back when we had soft land-based weapons systems, these were vulnerable to missile attack. That's why our fear, that the other side might get many missiles at a time when we had none, was particularly distressing. Even when both sides have missiles, if the missiles are soft and if there's an exchange ratio such that one missile can kill many missiles, then the side that strikes first has an advantage.

But that has changed?

Yes, as we went to smaller missiles, which could be put on submarines or could be hardened at acceptable cost, the exchange ratio changed. It now takes several missiles to have a reasonable chance of knocking out one missile on the ground. That situation is obviously stable in a simple arithmetical sense, in that no great advantage attaches to the side that strikes first. The side that strikes first is not able to knock out the retaliatory capability of the other side.

Also, in a way the great increase in damage-producing capability, all by itself, is part of the stabilization of the political situation. When even a fraction of the retaliatory capacity is still enough to do enormous damage, a potential aggressor is less likely to make the mistake of thinking he can get away scot free.

You implied in your speech that some technical advances might have the opposite effect.

One thing that might be unstabilizing is a really effective anti-ICBM. I don't consider that likely—and that's what I meant when I said I don't think this sort of shift is likely to come about.

You don't worry about it.

One thing to remember is that there is a long lead time now on all big systems. A new development can be conceived in a short time; a new physical principle can be discovered very quickly, and it can be turned into a laboratory application or even breadboard hardware fairly quickly. But developing and producing and deploying a major system takes years—four years, five years, seven years.

Breadboard: a lab bench hookup to make sure an idea works at all.

That factor was at work in the ballistic missile scare you spoke of.

I think that is an instructive lesson. We became worried about Soviet missile development in 1953 and 1954—and as a result we started a development of our own which produced a force in being in 1959, 1960, 1961, a substantial but not an enormously large force. It takes a fairly long time. The interesting thing is that the interval between the time we became really worried and the time the Soviets themselves had a substantial force was also seven years or so. It was possible for us to work on a similar capability, and to achieve it, without having the new technological development produce an unbalancing situation.

It's pretty expensive just to stay stable.

It's very expensive. And it takes a great deal of effort, that's right. You have to try to think ahead—recognizing that you can't always think ahead correctly. You do things which later turn out to be wasted. If you're in an arms race, you more or less have to behave that way, and we do behave that way. I think so long as we have an arms race it would be dangerous to behave any other way.

There's another aspect to this question. Over the past fifteen years we've been in a situation of very rapid change in the technology of war—megaton weapons, ballistic missiles, radar. Is the rapid change likely to continue, or is the technical situation itself more stable?

The rate of progress has been very high and continues very high. However, doubling your capability or even multiplying it by ten doesn't have the same effect as going from no capability at all to some. That's why the pace of military technology may appear to have slowed; the biggest change takes place when it is born, and forever after the pace is slower.

1 megaton = explosive power of 1 million tons of TNT. The "blockbusters" of World War II contained about 1 ton of TNT.

You have to look for new areas, for the birth of new ideas.

Exactly, and I think there may be a few of those floating around, although it's difficult to tell from this end of their history. Laser technology might well produce an effect that's comparable to jet aircraft or nuclear submarines. . . . I'm not sure it will, but if it does, it will be apparent in retrospect.

Lasers produce very intense sharply focused light.

If you're looking for radically different developments, maybe you look outside the physical sciences altogether. To the social sciences, maybe?

Yes. I think that—or to the biological sciences. The scientific revolution that corresponds to the revolution of physical science in the twenties and thirties may well turn out to be in biology. It's not obvious what military applications that will have—and I don't think that anybody's activities in that field need to be either perturbed, accelerated, or perhaps prevented because of any hopes or fears of what may come out militarily. But it is quite possibly there that the big scientific advances are going to be. Of course, applied science may be doing something in a field that is not the one where fundamental science is flourishing. In the late thirties, when the fundamental science was atomic physics, the most interesting applied science, from a military point of view, was the application of principles at least fifty years old, the principles of electromagnetic wave propagation.

Electromagnetic wave propagation = radio, radar, etc.

The future is very hard to predict.

When it comes to the psychological sciences, behavioral sciences, we do believe that there are likely to be fairly important military applications. The problem is to pick them out. It's much less possible than in the physical sciences for everyone to agree on who's an expert and what the important fields are. So we tend to demand a more direct application of the science to technology—not because that's a good idea generally but because it's an anchor. The problem is not so much to find a good criterion as to find any criteria at all.

Could you make that a little more specific?

One area in which behavioral sciences are important is the command-and-control area—because here you have an interaction between physical and human systems. There's a limit to the amount of information a person can absorb; and one of the things you want to find out is how to present the information so that somebody who is making a decision can absorb the maximum information. We have a number of such projects; we have some rather good work going. But it's hard to keep this from turning into a sort of hobby for the people who are interested in it. You start with a fairly specific problem: "How much information can you present to a decision maker?" And if you're not careful you get into acting-out situations, into replications of real situations using people who are supposed to act them out. This may be fruitful in some areas of science, but I think they can be very dangerous if you take them too seriously in a military situation.

Could we go back a bit? You said earlier that you see no real prospect of an effective defense against ballistic missiles. Why is that?

I don't think I quite said that. I said I think the offense has an advantage, so that a ballistic missile defense which can take care of an unlimited attack is going to be very, very difficult to achieve. The offense can concentrate, whereas the defense has to defend many places. The offense has the last word on how many objects it throws, and the defense either has to distinguish all the missiles from the decoys or it has to shoot at all the ones it doesn't distinguish. Finally, the offense is probably able to react faster; it may be able to deploy changes in what it's going to send in faster than the defense can respond.

What does this sort of situation do to the intellectual glam-

Command-and-control systems are computerized information systems to speed a military commander's assessments of readiness and of field situations.

our, the excitement, of military technology? Does military
work appeal to the scientist as much as it used to?

The challenging problems are a smaller fraction, perhaps,
of the big programs now. But of course there are more big
programs now than there were then. So I think you have a
comparable amount of effort that is interesting. I think the
antiballistic missile . . . and the reverse of that coin, pene-
tration aids . . . these are just as challenging technically.
They have more scientific content than ballistic missiles had,
as much engineering challenge as early warning or SAGE
systems. The communications satellite is interesting. It's just
that people aren't quite as able to convince themselves that
any single thing they do is going to make a significant difference in the balance.

*SAGE = Semi-Automatic
Ground Environment,
one of the earliest
command-and-control
systems for air defense.*

That sort of difference just isn't in the cards?

There are always ideas floating around which, if put
together, do offer a change in the military balance. They're
not such as to completely upset things. They are not such as
to give us an easy first-strike capability or to cause us to lose
our second-strike capability. But they change the military
balance enough so that both sides notice it—and if both
sides notice it, I think it has a big effect on the political situation. Even unreal changes have a big effect once in a while.

*First strike = initial
attack. Second-strike
capability = retaliatory
attack strength after
suffering enemy's
first strike.*

What I notice is that the younger technical people don't
need to be convinced of the importance of new developments. It's the older ones—like me—who have been through
the past revolutions who feel all the revolutions are over.
They mean that theirs is over. And there's another thing. The
closer you are to an enormous bureaucracy, the more you
may believe that nothing can get done, nothing's important,
nobody cares.

*You've been close to this bureaucracy for a while. Does it
feel immovable to you?*

No, not at all. I think it can move; it can be moved. It's
hard for one person to move it. The right way is to gather
enough other people around him with whom he feels some
community of interest and purpose, some rapport, and all
keep pushing on things they believe important. It's like one
of those enormous push balls in a game in which dozens of
people play . . . they all try . . . some try to push one

way, some another. In any big organization you're likely to get a distribution of molecules, all pushing on this ball, and on the average it'll hardly move at all. If you can get a few hard pushers pushing in one direction, you can move it. I think we have moved it quite a lot in the two years I've been here.

Where has the ball moved in those two years?

I think the ball has moved toward an insistence that— except for supremely important projects, of which there are never more than one or two and at times there are none— except for these you prove out what you are trying to do before you make a big-system investment. You do support technology and new ideas for their own sake, and you don't insist they be tied into systems. But on the big systems we require an understanding of what the requirements are and what technology can do to meet them before we go ahead.

Are there changes in what you're trying to do as well as in how you do it?

We are paying more attention to the importance of being able to respond to force at lower levels of violence. The potential use of force is the responsibility of the Department of Defense. This is an era when both we and the Soviet bloc have the capability to respond to nuclear strikes with enormous damage on the attacker. So if you're deterred by the level of force implicit in strategic weapons, you have to be able to respond in other ways, at a lower level of force. We have put considerably more effort, percentagewise, into conventional arms—which do have some very interesting developments.

Is there really much room for development there? Most of us think of preparation for limited war as a matter of digging out the old World War II blueprints.

On some things, I think our capability has dropped below World War II; it might not be a bad idea to dig out some of those blueprints. But we're going to go beyond that, too. I think we already have, for example, in antitank weapons. When it comes to close air support of troops, we may not have gotten beyond where we were—or where the Germans were—in World War II. We're devoting more attention to the acquisition of targets—which is a harder job in many ways than their destruction. The payoff from increasing firepower, when you don't know what you should be shooting at, is a lot less than the payoff from improved tactical reconnaissance.

Target acquisition = locking sights on a chosen target (decoys and electronic deception of radar make it harder these days).

But these improvements in limited warfare capability can't really produce any drastic change in the basic situation, can they?

Can you ever get an enormous advantage at the middle and lower levels of conflict? Perhaps we haven't been imaginative enough. I think it's clear you can't get any enormous advantage just in firepower—because firepower goes all the way up to the nuclear level now. Perhaps the fundamental limitation at levels below the strategic level is that numbers count. That keeps the technical factors from being as important as they are in strategic warfare.

Maybe that is where your work in the behavioral sciences could pay off. Do you think the performance of the individual soldier could be radically improved?

Yes, people have suggested that. I think the behavioral sciences are only one element of that problem. I think the engineering and physical sciences also have a role there. It is worth thinking about what you can do with an individual soldier or a very small military unit by making a very large investment in them, their training and their equipment, make them mobile, able to communicate, with large firepower, good target acquisition capability . . . and see how much their effectiveness can be improved. It's a fascinating concept, but no one has quite brought it off. We've done some of the component work, but we haven't tried to put it together into a system.

Do you think it might . . . ?

It might . . . It might.

Harrison Brown

*O*ne would think that with all the technically trained people around, Uncle Sam would have little difficulty getting the
technical advice he needs. To get the best advice, though, it's
necessary to put the government's problems to the right problem solvers. Much of this, of course, is done through the
President's Science Advisory Committee in ways that show
clearly in the interviews with Kistiakowsky, Wiesner, and
Hornig elsewhere in this volume. However, for the important
but less urgent questions there is a more traditional advisory
organization—the National Academy of Sciences. The NAS
was chartered by Congress back in Lincoln's time in the
somewhat paradoxical form of a non-governmental organization created expressly to investigate and report on any aspect
of science and technology called for by the government.

One of the Academy's outstanding "brokers" in lining up
technical advisers is Harrison Scott Brown, professor of geo-
chemistry at CalTech and, over the last few years, foreign
secretary at NAS. In the one-third of his time that he spends
as foreign secretary, Dr. Brown may be involved in any or
all of three main areas. There is the quasi-diplomatic one of
scientific exchange agreements with other countries, including
those of Eastern Europe; there is the administrative one of
looking after the U.S. participation in ICSU, the International
Council of Scientific Unions; and then there is the relatively
new and important area of providing advice on how science
and technology can assist the developing nations. In this
last area the office of the foreign secretary may, for example,

organize an ad hoc *panel of experts at the request of the Agency for International Development at State, or a "country-to-country colloquy" on some technical problem abroad.*

Amid all of this, Harrison Brown is the energizer, a dynamic man admirably suited to his task and confident of his ability to carry it out. A scholar of repute in his own field of earth chemistry, he has a supple mind that ranges over the whole gamut of technical problems facing us today. He is a political activist as well. As a panelist on disarmament for the Democratic Advisory Council (formed during Eisenhower's last term) he is credited, along with Trevor Gardner, with providing the early impetus for the new initiatives in this area during the Kennedy years, culminating in the test-ban treaty of 1963.

Dr. Brown is perhaps best known, outside his own field, for his two provocative books: The Challenge of Man's Future *and* The Next Hundred Years, *a volume coauthored with two of his CalTech colleagues. In any sense of the word, he can be considered one of America's scientific elite. So our first question to him, not surprisingly, was:*

Do you think there is a scientific "Establishment" developing in the U.S.?

Not as such. The people involved in science policy in our government, of course, all know each other. I doubt that there is what you would call collusion. Each has his own job to worry about. I frankly am very much impressed by the caliber of men who have come into this business recently. We have in the chairman of our Atomic Energy Commission, Glenn Seaborg, a man whom I have known since I was a student, a man of extraordinary capabilities. You have Jerome Wiesner as the President's science adviser. I find Herbert Hollomon, the Assistant Secretary of Commerce, whom I had not known until he came to Washington, a very competent man. You have Roger Revelle, who is science adviser to the Secretary of the Interior.

Wiesner is now Provost at MIT; Revelle now directs the Center for Population Studies at Harvard.

Will such men automatically appear, or do any special steps have to be taken to encourage them into government?

They're not going to just appear. You're going to find a great flux. For example, I believe Revelle is leaving the government soon. He has done two years of very hard work and he wants to go back to his university. Walt Whitman of MIT has left as science adviser to the Secretary of State, and has been replaced by Ragnar Rollefson from the University of Wisconsin. Now this is healthy, I think, as long as the tours of duty aren't too short.

What about the elective prospects of men like these?

I really don't think you're going to find an appreciable number of scientists going into active politics in the sense that they will seek elective office. It's difficult enough being a scientist and an administrator. I would say that being a scientist and a truly effective politician—these are mutually incompatible.

Wasn't there a kind of ad hoc *committee, or perhaps even more than that, during the 1960 Presidential campaign?*

Well, before that, the Democratic party established something called the Democratic Advisory Council. There were three major panels. One was on foreign policy. Another was on economic policy. And then there was a third panel established, on science policy. This turned out to be really quite an effective panel. It came up with some important recommendations, one of which got into the 1960 platform and has since been enacted into law.

Which one was that?

The formation of the Arms Control and Disarmament Agency. The original draft for that was written on my kitchen table by Trevor Gardner, the former Assistant Secretary of Defense, and myself. We were both on that panel.

Returning to your statement about the incompatibility of the scientific and the political mind . . .

Not the mind. I would say the general life led by a politician is incompatible with the life of a scientist. That is, you'd have to completely stop being a scientist. Take what I'm doing now here at the Academy. I stop being a scientist one-half of the time, but I don't stop completely, so I don't lose touch with the world of science. I speak with some authority because my wife has run for Congress twice, and just living in a house with a political campaign going on is not conducive to quiet meditation.

Is she determined that you shall be the next one to run?

No, no. . . .

Nonetheless, a technical man or two in Congress might be welcome. . . .

The scientific section of the Legislative Reference Service of the Library of Congress, established two years ago, was a step in this direction.
Yes, it would be a very health*i* thing. And the next best bet, I think, is for Congress to establish a system of some sort which enables it to secure, with confidence, the most knowledgeable and wisest advice in the scientific-technological area that it can get.

Isn't the situation improving, with some of these advisory panels being formed?

It is improving enormously. I think that Congressman George Miller has done a good job of forming his advisory panel for the Science and Astronautics Committee. There have been other occasions, however, where one might . . .

Isn't there a kind of limitation built into the advisory panel system? Aren't the men who know what science is about too heavily committed elsewhere?

Not in my experience, and I have been involved in forming quite a few panels quickly here at the Academy. I've asked people to come to Washington at no fee, with just traveling expenses and the privilege of living here on $16 per day. The refusals I've gotten are very few and far between.

Could you cite an example?

Yes. Very suddenly, the Academy was asked to help formulate perhaps about a third of the American program for the recent Geneva Conference on science and technology for the less-developed nations. And in three days I had five panels formed with some thirty-five or forty people—men of the caliber of John Pierce of Bell Labs, who chaired a panel on communications; Julian Feiss of the Geological Survey, who chaired a panel on mineral resources; and Abel Wolman from Johns Hopkins, who took a panel on water-resource problems. After calling this whole group, I had only one person who said he couldn't help us, and for a legitimate enough reason.

This conference was held in February 1963.

This is a peculiarly American attack on the problem of scien-

tific advice to government. From your observations of the Soviet approach, how would you say it differed?

Here in the scientific community we rely almost entirely on what you might call volunteers. In the Soviet Union, the Academy of Sciences is really a branch of the government, and until recently the president of the Soviet Academy was responsible to the Council of Ministers. You do this kind of thing as part of your job; you are told by your superior to do it. Take the Geneva program. The part we worked out here was done extragovernmentally. The Soviet program was worked out under their General Scientific Secretary, Federov, and done within their Academy.

You have come to know a number of Soviet scientists, have you not?

Yes, at two levels. As you know, this office is charged with the responsibility of negotiating and operating the Soviet-American scientific exchange agreement. We have had a number of distinguished Soviet scientists here both doing research and visiting laboratories. And we have had quite a number of eminent Americans doing both long- and short-range research in the Soviet Union. I've visited there four times myself. My own personal relations with the Russians are quite good; I think we understand each other.

To what do you ascribe this?

I suppose it's based on the fact that we haven't double-crossed each other. We're men of honor. In any agreements I've reached with one of my Russian colleagues, he has always kept his part of it, and I've always kept mine.

Could we turn the conversation just a bit? In your book The Next Hundred Years *you were concerned about our resources of brain power. Are you still worried?*

Yes, because I think we're headed for a major shortage of really highly trained and competent individuals.

In terms of our own needs . . . not just as a response to a Russian threat?

No, I'm speaking of our own problems. Now, some maintain that if the arms race were to end, we would have engineers and scientists running out of our ears. I don't think this is true. If it were to happen overnight, which it won't, you would have a dislocation. But I think there is going to be an expanding need in the future for scientists and engineers. Take our interests in Latin America or in Africa. I believe that with respect to science and technology we've got to face up to our responsibilities. The Africans, for example, are not going to be able to provide the levels of higher education for themselves that they need. They might be able to put some funds in, but they just don't have enough trained people. And there is a great deal of discussion now as to providing a mechanism whereby it will be possible for American university people to accept posts in Africa, as well as in Latin America, with reasonable security.

What sort of mechanism?

This organization has been set up, with money from the Ford and Carnegie Foundations, as Education and World Affairs. Teaching exchange problems are handled by its subsidiary, Overseas Education Service.

Well, one attractive approach that's being discussed is the creation of an institution here in the U.S. that will recruit professors to go abroad, one that will handle all of the administrative aspects . . . problems of salary differentials, annuities, insuring job tenure, and so on. The funds for this would come from private foundations in part, from government agencies in part, and from the countries receiving the people they need. Something of this sort is necessary, and helping to organize it may be one of the Academy's projects.

Going back, if we may, to the problem of more graduate students and more people in science and engineering . . .

I really think the bottleneck is one of education, of stimulating more youngsters to go into science, of endowing them with a curiosity about the world around them.

This raises an interesting question: If you were a student today, what do you think you'd be studying?

It's hard to say; you'd have to tell me what else I'd be exposed to at the same time. My guess would be that I would go into science again, although other fields are enormously attractive to me. I find anthropology a fascinating study; history equally so. But I'd probably go into science.

What sorts of avenues are you following in your own current research?

Well, I am part of a team that has an experiment on one

of the Surveyor space vehicles designed to determine the chemical composition of the lunar surface. Also, I have been heavily involved in establishing a laboratory at CalTech that can be a focal point for geologists and astronomers working together on lunar and planetary problems. Two men there, Bruce Murray, who's a geologist, and Robert Wildey, who's an astrophysicist, built an infrared telescope that has just given tremendous results. It's a very exciting development. They found these hot spots on the dark side of the moon. And then something, so far unpublished, that they did on the night of the Mariner fly-by: They obtained a complete scan of Venus and got the most beautiful temperature-contour map of the planet that you would ever hope to see!

Stevan Dedijer

*T*his is a discussion of "the science of science." What is the meaning of this expression? You should picture it as a composite of things. For instance, the history of science is one of its important components. The philosophy of science is another. And the sociology of science another. Also the problems of decision-making on science and the practical organization of science. When these various fields are pulled together, we have a base on which to build a science of science.

The sort of man who is expert in such a field is likely to be one whose professional career has taken him into many fields, many disciplines—a man of wide-ranging interests, in other words. He will have an interest in history. And he will also have an interest in politics. He will know science as a scientist knows it, but he will also know something of the utilization of power as only the practicing politician can know it—from firsthand experience.

Stevan Dedijer is such a peripatetic. He has done neutron physics in Belgrade. He has run a Slavic newspaper in Pittsburgh. He has directed atomic research in his native Yugoslavia. He has even served and fought with the 101st Airborne Division of the United States Army.

In recent years Dedijer has lived in Scandinavia, working at the Institute for Theoretical Physics in Copenhagen, under the great physicist Niels Bohr, and at the Institute of Theoretical Physics in Lund, Sweden, where he has been study-

ing the problems of establishing research policy in underdeveloped countries.

In the summer of 1963 Dedijer visited the U.S. for several
weeks, as a guest of the Department of the History of Science
and Medicine at Yale. This is where our conversation took
place.

When you meet this big, happy, shaggy-sweatered fellow
and hear that Serbian ring in his voice, you think there is a
mistake in the dossier, which says, "Taft School, Watertown,
Conn.—1930 . . . Princeton University—1934." But there
is no mistake. Says Dedijer, "I had a very energetic mother."

Our conversation began with a question relating to the development of science in underdeveloped countries. But it
was not limited to this, as you shall see, for the mind of
Stevan Dedijer is fond of roaming, exploring, provoking.

267

How does the young, aspiring nation get going in science? And how does the big nation help?

That's the problem: What is your social mechanism for developing your own science? These people have to become aware, first of all, of the importance of research, then find their own internal ways: "How am I going to build a social mechanism which will give me information of what I should do in science?" They have to make their own stupid mistakes. That's one characteristic of independence. They want to do research through their own forces. We've got to help them so their mistakes are fewer.

There is not enough time to allow so many mistakes, is that the idea?

They have to build science themselves. Once they decide that, they have to analyze their own problems of developing science, because developing science there is quite different from developing science in developed countries.

We can tell them how to build a railroad. But we know less about planting the seed of science. We may know less than the science group from India or Ghana . . .

You haven't systematized the knowledge you have. I don't think you know enough—nobody knows enough—about underdeveloped countries. You offer them a reactor—they take it because you're giving it to them, even if they don't need it. They'll take anything you give them.

Because they may as well take it.

Of course. And then you can wreck their science by that, by orienting it into nuclear research, and then they are bound for years. And there is the other extreme. I don't know about the Russians; I haven't had enough contact. But I know that Western scientists—I can name a couple of Nobel prize winners—will say to them privately, "Well, listen, do you really need research?"

You believe they do. Why do you think so?

There are several reasons. It's taking a long time for the West to realize that to develop you must plan. And that's becoming the U.S. policy now. But to plan, you must include research. You cannot make a single move in economic development without basing it on science and technology. If you want to know what you have—your resources—you've got to develop your own geologists. You can't keep importing geologists.

The U.S. had speculators—prospectors—when the West was opened a hundred years ago. Is the speculator obsolete? Does today's geologist in India have to be better educated than the American prospector of 1849?

I think yes. You want to do it the best way possible. You can't do it any other way. The biggest invention of this century is not the theory of relativity or quantum mechanics. It is the invention of planning, social planning. It's a short cut. Every country will have to make research policy one of the major plans of its national policy.

What do you mean by research policy?

I mean a theoretical solution of how you're going to merge science with all your other problems of the government and national life.

But you need drive . . . a drive to discover. Don't you want speculators, entrepreneurs?

This is difficult. In Yugoslavia, they saw that schematic rigid planning kills off initiative. They don't admit it in public. But they must find out how to get people more interested in what they're doing. It is very difficult to combine the two—planning and initiative.

Well, the U.S. combined them in agriculture.

Very true. You combined it very much in agriculture. That's your first research policy really starting. Underdeveloped countries should study how you combined the two. So you see, the West has the idea that in everything you do, you introduce research. But at the same time you say, "Oh no! *They* shouldn't." I have actually seen this. I have a friend in India who got very angry. A prominent sociologist and economist told him, "India doesn't need research." Yet every one of these countries is developing research, no matter what you tell them. They're independent.

India decides it needs more educated people in science. It educates them—many going away for education; and many never come back.

The only force that can start research in the underdeveloped countries is the government. In the West, you have industrial research, very powerful. You have university research with a long tradition. There they've got no tradition. So the government has to build a research community which will influence the development of science. If it starts by developing policy through its reactor . . . OK, that becomes its science. But if there is a man who is interested in some very abstruse research, he should be given money to do it.

Compare what Abdus Salam says about the role of the abstract scientist in a backward country.

So the man is the key. A Niels Bohr in Copenhagen. But how often is a government wise enough to know the importance of that man?

Well, they have no experience in the development of science. Underdeveloped countries have underdeveloped governments with respect to science also.

Supposing Bohr had been born in Yugoslavia.

He'd have worked in Copenhagen . . . or England. In the country with a scientific tradition, the scientist has status; he has support. The underdeveloped country picks "Joe." Why? "Because Joe belongs to the party" or "Joe has good friends in the government."

The thing is to develop policies that will enable young people to push forward, to develop mobility of scientists within the country. In many countries, the people in nuclear research get three times the salary of others. This locks them in. Many countries are trying to abolish these barriers to mobility.

Then there is the status question: In many countries, the governments are basically anti-intellectual.

In Yugoslavia more so than in the Soviet Union would you say?

Yes, that's very strange. And I've pointed it out when I was in Yugoslavian trouble. This is where we come to Marxist ideology. This is how the Russians came at their science. Lenin in 1918. One of the first acts he wrote was on how to merge the Academy of Science and the planning of growth of science and the economy. With his own hand, he wrote a decree giving Pavlov—who was *against* the Bolsheviks—all the things he needed: literature and a double ration of bread for his family.

In Yugoslavia that wasn't the case, although Yugoslavia has since done quite a lot. It has overcome its infantile disease of developing nuclear research at the expense of everything else . . . and now I think there is quite a lot of discussion of the problem of the development of research.

But Yugoslavia is losing scientists. And they are apparently going the wrong way to solve the problem. They seem to be trying to solve it through administrative measures, including the restriction of passports. Now that's wrong because they have to analyze *why* the scientists are leaving.

But to solve that problem, they must change the system.

Well, the system is changing. The elite learn. They increase freedom in exchange for information. It does not matter that they label this "the biggest discovery in Marxism." That's not important.

You think they may discover the free society one of these days?

I think they are discovering that—the Russians also. The role of a Soviet scientist in policy has been very great, although they don't say this openly. And my impression is now that the Soviet scientists, among themselves, can practically kick any idea around.

Among themselves. . . .

Look, I look on all of these problems on a relative scale: How was it before, and how is it now? In your eyes, it's nothing. But when you live in such a country and you see that one swallow arrives . . . You see, I knew the old Soviet scientists. And then I met a new generation. It's a shock. It's a completely new phenomenon. That's happened in Yugoslavia too. The new generation considers intellectually every problem. Now in the developing non-Communist countries you have social pressures which thwart expression of opinions.

If you work in a nuclear institute and your country is pushing nuclear energy, the man in charge of nuclear energy is politically powerful. You wouldn't write articles *against* nuclear energy. You would lose your grant if you stepped on somebody's toes. So these pressures are very strong.

But if you have a strong research council which will join all the scientists . . . which will show the government how to *build* science . . . which acts as the government's eyes and ears in science . . . But it must be free to act . . . financially independent.

Is this council a fluid organization? Is it continually changing, as advisory bodies to governments in the West?

You see science councils of different kinds. I think about thirty countries today have science councils or research policy bodies. You have to find people who will be wise— human-wise. You have to do what Churchill did. He said, "I don't know anything about science, but I knew something of scientists, and I knew how to make decisions in fields I didn't know anything about." Now you pick a dozen or half-dozen such people. It's very important to pick young people, even without experience. You have to pick people who are really socially oriented—who are interested in developing their own country—who are willing to say, "I'm not interested in my own particular career in this field of science." Then they pick problems—especially social, psychological problems of science. They ask, "Why do people leave here? Is it salary? Social status? Do we orient our young scientists in the wrong ways?" Then they start analyzing: "Where are my researchers going to be trained? What are our universities doing?"

You distinguish between university training and research training . . .

A lot of universities teach science, but they don't do research. Researchers can only be trained by people who do research.

What does the word "research" mean to you?

Research for me means everything from detecting the expansion of the universe to making a better fountain pen. You really use some basic elements of scientific method in both.

Now, many countries start in science with the idea: "I'm going to get all the scientists I can and close them in the institutes." They do that. This helps to develop a certain number of scientists, but it wrecks the universities as research centers for training researchers. Once the decision maker clears that up, he's got all kinds of tools for fostering research in the universities. If you decide you need big institutes, then make sure the people there are closely connected with the universities, that they pick their young people from here.

Where do you see this integration of science and national policy taking place with some success . . . in what country?

I think perhaps India is one of the best examples. I went to India with certain preconceived ideas. I told myself, "Here's a laboratory example. I know a little bit about Indian science . . . I'm going to test these ideas to see if I'm correct." And every step I made in India, I found myself saying, "I've been here before."

What did you find that you liked?

First of all, the top man is very much aware of the importance of science. That's extremely important. Second, you have a relatively large number of people who are first class scientists . . . and they are closely connected with the development of science.

But India suffers from many of these infantile diseases of science. One problem—in all these countries—applied research is really futile, because it rarely gets applied. They have numerous institutes doing applied research. I asked the leader of one of the best, "How many rupees does India get from every rupee invested here?" He hit the ceiling. "NOTH-ING. We've got the results, but our industry is not ready to accept them." Now that's another policy governments have to be conscious of.

You have these countries that are starting to develop science. I think their problems are so similar that there is a field for sociology of science. I really think there is a problem of study for sociologists and economists and everybody else in this field—social psychologists—to bring things out. To save headaches and wasted money. The diseases are the same. And I think the preventive medicines should be the same. The cure should be the same. I feel very hot about this subject.

Do you think the same medicines work in every political climate? . . . Can good science grow in other than free soil? You see it growing in the U.S.S.R., in Poland. . . .

It's growing in China: They're spending now what India will be spending six years from now. It's a paradox. The social scientists in the West were extremely surprised by the Sputnik. My theory is that you can develop much quicker and much cheaper and with fewer diseases if you have democracy. . . . Now that doesn't mean democracies in which you have three parties to vote for. But let's say a democracy within your scientific community—where the scientists can influence the government, where there is a candid exchange of views.

It's extremely important that scientists have freedom to influence the formation of research policy, and to criticize its implementation. I think the Russians have come to that conclusion.

Just as an aside, it would be very interesting to know how the Soviets started their space program, which paid off so well in propaganda. Which scientists advised them to start investigations in this field? There must have been a terrific nice exchange of information between scientists and government to launch themselves in that field.

Now the Soviet scientists feel as a community that they can tell the government some things. There is evidence for that: Khrushchev telling his adviser on agriculture in the Ukraine, "You called me an expert on agriculture, on research in agricultural problems. . . . Well, *you're* the expert. You're the fellow whose opinion I should follow, because you're the scientist and I'm the secretary of the party. I could be very wrong in your field."

You cannot formulate research policy, you cannot implement, you cannot get advice . . . unless you create that atmosphere. Otherwise, your scientist will tell you what you want to hear. I know from personal experience.

In your writing, you have called this "the science of science." Where does the term come from?

The Poles in 1936 first gave the name "science of science." The history of science has existed for some time. The philosophy of science has existed. Sociology of science is a minor brother. Then you have problems of decision-making of science, the practical organization. Now there is the approach to make all this one science. If you want to apply science of science, you've got to study all aspects of man in research, because man uses all these sides in doing research work—sociology, psychology, everything.

And the demand for science of science is increasing, mainly from the decision makers and advisers on science. Look at the White House paper on supporting the behavioral sciences. You have more people saying, "Now we've got to start knowing more about research and research policy. We've got to do research to increase the knowledge of science of science."

Where do you find strong programs in the science of science?

In Russia they are beginning to study. And who is pushing for it? The government. It is very interesting. They had a meeting with the slogan: How to make Lomonosovs. Lomonosov was the most prominent Russian scientist in the eighteenth century. Now *you* are discussing how to make Newtons . . . highly creative scientists.

Aren't we rediscovering things about creativity that the Poles, say, worked on before us?

That's a problem. Natural science is cumulative. Social science isn't. You write a paper in physics and accidentally include somebody else's formula; you're discovered very quickly.

In social science, there is a need for summation of practical knowledge: What do we know? Fourteen generations of scientists have been trained. Every one of those scientists had a teacher. That teacher had *know-how*. But very few have summed up that know-how.

I like to cite the example of J. J. Thomson, who had nine Nobel prize winners, thirty-two fellows of the Royal Society, and eighty-three professors of physics among his pupils. . . . Yet, when you look—what were his rules of thumb? how did he teach?—you find practically nothing. I think if we examine present teachers—how do they teach?—I think we'll come up with information that will be useful to the decision makers.

J. J. Thomson discovered the electron in 1897.

Where do you think social science will stand in the Communist world in another twenty years?

Social sciences, East and West, both apply Meyer's law:

275

If the facts don't fit your theory, you've got to ignore the facts. Western social science applies this to the existence of the Communist world. Eastern social science applies it to the lively existence of capitalism.

But in the West, there is much more freedom of exchange of opinion, of information . . . that is the biggest advantage the West has over the Soviet Union.

Now, I think the interesting thing is this: For ideological reasons, the Soviets did not recognize the existence of operations research, linear programing, cybernetics. Yesterday, I saw in the library the economic magazine of the Soviet Union. It's full of articles about the ideas of cybernetics, linear programing . . . so they realize that the old philosophy in this case is nonsense. And you see Leonid Ilyichev's speech—remarkable for many things: He recognizes social psychology. So they are borrowing from the West. Of course, he says, "We're going to do it differently."

In 1963, Mr. Ilyichev was secretary to the Central Committee of the Communist Party. Today he is deputy to the Foreign Minister.

Well, that's a beginning. But the key is this: Up to now, the social scientists have played a small role in policy-making in the Soviet Union. It was done mostly through the party

apparatus. Now, if the party wants more information from social science . . . they give the social scientists a little more independence. And somebody comes up with the idea —"We need a profit motive! But a *socialist* profit motive." Then these Soviet social scientists begin to communicate with the Western scientists . . . start using the same methods, talking the same language. And then the two social sciences are going to start closing up, merging into one social science, just as there is one natural science.

Your decision makers are saying, "The winds of social change are blowing." But your social scientists never answered the question, "Which way are the winds blowing?" The Russians say that capitalism can never develop science, ignoring the fact that the current scientific revolution was made by capitalism. But I am studying . . . and I am comparing here the Republican party program—in the U.S.— and the Bolshevik party program, relative to science, and I'm showing that they use the *same* ideas . . . the relation of science to society . . . . *exactly* the same ideas.

So it's a very interesting field, this field of research policy.

Clinton P. Anderson

Nobody in the United States Senate or the House of
Representatives commands more respect among scientists
and engineers. To many, Clinton P. Anderson is one of the
"heroes" of science.

Yet, he is no scientist. He is an ex-reporter. An ex-insur-
ance salesman. An ex-bureaucrat. He is a Rotarian. A
Mason. An Elk. A politician. And those scientists who have
encountered him—as chairman of the Aeronautical and Space
Sciences Committee of the U.S. Senate, or when he served
as chairman of the Joint Committee on Atomic Energy—
will tell you that he is tough, a hard man to convince, a
tight man with a dollar.

Anderson has represented New Mexico in the Congress
for most of the years since 1941, when he was elected to the
House of Representatives. In 1945, President Truman appointed him Secretary of Agriculture, where he served for

the next three years, until he ran for the Senate in 1948. This year he will complete his third term, eighteenth year, in the U.S. Senate.

Anderson has made his reputation in Washington by pushing programs he believed in—as an early advocate of the use of ballistic missiles for space vehicles, of atomic power for submarines—and by challenging those that seemed wrong or suspicious. For instance, he led the fight against the Dixon-Yates power project, during the Eisenhower Administration.

He carries many committee responsibilities, but science is his broadest domain. Why his interest in science? "Because it was in my state." How does he get to the core of a technical question? He asks "stupid questions, silly questions, questions that scientists don't ask."

Our conversation began with politics.

Senator, let's talk about politicians. How do you view the politician? What is he?

Well, a young boy wrote me not long ago and said, "I would like to be a U.S. Senator. How do I do it?" And I said, "Live the first forty or fifty years of your life without any thought of that and in time it will come to you." I think a politician is someone who has learned that people have interests. They want to find someone who can conserve those interests. And when they've found him, they do like it says in the song, they never let him go. Sam Rayburn said to me when I was in the House, you have two groups of constituents. The first is a constituency at home. The other is the membership of this House. If you don't take care of those other 434 members of the House, you then can't take care of your constituency at home. If a man has not served the other members of the House, or the Senate, he can't be helpful in preserving the programs in which he is interested. That's a politician, but it isn't quite our concept of a politician. He doesn't go around doing "good," but he at least goes around trying to understand what other men want.

You're defining a politician's politician.

Frank Carlson is a Republican Senator from the state of Kansas.

Well, maybe; but some weeks ago, Frank Carlson was interested in the Glenn-Elder project. There was a fight going to be waged on it. We had tried to put it through as a Bureau of Reclamation project. Now Frank said, "I need help. Be sure you are on the floor and be sure you do something about it." And so I tried to be on the floor and make sure he got along all right. I'd want Frank to help me someday. And that's what I say: The Senate is still a gentleman's club! There is a relationship in the Senate and the House between members. You just don't define it in easy terms of is he a politician or isn't he a politician? It's the personal contacts people make.

As the technical man looks at the hearing transcripts, the question that always strikes him is, "How well do those elected representatives understand the technical questions that they are dealing with?" Take atomic energy. What is the nature of your understanding of it? It's not that of an engineer. It's a different kind of understanding.

And it's a slow process. Some of it works into your system finally. You never intend to be technically correct or an expert in any fashion. You want to be able to understand what the Los Alamos man and the atomic energy man say to you when they ask for their appropriations, but you don't try to be an expert in the field. For instance, we're building a reactor down in McMurdo, at the South Pole. It hasn't worked out very well. Now, why? The scientific answers would fill volumes. But we all knew we had to ask more questions than "Why didn't it work?" because the scientists' answers were not at all satisfactory.

What questions led you to an understanding?

Well, this reactor was going to be put in mothballs. Why? Well, because the Martin Company delivered it to the Atomic Energy Commission, but the Navy, which had to run it, was not satisfied that it was safe. So the next question was: "Why did the AEC pay for it? Didn't they have a guarantee?" Oh yes. The guarantee was that it would be a workable reactor. And Martin says it's workable. But the Navy says it is not, so put it in mothballs . . . for a year, or ten years, or twenty years. In the meantime, somebody would be putting out millions of dollars. So we have to ask stupid questions, silly questions, questions that scientists don't ask: "Why did you pay them if it didn't work?" That's entirely too simple for the scientist. But if you ordered a car, and they delivered you a nice-looking car, with a guarantee, but the motor wouldn't start, you wouldn't let it sit there in the garage for twenty years. You'd make it good. And that's what ought to have happened to this reactor. And what I think will eventually happen. Now, that's painful to Martin, the AEC, and the Navy. They are all suffering because the Joint Committee wants to know why they can't resolve this problem. And it's not easy to resolve apparently. But it will be resolved. And if it isn't made workable, the AEC will demand its money back. And Martin will have to prove it was workable, and that the Navy was messing it up. And they'll probably get Admiral Rickover to go down there with a couple of screwdrivers and a pair of pliers. He'll make it work.

By not being involved in all the complications, you are able to see the essential facts.

Well, at least we ask the questions that help develop the information that we think we need. It may not be what the

Navy needs. But the Navy just said, "Nothing doing. We think it is not safe. Close it up. Put it in mothballs." What good does it do to put something in mothballs? No good at all.

Let's look at this particular instance a little bit more. When it first came to your attention, some technical question must have come up. Levels of radioactivity, something like that. Did you call in one of your technical experts, or what?

As soon as the first reports came through that the reactor had been closed down, John Conway got busy on the committee. I've not wanted to have so many experts assigned to these committees. We have men who've worked with us right along and we have confidence in them which may be utterly disproportionate to technical experience they've had. But they tell us what we need to know: Number One—it was closed down. Number Two—who closed it down? The Navy. Was the Navy the one to accept it? No. The Atomic Energy Commission. Why didn't the AEC close it down? Well, because the Navy was running the place down there. It was a case of divided control. And the Navy thinks it's nicer to fly in these supplies of fuel oil. It costs a lot more, but you've got all that flying time for aviators. Now when the reactor won't work, what incentive is there for the Navy to make it work? None. They weren't for it in the first place.

John Conway is executive director of the Joint Committee on Atomic Energy.

We were trying to show that with atomic energy at the Pole, we would reduce the Navy's fuel costs. Then the Joint Committee got the Army and the AEC to come in and explain their problems. We got them to act up to the problems and reach some decisions on what should be done. We also demanded weekly letter reports on how things were going, so we could get some advance notice on things that might be going wrong—but more important, to let them know we were watching them.

Modifications were made on the McMurdo reactor, and the plant went back into operation in May of 1964.

Isn't the case of the Savannah *another instance of the trouble you get into with divided control?*

I don't suppose there has ever been a more graphic example. President Eisenhower had a very good point: He wanted to be able to bring an American vessel into the harbor of another country and light a whole city that night with atomic energy. The people would be invited to come down to a picture show the next night where we would show what we had done in the development of atomic devices. That might have been worth while, but it appeared to the committee that it was sort of a wasteful thing, because by the time the ship was finished, most countries would have their own atomic plants working somewhere. So we turned it down. But President Eisenhower very vigorously appealed for us to put it back in and we finally said all right. After all, he was the President; we weren't going to be just a little band of men who would keep him from having his ship if he really wanted it.

But it got mixed up in the House. The Merchant Marine and Fisheries Committee wanted a part of it. Other committees did too, so they finally ended up with a divided management. And what happened? Well, Mrs. Eisenhower broke the bottle of champagne and many of us had to go up there. But one man got there first. Mr. McCone, then chairman of the Atomic Energy Commission, went up a day or two in advance. And he knew a lot about building ships. The California Shipbuilding Company was a very successful shipbuilding organization and he was the president and the driving genius in it. So he looked at it, and the first thing he saw were the gears. Why? When I go into a man's office, the first thing I look for are the books. I have an interest in books. And he had an interest in gears. Gears were his specialty. And he looked at them and just was amazed. "Who made these gears? They're just as wrong as they can be." Of course, if the gears were wrong, then there was a chance that something else was wrong. So he sent for Rickover. And Rickover found about eighty things that were wrong. And he said, "Well, this is hopeless. You're going to have to change all these things over again."

Admiral Hyman Rickover who is credited with spurring the development of the atom-powered submarine.

Now, here we are. We have spent I don't know how many millions and millions of dollars on the *Savannah* and some of these days it will start to run again. But look at the money this is involving. The point is, if we had tried to use it for the purpose for which President Eisenhower had intended it, namely a showboat to go into Copenhagen and show the people what atomic energy was like, we would be the laughingstock of the world, because Copenhagen knows all about atomic energy and can see it anywhere. So the use of the

The Savannah *was licensed for operation in August of 1965.*

Savannah as a showboat, as President Eisenhower contemplated, laudable as his purpose was, just doesn't work out.

And yet presumably he was responding to technical possibilities that he had been assured about by his technical advisers in turn.

Yes, but the atomic energy people, who should have been the last word, were not the last word. They let the Merchant Marine group build the ship. Then they put the atomic power into it. But in the nuclear submarine program and in the nuclear-propelled aircraft carrier, Rickover has proved that you have to design them together. You have to make sure the entire vessel is built for nuclear propulsion. Now, the *Enterprise,* our aircraft carrier, is a great success, because the entire matter was designed by people who were able to contemplate not only the ship, but the motor power for the ship, whereas in the *Savannah,* the AEC had responsibility for the propulsion in it and somebody else would order the gears according to the place where the propulsion was put, and it didn't fit together at all.

You've had a very large number of technical people appear before your committee. And you seem to have an instinct about what to believe. What seeps through your pores at hearings?

Well, I'm afraid that we do it by guess. By the time you've been elected to office a few times, you learn that not every precinct chairman can be trusted, and you find out very quickly which precinct chairman delivers for you and which precinct chairman doesn't; which man will make a good postmaster or which fellow will be an ingrate the rest of his life if you make him postmaster. The lessons you learn in that way carry over to the witness stand. And very quickly you'll pay no attention to a certain person because you know his testimony isn't worth depending upon. That's why Rickover has a great hold, I think, upon the Congress. He tells the people the truth, to the best of his ability. He's intemperate sometimes. He has prejudices like some of the rest of us. But he's never tried to mislead the committees.

I remember the first time I listened to him, when a decision had not yet been made to go for the nuclear submarine. And, frankly, I was not impressed when he walked in. I was not sure this wizened-up individual was the genius some people thought he was. But after he talked awhile you realized that here was a man who was an evangelist, practically, who was totally absorbed in his idea. He was pulling all the little atoms of his being in one direction and driving forever toward that goal. I became persuaded that if anybody could build it, this zealot could. Greater engineers might fail. But this man who had a complete singleness of purpose and a determination to see one thing through was exactly the sort of fellow we could entrust this thing to. So I just followed him blindly and never had occasion to regret it. He has a tremendous hold on the Joint Committee.

On the other hand, without giving any names, there was a man we had a great many times on the witness stand whom I listened to politely, but never allowed myself to be persuaded that he ever was telling the truth.

What is it about these precinct captains of science that tips you off?

Oh, I don't say you're tipped off. You have three precinct workers and one fails you. And you say to yourself, "Why was I misled by that fellow?" You never know, but you never trust anybody who looks just like he looks. And that's the way with these scientists. We're never real sure.

I remember the first time I talked to Ernest Lawrence. I didn't know much about him, and I wasn't disposed to spend much time with him because I was trying to talk to some other people, too, and he finally said, "You're from South Dakota, aren't you?" and I said, "Originally," and he said, "So am I." We just adjourned everything and talked about all the people we knew who were from South Dakota. And I found he had other interests in life besides his scientific interests. He had a family in which he was interested; he had friends in whom he was interested, and they had families and so forth. I decided that he was a better sort of person than I thought he was the first time I saw him. And anything he asked me for from that time on, I tried to do.

Ernest O. Lawrence was a Nobel laureate and physicist from the University of California. He was the developer of the cyclotron, the device which made it possible to bombard the nucleus of the atom, and hence to produce radioactivity artificially. He died in 1958.

You depend on your faith in people and on their capability to do a job.

I do think we pick individuals by use of a queer yardstick. We pick the ones we trust. If Norris Bradbury came to me

*Norris Bradbury is a
physicist and the director
of the Los Alamos
Scientific Laboratory in
Senator Anderson's home
state of New Mexico.*
and said, "I've found a new way to make a bomb. I'm going
to take three scoopfuls of common dirt, an ounce of paregoric
and an ounce of something else, and shake them up," I would
know it would work. Norris has a sure instinct. He can't tell
you why sometimes, but I trust him even if I don't know the
scientific reason for what he's doing, or couldn't understand
the scientific reason if I knew it.

*In modern government and big science, you and the Congress
become part of the whole process. I think of the nuclear
rocket program. You're an espouser of the rocket, and I've
had the feeling that the technical people were a little faint of
heart about it.*

I would hate to see in nuclear rocket propulsion the sad experience we had with the nuclear airplane. We never got started
with the nuclear airplane in a way that meant we intended to
finish it. We had a competitor, the airplane industry. And
many people worried that the airplane industry would suffer
if a nuclear airplane were constructed. I don't think that was
a sensible viewpoint at all, because the nuclear airplane had
such limited uses. It was a patrol vehicle. It was a policeman
who could get out and walk the beat and could walk it a
long, long time. And that's all we saw in it. But we spent
over a billion dollars on it and then, when it looked as if it
might work, it was abandoned. And now there is talk that
it may be the most interesting development we could come
to, and that maybe we ought to revive it. Before long you'll
see the military asking for it, because it can patrol. I hope

*Rover: the nuclear
rocket program.*
this wouldn't happen with Rover. The devices we are going
to send to the moon will need enormous propulsion power.

*What does the nuclear engineer tell you about the feasibility
of nuclear rockets?*

When I talk to some of the people who have responsibility
in that field they take the position that the project will never
work, that we'll never get a propulsion device that will be useful, that it can never be the third stage of something or other
we hope to build, and therefore that we might as well take
it very slowly in the laboratory. Well, we had a hard time
with many of our devices by letting them go too long. At the
time the first proposal was made for the hydrogen bomb,
they would have built it very quickly if they had really gone

ahead with the engineering they had at hand and the inventive devices they had in mind. But we postponed it. And it was hard to go back, pick up the pieces and start over again.

I wonder how you feel when you go down to Los Alamos for a visit. Is there any part of you that itches to put your hand on the valves? Is there a frustrated scientist inside you?

No, there's not. Not in the slightest. When we had President Kennedy down there, he saw a little device—you put your hand in the mittens and control something out ahead. You couldn't get him out of there until he'd tried it. But I've been in there about a dozen times and never wanted to try it.

What was it, Senator, that attracted you to atomic energy and space activities?

Well, it was in my state. You know, a little state gets tired, eventually, of hearing how wonderful it is in New York, Massachusetts, Illinois, or California. You think there are things out in your country that are worth while, and I became very proud of the people in the Los Alamos Laboratory and the things they were trying to do. I made up my mind that as soon as I could, I wanted to get better acquainted with them. Afterwards, I went to Vice President Barkley and told him I'd do anything I could to get on the Atomic Energy Committee and work. I was appointed, and right after that they had the first test in the Nevada area and so I went out. I was the only member of the committee who went. I took a short briefing and saw one of the bombs assembled. And I thought it was sort of a nervous business. They got us into a room, picked up these pieces of high explosives and put them into place, and the man said very casually, "You know what would happen, of course, if we dropped one of those." I wondered what would happen if the suction device got clogged somewhere and this thing was dropped. But I saw the whole bomb finally put together, and then we went out and watched the bomb explode. It gave me a little different feeling.

Can you tell us a little about your own educational process? One gets the feeling from reading the hearings that you people are very knowledgeable about the program these days.

Well, you have witnesses to help you. One day it's some-

body from Oak Ridge, and one day it's somebody from
Los Alamos, and one day it's somebody from some other
spot. They've been working very hard for a long time and
getting nowhere. And in desperation they come down and
sit in this office and start telling me what their problem is.
In a way, I couldn't care less, because I don't know a thing
about their idea and what they want. So they explain it to
me. By the time you get through, you ask yourself, "Is it
necessary or would something else serve the same purpose?"
So you make some inquiries and you read some books and
magazine articles. It's quite different from going to school.
But the scientists will educate you if you give them a chance.

*What about the role of the legislative branch in establishing
goals in science?*
Well, I don't know whether we do much in that way.

You certainly push certain things. . . .
Well, let's take saline water. We had a panel. I wanted
to find out what the importance of atomic energy might be and
how long it was going to take to get where it might be competitive with other types of fuels. We had study teams of all
kinds, and one day I began to wonder if this problem of
saline water might not be solved by atomic energy. The reason was that I was on two committees. If I were only on
one, I wouldn't have encountered these things. But one day
somebody said that to get salts out of the sea water the
water had to be lifted to about 1400°. I went from that
meeting to another in which they were talking about a certain type of reactor. They said when you run water through
there you use water as a coolant, it rises to about 1400°.
And I said, "Why not consolidate these two things?" So I
wrote to Los Alamos to see what they could suggest. Sure
enough, Dr. Philip Hammond had made a study that showed
for about $600 million he would build a plant that would
satisfy Los Angeles and its water requirements and give them
a boundless, endless, eternal supply of water from the Pacific
which they couldn't get by any other device, and give them
electricity as a by-product at a cost below anything they now
have.
Well, that answered the scientific question, except who
would turn a card for $600 million? It's like going into a

gambling game. You don't mind taking a hand of blackjack at fifty cents or a dollar, but if it's fifty thousand, you leave that for Nick the Greek. So I had to write to Phil Hammond and tell him that this was a fine gamble, but I just didn't know anybody who'd be fool enough to gamble $600 million. I asked him, "How big should the pilot plant be?" His reply was, "A pilot plant would teach you nothing. You have to build it big."

Well, Hammond kept on working on it, because I needed help and he was kind enough to keep giving it to me. And then, sure enough, the Atomic Energy Commission got more interested and the Secretary of the Interior, Mr. Udall, got interested. And now Hammond is working at Oak Ridge in the cooperative effort between AEC and the Department of Interior, trying to project what a plant can do. The plant he's proposing will develop enough electricity for the greater metropolitan area at a cost of two to two and a half mils per kilowatt-hour, which is lower than Bonneville, lower than what they're going to be charging in the Great Northwest in a short time. The present figure on saline water is about a dollar per thousand gallons, give or take a few pennies. We hope to get it down to forty cents or fifty cents. At twenty cents it's a godsend, but Hammond expects to get it even lower than that figure. You can water all the area around Los Angeles with that endless supply from the Pacific Ocean. And that's why I've been interested in saline water. We can take it to parts of the earth where we're not making any impression with our foreign aid programs. We can do great things with it.

There are proposals that Congress be given some sort of super technical staff to advise the whole body of Congress. How do you feel about that?

I don't believe you're ever going to be able to give Congress the information it wants by trying to build into every staff the complete answer to every question. I think you have to develop a few staff men in whom you have complete confidence. They go out and gather information. I don't think you could staff every committee with the men essential to give the members the information they need. For instance, we sit down there now in the Finance Committee and we ask what the effect of a certain amendment is. We get one answer from Treasury and a different answer from the so-called professional staff, and then we have to go around and ask a few people. We write our local banker and say, "What does this mean to your bank?"

You've only a few people on the staff of the Senate Space Committee. How can these few keep tabs on that enormous organization?

Well, probably they can't. But you can ask questions that reveal they aren't doing their homework. I don't say that any

Congressional staff keeps complete contact with everything that goes on inside of its organization. But let's go back to the Dixon-Yates contract. No member of the staff of the Joint Committee on Atomic Energy gave me a bit of information on the Dixon-Yates contract that was of any value to me. I tried to get a copy of the contract and finally one was sent to me at Albuquerque. Nobody expected me to do anything with it. Well, it was a fairly quiet night when we flew, all night long, from Albuquerque to Washington. The hearing was to be the next day. I went through that contract as if I were buying the plant or building the plant. Then we went to the meeting of the Atomic Energy Committee and heard all the beauties of this contract and I asked a question. And there was absolute silence. You shouldn't ask that question. I think the question had to do with what the tax advantages were. With absolutely no dangers, the promoters had a chance to make $150 million. So I began asking lots of questions. Well, the Atomic Energy Commission met and revised the contract and went over some of these things and brought it back again and revised it twice more. By that time, I knew there was something wrong with it. So we fought it as hard as we could fight it from that time on.

So the Joint Committee staff did not rouse you to the dangers of Dixon-Yates.
   That's right.

There was a need for strengthening that staff. What kind of need?
   At that time the staff was not built to alert us to what the Atomic Energy Commission was doing that was wrong. When Jim Ramey came in, we told him to watch the AEC. If we found they'd swept out the office and hadn't told us about it, we had somebody down there to find out why. We got into a few fights, but people began paying attention to things and before long we had a staff that really went into these questions hard.

James Ramey came in as executive director of the Joint Committee on Atomic Energy. He has since become one of the five commissioners of the Atomic Energy Commission.

Richard Crossman

*T*he British elections of 1964 were doubtless the first *major elections in a major nation in which policy toward science and technology was explicitly recognized as a major issue. In that election campaign, Harold Wilson was trying to do at least two things. First, he was trying to woo the rising class of technical specialists into the Labour party, trying to present himself as their spokesman, whether they were electrical engineers or market researchers. Second, he tried to establish the idea that Labour could regain for Britain the position of technological leadership in the world which it has lost to nations which came later to the industrial revolution.*

Like Kennedy's election four years earlier, the Wilson victory was a hairsbreadth one, and it will be a long time before anyone knows how far Labour can actually get toward its technological goals or even know how vigorously Labour can pursue its goals now that it's not crippled by an almost nonexistent majority in Parliament. Wilson has created a new Ministry of Technology—with a union leader (Cousins) at its head and a novelist (Snow) as Parliamentary Secretary. The new ministry is trying out some programs to encourage technical advance in computers and machine tools, programs whose effects no one can yet judge. Today you can probably get a clearer idea of Labour's ultimate relationship to science and technology from the discussions that went on in the months just before the election than from anything that has happened since.

In the summer of 1964 Richard Crossman was the shadow minister of science in the Labour opposition—the Labour MP whose assignment it was to keep track of science issues, formulate party policy, criticize the science actions of the Conservative government. Crossman is not at all a scientist himself and is quite ready to present his own classical education as an example of what's wrong with Britain's governors. When Labour set up its non-shadow government after the election, Crossman became Minister of Housing rather than of science.

In his late fifties, Crossman has been a journalist most of his life—an editor and later a columnist on The New Statesman, *the left-wing weekly. He has a journalist's suspicion of other journalists, was hard to get hold of for an interview, vigorously resented the camera and tape recorder. But he also has a journalist's facility with words and ideas, and he was easy to interview once his reluctance was overcome. He talks fast, snatches at an idea and develops it enthusiastically and at length. The difficulty, indeed, is to finish a question. He is impatient of slowness, grasps the question—usually correctly—before it is half stated, and plunges into an answer.*

To an American familiar with Washington, there is something casually amateurish about the way Parliament works. MP's have no offices, no paid staffs. When Parliament is in session, Crossman uses a small old-fashioned house on a quiet square within walking distance of the House of Commons. It was in the dowdy little parlor of that house that we interviewed him one rainy morning. We began:

Why is it that science and technology have suddenly become matters of intense political concern here in Britain?

It's a delayed reaction to the technological revolution from which people have been averting their eyes for many years. Suddenly it's hit them in a number of concrete ways. The most obvious is the motor car. Some time between 1959 and 1964 we passed the critical point where a motor car ceases to be a privilege and becomes the right of every citizen. You Americans passed it years ago. We passed it in a very small country with very little space and very bad roads. Now remember, this was a crisis of freedom. You buy a motor car to get free; you believe in free enterprise, your own individual free enterprise. You say, "I want to move anywhere, travel anywhere; I want to go where I like with whom I like." And the net result is that every Saturday you sit in a traffic jam solid from London to Brighton. Your vehicle of freedom has become a static status symbol.

And this put technology into politics?

This demonstrated to the British that technology impacting on an unplanned society produces chaos. It was a demonstration of the case for socialism. This is why we are going to win the next election. At the Labour party conference last year Harold Wilson was able to have a day devoted to science and technology on this very theme. It suddenly became relevant.

It sounds as if you saw advanced technology as primarily a threat, a trouble.

No. Technology is simply an instrument of power over nature. Power to do good or do bad. The computer is an enormous advantage, but it brings social problems with it. Unless you have social planning, the damage could outdo the advantage. That's all. This is nothing new I'm saying. It's what Karl Marx saw—that changes in the techniques of production, distribution, and exchange determine the character of social relations.

What kind of steps does it take for a country like Britain to adapt itself to the technological revolution?

You're asking me what the policy of the next Labour government is going to be. Because this is what we regard as the central issue—what Wilson regards as the central problem facing a Labour government, to be the first science-based government in Britain. Science-based in two senses. First, that it recognizes the enormous importance of technological change. And second, that it bases its actions on a scientific assessment of the facts. Now this is quite new in this country. The British government is traditionally the worst-informed in the world, because it prefers not to know what it does not want to see. Sometimes the results are brilliant;

in 1941 Churchill averted his eyes from the certainty of defeat and was able to resist Hitler. By defying the laws of gravity we had our finest hour. But normally speaking, defying the laws of gravity is an expensive process.

Might there be some defiance of the laws of gravity in trying to create a science-based government in a country that is not always technologically minded?

The oligarchy here, the Establishment, the people who run Britain have been deeply anti-technological. First of all in the preference for pure science as against technology; we are very good in Nobel prize winners in pure physics and chemistry, but we've never been as good in applied science. And second in the dominance of arts-trained people as against people trained in science and technology. At Whitehall, policies have been dominated by people trained in the humanities—and in a kind of humanities which is extremely anti-scientific. I am a perfect example of this, and so is Quintin Hogg. The men who are now Minister of Science and shadow Minister of Science were both trained in Oxford Greats. The Greats course in Oxford is two years of Latin and Greek philology followed by philosophy mainly confined to Plato's *Republic* and Aristotle's *Ethics*. Then we did Greek and Roman history, but of course not later than the third century A.D. Hogg and I are perfect representatives of the prescientific age. The difference is that I know it and he doesn't.

Quintin Hogg, who was Lord Hailsham until he gave up the title in 1963, was Minister of Science in the Conservative government.

What will a science-based government be like? How will we tell the difference?

Probably the first thing it has to do is end the domination of planning by the Treasury; a government which is planned by the same people whose job it is to reduce expenditures to a minimum can't really be planned at all. In America you've never had the kind of Treasury dominance we have. The head of the Treasury is the head of the civil service, and, with the Prime Minister's permission, he appoints the heads of all departments. There is what you might call a mandarin class at Whitehall. I'm parodying, of course, but basically there is a view that the best man to head anything doesn't know anything about it; the scientist should be treated always as a technical expert, and our wise, well-educated, cultured men will make the decisions. I regard this as fair nonsense. Of course, the scientist who has no training in history and the social sciences and despises them is just as blind as the other. The wise man we have to create is the man who is literate and who is also conversant with the world of science and technology—at least, let's say, he's numerate. Today the scientist is illiterate and the humanist is innumerate. I'm innumerate.

You will want to change the civil service?

There is a great deal to be said for having a corps of responsible, professional civil servants. But I think we have to have them refreshed and constantly jolted by temporary people from outside. In wartime we always flood Whitehall with temporary people from the universities and from business. And the great periods of advance in Britain have been times of war. In the nuclear age we can't have another war, so we have to have the sense of emergency without the actual war. If you ask what the Labour government will be—it will be that. We must get this circulation among Whitehall, industry, and the universities. I think that between 1940 and 1945, Britain was better governed than any country in the world. Our wartime planning was the best: We used our resources most economically; we retained our civil liberties most successfully; and yet we had far more total mobilization than the Germans or the Russians. Now I can see no reason why, in the modern world, we shouldn't introduce peacetime planning. But in order to do this we have to have an optimum combination of professional civil servants with specialists coming in and going out again.

If you had such people, do you think you could improve the ties between technology and science?

We have to narrow this terrible gap between university science and technology, between university and industry. When I go to Boston, I am struck by the influence of MIT on the industry around; and there's no shame about this. We haven't yet done this kind of thing here. This type of relationship, which is perfectly common in Germany and Holland, is something we have to establish here. I don't think we should establish it merely by upgrading our colleges of technology and calling them universities; there's a great

danger, if we do, of turning them into old-fashioned British universities.

Can you establish basic social changes like these by planning?

No. This has to do with education. The biggest job we have to do is to get an educational system of such a sort that people naturally grow up having these ideas. For instance, we have a unique specialization in this country. Starting at the age of fourteen, boys and girls are compelled to specialize either in arts or science—appalling/y early. This is mainly because of the scholarship system to Oxford and Cambridge. A lot of people who could be perfectly numerate are rendered innumerate at the age of fourteen. This is one of the things we shall have to deal with.

But isn't this specialization often considered one of the glories of British education?

True enough, if we destroy this specialization we shall be in danger of lowering the standard of our honors courses —which we are proud of and which have great advantages. But the disadvantage often is that to get a student so good in, say, medieval history, he has to be far too specialized in his last two years at school. If we're going to have more generalized courses, then we must have more postgraduate work. There's where the specialization should really start. The whole process is going to take longer. I think America is quite correct in holding that in the modern world the process of education takes longer. The same thing is happening in Russia. For once, we have got to realize that in this respect we are behind the times.

Compare C. P. Snow's thoughts on British education in the interview with him and the attitudes expressed by British émigré scientists.

298

Would that create the psychological change you want?

It would have an effect on the outlook of the people we are training. If you ask boys nowadays what they want to be, engineers or nuclear physicists, they nearly always want to be nuclear physicists. Not that they want to create bombs, but it's socially superior in Britain to do something useless. This is the old Greek view. You know what Aristotle said: "It is the mark of a gentleman to be able to play the flute —but not well enough to be thought a slave." This is the British tradition of the amateur. This we've got to get rid of. It may have been OK in the nineteenth century, but for running a complicated traffic system, for instance, I really think you'd better have some professional traffic people.

I have been gathering the impression that the Labour party is trying to become a spokesman for these professionals, for the technical people in Britain. Is that in the cards?

I hope so. We are aware of a tremendous frustration—the frustration of the professional man, the man who really knows his onions, who is a technologist. I think Harold Wilson consciously feels that he can represent these people. He is himself a trained statistician who first made his name because he organized a statistical system for the Ministry of Fuel in the war—the first proper statistical department in Whitehall, as a matter of fact. He feels himself genuinely a spokesman of the professionals.

In conventional terms, how much socialism is there to the sort of science-based government you are talking about?

Well, in my definition socialism is based on the proud

rationalist assumption that human reason can solve the problems of society. If you're a Communist, you think you can do it by ruthless centralization, that a small elite will impose a rule. What we mean by democratic socialism is that rational solutions can be achieved with the voluntary assent of an educated people. That they will acquiesce, for instance, in the necessity for a public sector far larger than the present and absorbing far more of our wealth than is at present absorbed. Your countryman Galbraith is quite right. The great issue is the relation between the public sector and the private sector. You've only got to tot up the bill for education, the bill for health, the bill for all these public services—you cannot pay this bill unless democracy is willing to stop insisting that each year there should be so many extra pounds, shillings and pence to spend each week or each month on individual purchases in the shops. Now this is quite a thing to do. And this is why I say education is the central theme.

You have been pointing out ways in which Britain is now less science-based than most of the industrial world. Suppose there is a Labour government for five or ten years, do you see a possibility that Britain might become a peculiarly science-based country?

It sounds very arrogant, but I think there is something to be said for the view that we and the Scandinavians have special advantages here in a long tradition of democracy and a long tradition of personal freedom. In order to do something, we don't have to risk the danger—not as much as other countries—of scientific despotism or of anti-scientific anarchy. I think our size is an advantage, too. I think it is much more difficult to do this on a continental basis than it is to do it in a smallish nation-state of something like seventy million people. I'll be quite blunt. We do have special conditions for succeeding. I think we have a special chance.

A SHAPER OF SOCIETY

The impact of science and technology on nations, on regions, on industries

British Emigrés

Scientists have always been travelers. Whether they went
to other laboratories so they could compare results with
colleagues struggling over similar problems, or to centers
of learning, for study under a great teacher, they have never
found the boundaries of country or continent as inhibiting
as the average citizen does. Since World War II, however,
a new dimension has been added to this picture of mobility,
as significant numbers of scientists and engineers have mi-
grated to the United States. Unlike the wave that came
from Germany and Austria during the 1930's, most of them
have come not to escape persecution but to find the advanced
facilities that are becoming more and more vital to the practice of science. From 1949 to 1963 some 55,000 scientists
and engineers were admitted as immigrants, and of these,
10,000 came in 1962 and 1963 alone.

Needless to say, this outflow of technical manpower has
caused considerable concern in the countries affected, particularly in Britain, which is the birthplace of the highest
proportion (20 per cent) of those admitted in 1962 and 1963.
In Parliament and in the press there has been a continuing
debate over this "brain drain." Why is it happening? Is it
hurting Britain? Can it be stopped? Should it be stopped?

These questions reached a peak during 1964, when an
important nine-man medical research team decided to move
in a body from Birmingham University to the Worcester

Foundation for Experimental Biology in Massachusetts. So in the spring of that year the editors decided to gather a few technical men who had come here from Britain and ask them to discuss their experiences and attitudes in the hope of getting some insight into the causes and the significance of the brain drain. The group we brought together around a Cambridge (Mass.) dinner table was a thoroughly unscientific sampling. Its members, who ranged in age from thirty to forty, were chosen simply because they were in the Cambridge area and were free to join us on the same evening.

Professor Patrick Wall of the MIT biology department is a medical doctor and research physiologist who received his education at Oxford. He came to the U.S. in 1948.

Professor W. D. Jackson, also at MIT, is an electrical engineer who works nowadays in magnetohydrodynamics (the behavior of electrically conducting fluids in magnetic

W. D. JACKSON

PATRICK WALL

fields). *Trained at Glasgow University, he first came to the
U.S. in 1955 as a visiting scholar in the Fulbright program.*

*Dr. John Evans is the youngest in the group, and his work
at Lincoln Laboratory deals with one of the youngest areas
of science—radar astronomy. This is a branch of astronomy
in which we bounce radar signals off the sun, moon, and
planets in order to learn certain things about their characteristics. Evans studied physics at Manchester University and
learned his radar astronomy at the university's Jodrell Bank
research station. He left Britain in 1960.*

*Robert H. Colbourne is a systems engineer at MITRE
Corporation. Educated at London University, he came here
in 1956.*

*David Lutyens, educated at Cambridge, is a teacher and
science writer. He emigrated in 1961 and is now developing
educational films at The Ealing Corporation.*

*The conversation developed with a most British-seeming
combination of passion and decorum. The subject was clearly
one about which the participants had thought a lot and felt
strongly. But the discussion stayed on the point and moved
in an orderly way with almost no intervention by the editors*

305

DAVID LUTYENS

—except for an opening request that each of our guests tell something of why he had crossed the Atlantic.

WALL: I came here in 1948, immediately after finishing medical school, as an instructor at Yale. I had assumed that I would return, but by accident or inertia, I stayed on here —stepped onto the American academic ladder and proceeded on.

EVANS: I came here four years ago, in 1960. I went to university in Manchester at a time when it was quite easy for someone to get a PhD regardless of his parents' income; the educational act allowed one to go through college and postgraduate work with government support. So by the time I was twenty-four I had my PhD in the rather strange field of radar astronomy—even today there must be fewer than ten professional radar astronomers in the world. So I was a bit of a freak, and the problem was what to do next. I graduated at Jodrell Bank, and the only other organization in England with a program in this area was the Royal Radar Establishment. I didn't entertain the idea of becoming a civil servant, so I stayed on at Jodrell as a research fellow. But

A radio telescope, such as that at Jodrell Bank, detects radio waves coming from space. To do radar astronomy, however, an extra step is necessary. One must send out a signal and then receive the echo coming back.

JOHN EVANS

after three years it became clear that either I had to leave this field or leave the country. Although we had a large telescope, we didn't have the associated equipment, the large transmitters and sensitive receivers, to compete with what was being done in America. So with some reluctance, I came to Lincoln Laboratory, where I have been allowed to pursue this kind of work with much better support than I was getting at Jodrell. In that sense, I have no regrets.

JACKSON: My story really begins with leaving Glasgow University, where I did my bachelor's degree, for an appointment at Manchester as an assistant lecturer; that would be instructor at an American university. I worked for some time on my thesis research in magnetohydrodynamics, until it began to have implications beyond the capability of the university and the people I worked with. Moreover, as an instructor I became aware of the revolution in engineering teaching at MIT which Dean Gordon Brown—then head of the electrical engineering department—was initiating. I came to MIT on a nine-month visiting-lecturer appointment because, in the first instance, I wanted to find out what Brown was up to—for I felt the need of some substantial

ROBERT H.
COLBOURNE

revolution in engineering education at Manchester and elsewhere in England. Secondly, I knew some people at MIT
were getting interested in my research field. So nine months
stretched out to two years. I did return to Manchester, but
I wasn't there long before I decided that the professional opportunities at MIT were to be greatly preferred to the life
of a revolutionary at Manchester. So, as Wall said earlier,
I stepped on the American academic ladder.

COLBOURNE: I represent applied science here. I will go
back a little farther than other people to point out that I
was in school when the war started. I served five years in
the RAF before going up to university. After graduating
from London, I joined the Royal Naval Scientific Service,
in the microwave field, working on what I would now call
a weapons system. In 1954 it became obvious that if I were
going to get anywhere, I would have to leave the rather cozy
little nook I was in—and if I were going to move, I might
as well make a real move. So I succumbed to an offer from
a Canadian company, thinking that two years over there
would let me see the other side of the Atlantic. But at the
end of those two years I came down into the States, because
it seemed silly to be over here and not see this part of the
world. That was in 1956 and at the moment I'm still here.
It comes down to the difficulty of going back.

LUTYENS: I first came to the States in 1957 on a Com-
monwealth Fund fellowship. I came as a teacher. I had been

teaching for some years in England, after being trained in science, and it is a terribly corny thing to say but really I think the moment I first decided I wanted to live in America was when I saw the Manhattan skyline—the conventional immigrant's reaction. I taught at Harvard for a year in a very minor capacity and spent the rest of the time studying American techniques of teaching science. It took me about six months to unlearn the dogma I came equipped with— that the British education system was the best in the world. I became fascinated, above all, by the American talent for experiment. My arrival coincided with the arrival of Sputnik, and this was a time of tremendous ferment; I was immensely stimulated by Zacharias' curriculum reforms. When the time came to go back to England, I still had the urge of a frustrated scientist, the urge to explain science to other people. I went into television and newspaper and paperback publishing and spent a rather miserable two years in an atmosphere where science just isn't understood and I decided to come back to the States. In the meantime I married an American girl, and that helped. So here I am.

WALL: I wonder if we'd like to discuss why we are here, really. People have been leaving England since before the Crusades, coming to America since after Columbus. I think there is a real question whether there is anything new now. One thing, it's clear, is new: It's become a political issue, particularly between Quintin Hogg and Harold Wilson. I suspect Hogg's friends have quite a two-faced attitude. They have to regret this emigration, *pro forma,* but they are a past-oriented group who look on England as a place where you distill off the low-boiling-point types to India or any other place that will accept them. The implication being that those who remain get better and better. Now what about Wilson and the Labour party? They are concerned, of course, with an improved living standard in Britain. Now a living standard doesn't come just from having good ideas. It comes from applying good ideas—and this needs large numbers of people. So Wilson has a very good point; now really is a time to be worried.

Hogg was at that time Minister of Science in the Conservative government. Compare the comments on Hogg in the interview with Crossman.

COLBOURNE: I'd like to add to your analogy. Distillation is fine, and pure metals are fine for ornaments, but if you want strength you look for alloys—and I think the alloying agents are being lost in Britain. After all, who went to India? Not the elder son. He looked after the estate. It was the second or third or fourth son, who would be nothing in England, who became the administrator of some Indian province. There is a little of that here. I think we have to face it.

LUTYENS: Britain is no longer the center of an empire. And the professional class, the class that finds it easiest to emigrate, is precisely the one which should be staying home and helping to build a better Britain. I think Wall is right that the political party in power has a very nineteenth-century attitude toward the loss of these people.

Is there any feeling of guilt around this table?

WALL: Oh certainly.

EVANS: Particularly in my case, as one of the younger members present; my education was paid for by the state. On the other hand, this feeling of guilt has to be reconciled with one's own selfish desire to do as well as one can in one's science. Wherever you can do your best, you must go there and do your best.

COLBOURNE: I don't feel a sense of guilt. When I left in 1954, I remember thinking, I don't feel I am leaving a sinking ship. Britain was back on its feet. And then there was the question how valuable one was in England, and how valuable over here. The people from Canada made me feel I would make a more important contribution in Canada than where I was. I was not irreplaceable, and it was fairly obvious I was never going to be on top of my little group because there were other people of my age who had four or five years more experience, acquired during the war years. I felt I had a greater breadth of vision, but it wasn't really needed in that comparatively limited scientific field—the job was fairly well spelled out.

EVANS: This is a very important point. People say this loss of brains damages the rate of scientific achievement in England. I really question this. If I had stayed in England, I know what would have happened: I would have gone to the Royal Radar Establishment. A colleague of mine did just that, and I visited him a year ago. He's struggling to do, with inferior equipment, what I'm doing over here much more easily with much better support. He is not benefiting England any more than I am. The country's use of brains is not that efficient.

WALL: After all, none of us have rejected Britain in the way a political refugee might. You have all sorts of emotional loyalties to friends and the country in which you were born, but in addition you have a loyalty to fulfill yourself in research; loyalty, if you like, to humanity—to produce the maximum you can. What we really want to know is: Why did we not feel ourselves fulfilled in Britain? What was wrong with Britain for us?

JACKSON: One thing that makes us different from the political refugee or the immigrant of the past—we work in a sort of international fellowship of science and technology; our friends are scattered around the world and because of the work we do we are able to get on airplanes and travel anywhere. We are part of a larger community.

LUTYENS: I think you research types have every excuse to go do your research where you can best do it. I don't have this excuse—but I would like to report that I don't feel any sense of guilt. None at all. I would feel differently if I came from Ghana or some other place which desperately needs technical help. But I am rather sick and tired of this moralizing by the politicians. I seem to have spent all my life working in institutions where I am told it is a privilege to work —from Winchester College to England. I am prepared to be rather aggressive in arguing that England ought to put its house in order before it starts moralizing.

JACKSON: I don't feel any guilt either. I made an attempt to work in a British academic environment. I went back and tried to be a crusader. . . .

LUTYENS: But they're not interested. The complacency is fantastic.

WALL: Yes . . . complacency. And there are those with shattered morale. When I had been over here and started inquiries about jobs back there, my old tutor at Oxford said, "Why do you want to come back? Don't you realize this

311

country's finished?" Now I think he was wrong, but I think it is important that a man in that position is making a statement like that.

COLBOURNE: I get an impression that nearly everyone around this table is saying that under a Conservative government we have an impossible situation and it will be all right when Labour gets in. I disagree. Not that I think it is better under the Conservatives, but I don't think it is going to improve overnight under Labour.

We hear it said that science has more freedom in Britain than here because so much of it here is sponsored by the Defense Department or NASA. What about that? Do you feel less free than your friends at home?

Compare Donald Hornig's comments on the American system.

WALL: On the contrary, I believe the method of distributing funds here gives increased freedom. In England, most money for the universities is distributed through the University Grants Committee and is distributed down through a hierarchy of people. Here the young man in a university applies for his own grant and is not dependent on his department chief. This is really a fundamental difference.

You indicated before, Evans, that you don't think you could do in Britain, financially, what you do here?

EVANS: Well, the large telescope at Jodrell, complete with the buildings and peripheral things, cost something like three quarters of a million pounds. But there was a shortage of money with which to buy receiving and transmitting equipment to use with this splendid instrument for radar. The kind we wanted would have cost about a half million dollars. Even had we had the money, we couldn't have gone to an English company to build one, for the simple reason that

A klystron is a special kind of electronic tube used in radar sets.

the high-powered klystrons weren't being developed in England. There is no market. In this country the military requires these large devices, and then industry can sell them to other organizations at a fraction of the development cost.

How easily can you come by a half million dollars here?

EVANS: That's a good question. The only personal experience I have had was when I wanted to build an antenna to use with an existing transmitter. The antenna was to be 220 feet across, that's about the size of the Jodrell Bank instrument. Mine is fixed to the ground and not steered, and therefore less expensive. It cost about $150,000. It was only necessary to convince the senior people within the Laboratory that this was a good project, and they carried it from there. At Lincoln, funds can be made available for a worthwhile project.

LUTYENS: I worked for two years for a company which makes particle accelerators—off the shelf as it were—varying in price from $25,000 to $3,500,000. Now the interesting thing is that this company sells about 80 per cent of its business to universities who get the money from the National Science Foundation or the like. This company could never have been conceived in England. It would have gone bankrupt in six months.

Compare what Robinson has to say in the interview with company presidents.

WALL: I think the important thing is not that money is easy to come by, anywhere, but that here your request is considered by a group of scientists. It is not automatically rejected as ridiculous by some civil servant. Here you have to get up to the level of the Mohole or the Stanford accelerator before the issues become so large that they are decided by general democratic process.

Mohole refers to the multimillion-dollar project to drill a 35,000-foot hole through the ocean crust to the mantle beneath. The problem of accelerators is discussed in the interview with Hornig.

COLBOURNE: We are comparing Britain with the whole of America. If the European scientific community really became integrated by the common market we might see a brain drain across the channel.

WALL: I think it is already happening. I think we have an example of what the common market way of thinking could do in CERN.

CERN is the European Organization for Nuclear Research.

JACKSON: When I was setting up to make a move from Manchester, I seriously considered the possibility of working with CERN, and some of my friends in engineering and physics are at CERN to this day. Others are in Switzerland working for such companies as IBM.

EVANS: Jodrell Bank lost nine of its doctoral graduates to this country, the last of whom came here about three years ago. Since that time none have come to this country but four have gone to Australia.

There is still the question of why people leave, apart from the fact that sometimes they can't get enough research money.

JACKSON: Could I say something about that? Getting money is one thing, but having people who can make good use of it is another, and I regard one of the chief difficulties in England as being the lack of graduate schools. One of the great strengths of American academic institutions is the existence of strong and effective graduate schools all across the country. People get known around the world, not for the books they write or as teachers, but for the research they do—and they do it with graduate students. This is a basic problem in British higher education. The tradition lingers that when a man has got a bachelor's degree he is educated and must not demean himself to sit in a class any more. And so one finds people doing research degree work of incredible triviality because their professors are constrained to give them work within their capabilities. One reason the brains are draining away from Britain is that in the academic world they do not have the opportunities which are available here to work with students.

LUTYENS: The British education system is living in a great self-deception—that it is the best in the world. If I may be forgiven an anecdote: The first morning I appeared as a teacher at what some people consider to be the best private school in England, a wizened figure with a chalk-covered gown came up to me in the faculty common room, a classics don of considerable standing, and said to me, "So you're the new stinks don." That very expressive British term for science derives from the chemistry lab of course, and conscious that physics is the queen of the sciences, I said, "Yes, I've come here to teach physics." Whereupon he said, "I said you are the new stinks don. I don't differentiate between one *kind* of stinks and another."

In a sense, you people have come to a society in which science outranks the humanities, and so you have upgraded yourselves. An American teacher of Latin or Greek might feel like an underdog.

JACKSON: That's how I feel. My high school education was obtained at a school in Glasgow, which specialized in sending people to Oxford and Cambridge. I did reasonably well in mathematics and such matters, but I was ruled out as a possible candidate because I could not attain the required proficiency in Latin—and that deflected me to Glasgow University. British education has a preoccupation with Oxford and Cambridge; they have an influence out of all proportion to their real importance. There is a hierarchy. There are those who are in the Establishment, the Oxford-Cambridge gang, and those who are out, the rest of us.

EVANS: Let me explain how this works. Any public school which is hiring a headmaster or senior master will, if it's possible, hire someone with an Oxbridge degree. You can go through the lists without finding a single headmaster who can't write *Oxon* or *Cantab* after his name. So, at the high school level, the headmasters deflect all their best pupils to Oxford or Cambridge. It's a closed circle, very hard to break.

WALL: I think this is something very important to say, here in America, because something very like this is developing in the States. Not as dramatically—but there seems to be a watershed, with universities collecting on the coasts and not as much happening in the middle as in 1900.

EVANS: One good thing about Britain is that it is possible for a boy who is bright to get through college, to get a good education even if it's second best, without the struggle that can go on in this country. In England the bright are pampered.

May I ask Jackson a question? Suppose you had been good in Latin as well as in math; suppose you had gone to Cambridge. What would your life as a scientist have been like?

JACKSON: I will use the example of a friend who did come to the U.S. but has chosen to return. He went to Cambridge, took a degree in engineering, came to Harvard for a year for a master's and returned to England. He did his doctorate at Cambridge and carried on for a while as a fellow—and has recently been appointed the professor of engineering sciences at one of the new universities—building up a new department from scratch.

WALL: The British educational system is really designed to select an elite. It may use nineteenth-century criteria, and the process of selection may well destroy some people, but once you've made it, there is no doubt that this is a fabulous bunch of people with excellent working conditions. The question is how much of their initiative is destroyed in the process.

COLBOURNE: It's very easy for a young man to determine at a certain level that he cannot make the grade, that he just doesn't have the background. Do any of us know of anyone included in the Establishment who has come over here?

LUTYENS: I confess that I am, in the sense that I suppose I could have gone on and become headmaster of a good private school. But I think this matter of an elite is just the problem. England has too much of an elite.

WALL: But there is fierce competition. The best do get trained, and so competition for a lecturer's post at a university is quite fierce. And the professor at Cambridge, someone who is in the Establishment, is as well off as a professor here. His standard of living is high, and certainly the respect which he holds in the community and throughout the world is very high.

EVANS: To take a field I know—there have been several groups of radio astronomers in the world. In England, in Australia, and over here. The only group that has been truly stable over seven or eight years has been the one at Cambridge. I believe this reflects the conditions peculiar to Cambridge.

COLBOURNE: This brings up another question. Can you go back? What are you going back to? It is nothing like so easy to organize as it was to organize coming over.

JACKSON: I did go back. And as near as I can remember, the thing that struck me was the high cost of living in the way to which one had become accustomed. Little matters like lighting coal fires—you could do it, but you had lived with central heat for two years. Now, I went back to the College of Science and Technology at Manchester, and I sort of expected there might be some interest in what Brown and Company had been up to at MIT.

LUTYENS: They recognized MIT's existence?

JACKSON: Oh yes, we were using textbooks that had

been written—before and during the war—by MIT staff members. But the reaction was: "Well, you're back. How about a game of table tennis?" I thought there might be some hope for the students, and I was teaching a course in circuit theory. Now, Professor Guillemin, who was active then at MIT, had a very elegant and general way of looking at this subject, and I thought I'd introduce some of this into the course. It was the only time in my career I've had any objection to my teaching. From the students! It wasn't in the syllabus; how could they prepare for the exams? I gave up. That very day I wrote to Gordon Brown.

It's hard to go back. But if you were offered a chance to become professor in your field at Cambridge would you take it?

WALL: Yes. There are a number of practical difficulties to returning. For a junior person, some simple ones like the time it takes for advertisements to arrive and the time it takes to answer them. And in any system, one tends to appoint people one is familiar with. Also, to get a job of any description in Britain you must put on a campaign for it; there is an expectation that a campaign will be mounted. Whereas here the system is that one is asked.

Yet if it were offered, you'd say yes. Why?

WALL: I still feel a foreigner here. Universities are universal places, and the people here are the same types I would mix with in London. But the man I meet on the street is still a stranger to me here. I still feel the chances of having an interesting conversation with the man in a garage are higher in England.

There is still a final question—whether something is going out of Britain that is really a loss to Britain.

WALL: We've seen examples in history of a country like Portugal, which, presumably, at the time of her expansion was a tremendously exciting place to live. Things happen to countries, and the worry is that England may be on its way out. You can't afford to isolate yourself—to lose the more enterprising people.

COLBOURNE: What would entice us back? I think the answer to that would be real long-term projects which were of use to humanity. I think there are a tremendous number of people who would go back for a real forward-looking project.

JACKSON: My own feeling is the hope for Europe, not just for Britain, is the common market.

LUTYENS: Britain is a very parochial country.

WALL: I think its parochialism may be the track that leads to another Portugal.

JACKSON: There may be an aspect of critical size here. That's where the common market comes up.

LUTYENS: I can summarize my thoughts in two brash sentences. I think the ideal environment is somewhere in mid-Atlantic, just slightly on the American side. I like living here because on the whole the people I deal with instinctively say yes to new ideas, whereas in England they consistently used to say no.

C. P. Snow

*S*cientists have long been pictured as people apart from
the rest of society—as denizens of ivory towers, unconcerned
with the turmoil and problems of the world around them.
Although technology is now so much a part of our lives that
this picture is changing, there undoubtedly remains a separation between science and the humanities, if only in the areas
where their practitioners fail to understand one another or,
worse, fail to try to understand one another.

Probably no one in recent years has done more to publicize
this separation than the British novelist-scientist C. P. Snow.
One of the very small number of literary men with a firsthand knowledge of science as well as of literature, Snow has
preached a deep concern about the gulf he finds between the
way scientists look at the world and the way other educated
men look at it. This concern has contributed a phrase—the
two cultures—to the language and has also brought him and
his novels under surprisingly bitter attack from the more
traditional literary men for whom he symbolizes a technological society they feel has little room for man's "individual
condition." Snow, in turn, feels literary people are insuffi-
ciently aware of, and in some cases opposed to, the scientific
revolution—a revolution he has written of (in The Two Cultures and the Scientific Revolution) as being the one way
out for a world facing the prospects of atomic war, over-

*population, and an ever widening gap between the rich and
the poor nations.*

*Snow's efforts to help bridge the gap between the scientific
and literary cultures have made him a close observer of those
areas in government and education where science intersects
with society. And doubtless this is why one of the first acts of
the Labour government that came into power in Britain in
1964 was to elevate him to the peerage and make him Parliamentary Secretary of its new Ministry of Technology.*

*When we talked to Lord Snow it was before the election,
and he was still Sir Charles. It had not been easy to get
together with him; he is an inveterate traveler with little room
in his schedule. When we finally met, it was at the London
headquarters of English Electric Company. He is a director
and keeps an office there, though it was plainly little used.*

*Snow was turning sixty when we interviewed him, but he
looked and moved as if he were considerably older. That day
at least, there was a weary massiveness to his speech. He
took no initiatives, broached no topics of his own, but he
turned a friendly and thoughtful attention onto each of the
topics we brought up. The first of them concerned fiction:*

*What about the appearance of scientists in fiction? Apart
from your own work, are there any fictional scientists who
seem real to you?*

There aren't many. Partly because most writers don't
know anything about scientists. Partly because they are relatively difficult to do. The much-despised Sinclair Lewis
made an honorable attempt, I think. . . .

In Arrowsmith?

With *Arrowsmith,* yes; it's much better than it's usually
admitted to be. One or two of H. G. Wells's scientists are
surprisingly lively and kicking to this day. One or two of
Nigel Balchin's are really pretty good. But there are very,
very few which are really viable, I think.

Why is that?

People, the readers, think that scientists are different from
the rest of mankind, and that makes it difficult to write about

them as though they are human beings. That's the typical fault.

Even in your own books, it seems to me, the scientist is often seen from the outside, where the lawyer or classicist is seen from the inside.

I think there is something in that. Of course it is partly the technique I've chosen. In using the first person in my novels, I'm writing as if I were a lawyer looking at scientists. My spokesman, Lewis Eliot, is a lawyer and couldn't know as much as I know about the actual scientific experience. It's part of the convention that he shouldn't. But I think I would agree that in my novel, *The New Men,* the scientists didn't . . . I think I'd do them better now if I had another shot at it. I'm fairly pleased with the scientists in my latest book; they don't play a large part but they are important to it.

You like them better than the scientists in, say, The Affair?

Yes, I think I do. This is a book called *Corridors of Power,* which is really about high politics; the scientists come into it in the way scientists do come into politics.

Is there anything peculiar about the scientist that makes him harder to handle, for a writer, than an artist or a lawyer would be?

If the public the writer were addressing were familiar with the scientific terms of reference, the scientist would probably be no more difficult and no less difficult than any other —except perhaps for this: I'm very dubious about how much any of our ordinary flux of experience is verbalized, but there is no doubt at all that very little of the scientific experience is verbalized. The more one thinks of it, the more certain that seems to be. Well of course that makes it very hard to put the actual scientific process into verbal terms. You have to find a sort of analogy for it, not a direct representation.

Do you feel that the crises of the scientific experience lack the drama you need in order to write about them?

On the crude level, of course, that's true. But I don't think it's very difficult to suggest to an audience what it must be like to discover the nucleus, as Rutherford did—or even what Dirac did with the relativistic extension of the wave equation. These are like all the great creative experiences—as sharp as any can be.

Then why did you make Lewis Eliot a lawyer instead of making him a scientist, say a spectroscopist, as you were?

I wanted his professional experience to involve no extra difficulties. I was going to do things that were difficult enough, and so I wanted to simplify that particular part of his experience. That was quite deliberate.

Perhaps some day it will be easier to write about scientists, as people generally learn more science. Certainly the American educational system does seem to produce a reader more aware of science. And British education seems to be tending toward the American model. Indeed some people I talk to in Britain are afraid it will move too far toward mass education and suffer a loss of standards.

I'm sure that won't happen. Our danger is that we may move too slowly toward general mass education. Most people genuinely don't like the idea of education at all, and certainly not education given to a really large slice of the population. The bitterest opposition to university expansion has come from relatively poor people of my own origins who managed to scrape a university education and have done pretty well—and are determined that nobody should have any university education ever again. I think you Americans have suffered from an extremely expansive attitude, but I'm sure you err on the right side and we've erred desperately on the wrong one. It's true—and anyone who knows the United States is aware of it—your high school education is very loose and ramshackle by world standards.

We are starting to change it . . .

It's changing very fast, but it's still very ramshackle by Russian standards for instance. On the other hand, you do pick up very fast at the college level, and by the last two years the catching up is going even faster. And of course at the graduate level you really put on the screws, and your graduate education seems to be far better than ours, as good as anything in the world.

In what is one of the classic papers of modern physics, the British scientist Lord Rutherford postulated in 1911 that certain phenomena observed in radioactive materials could only be explained by assuming that most of the positive electric charge and mass of an atom were concentrated in a small central region that was later to be called the nucleus. The Dirac reference is to the important step made seventeen years later by this British physicist in bringing the new theories of the wavelike nature of electrons into harmony with Einstein's theory of relativity.

What is going to happen to British education over the next decade?

We shall increase the amount of college education. And we shall do something you never felt a lack of—we shall try different kinds of college education. Education in England has been modeled absurdly faithfully on Oxford and Cambridge. The really new universities, the ones started in the last six or seven years, are starting out at the undergraduate level doing something different. This is very important.

Different in what way?

In the curriculum. At the University of Sussex they have broken down the ordinary English system altogether, and they pursue *groups* of subjects to a degree level. They take history, a language, and even some sort of sociology all in one school; they are divided into schools rather than departments. The University of Essex is doing something rather similar on the scientific and technological side.

How about secondary education?

At the high school level I'm not so sure. We tried the unfortunate expedient—ridiculous, disastrous—of splitting people up at a level far too young. It's meant a tremendous amount of strain and it's introduced a new and curious element into the class system: Parents of the emerging middle class are determined their children shall get into grammar schools—which happens if they do well enough in the eleven-plus examination, as we call it—and are desperately disappointed if they don't manage it. There are horrifying stories of parents refusing to speak to their eleven-year-old children if they didn't make this particular grade. This is clearly wrong and is being pretty well wiped out. We're going to drift toward something like your high schools—we call them comprehensive schools.

A friend of mine once characterized the American high school as the only institution except the church which believes that all souls can be saved. It does seem that the British believe in the elect and the damned. . . .

That's very nice. The British do believe in the elect, to an extent greater than anything I've ever known.

A moment ago you spoke admiringly of the Russian high schools. Is there something to learn there?

There's a great deal to learn from Russia. Their great strength is the most serious, widespread, and thorough education in the world up to the age of seventeen or eighteen. Unless you are living in the deep country you go through eleven years of school, and that course, which is the same throughout Russia, is extremely good. It's very wide, as wide as yours; you do Russian language, Russian literature, a foreign language really seriously for eight or nine years, mathematics, physics, chemistry, history. And you must do everything. The Russians don't believe in the elect at all: If you're bad at mathematics, then you damned well have to cope—and the better students are supposed to help you along. I think they believe too little in the elect and too much that everyone can do everything. They work the children much harder even than we do—probably too hard—but still they do very well.

Apparently the Russians are now cutting that eleven-year course to ten years. What do you think they are getting at?

I discussed this during my recent trip to Russia. Most Russian academics appear to be rather strongly in favor. They say the amount learned in the last year has proved disappointing—of course they did not go in for the extremely professional specialization of the English sixth-form course. They feel they can do a better job by getting into the university and beginning at a level which is similar to the first year of an American college course.

How about their college-level work?

It's all right—but no better than ours, I think. They split off research from the universities too much; the universities lose that stimulation. They are now rethinking that, putting a lot of research back in universities. They are very good at the fifth year of the undergraduate course—at letting a student really bite onto serious research or technological problems and get the feel of them. It's not uncommon for bright young physicists to walk out of Moscow University knowing enough solid-state physics to be a useful member of a research institute right on the spot. But the first great lesson they've taught us is that you can educate a really large slice

Solid-state physics deals with understanding the physical processes that go on in solids.

of the population thoroughly without losing anything—which is one thing we've badly needed to learn.

How far does an industrial society have to take that lesson? How much education does it need, to be technologically strong?

Technically, what you have to have is about 2 per cent of the population educated up to top capability in science and technology. That is the brutal requirement which you're approaching, the Russians are approaching, and we're on the way toward. In Britain we don't miss a lot of high ability, oddly enough. We're good at coping with high ability from poor homes. Our concept of the elect in education went fairly deep down to find able people—but it has drawn the limits of the elect much too sharply. We're very bad at dealing with people of modest ability—people who, if they had been born more lucky, would have been, oh, say, members of Parliament or successful businessmen. But there is another side to this question: I suspect that all you need for purely practical reasons is this 2 per cent intensively educated in science and technology; but in order to make the society tolerable you want a wide group who understand what we're doing.

I should think a modern, really technological society needs a whole spectrum of skills, not just a highly educated 2 per cent.

Yes, I'm sure this is true. And also to make it a decent society—so that far more people are capable of participating in it.

Can Britain become that kind of society?

I think we can hold our own. This is a thing which we all know is our best chance. We have certain advantages. We are a very homogeneous people and rather easily pull together, given anything to pull onto. I believe with good leadership some of the English skills at getting on with each other not too badly, at making certain personal compromises, might give us a certain edge. Some of our personal skills —and I mean here personal skills, not scientific or technological skills—may be very valuable once we get the impetus. And I'm sure that impetus is coming.

A few years ago, I remember, you were quoted as saying you expected atomic bombs to drop within ten years. You're more optimistic now.

No, no. I said that unless we began to get some rational approach, then the worst might happen within ten years. In fact we *have* got a much more rational approach since that time. We have stopped nuclear tests. I think we are pretty safe for ten or twenty years. After that I think the problem becomes acute again, for rather different reasons.

As bombs become widespread.

Exactly. I've always been worried about that. Obviously if all these weapons were held by you and the Russians, the equilibrium would be pretty safe for a very long time. But that probably won't happen. But still, I'm optimistic for a good long time to come. I think we are now discovering that the worst doesn't always happen, which is a very important thing to learn. People of our age have been through times when that was hard to remember.

We certainly have.

I. G. Petrovskii

*O*f all the nations of the world, the United States and the Soviet Union are the ones which have embarked on a policy of educating every youth just as completely as his abilities permit. France is striving to educate all of its brightest youths, with a rigid selection system. The British are still debating the merits of education for everyone as against education for an elite. For wholehearted mass education one must look to the U.S. and the U.S.S.R.

In the previous pages, C. P. Snow had things to say about the ways these two countries approach the problem of secondary education. For a look at college-level teaching, we talked to the head of Moscow State University. To an American, Moscow seems more a college than a university, since in Russia research and teaching are mostly separated, with research done in non-teaching institutes. Nevertheless, many of the concerns of a university head are the same in either country.

The main building on the Lenin Hills campus of the Moscow State University stands 720 feet tall, the second tallest structure on the continent of Europe. In a small tower office sits a man whose personal manner is modest, but who impresses the visitor every bit as much as the building. He speaks softly, struggling with his newly acquired English, but what he says has force and conviction, earnestness and obvious sincerity.

I. G. Petrovskii, rector of the University (in America we would call him president), is a mathematician by training. He's worked on partial differential equations, algebraic geometry, and the theory of probability. His career stretches back to 1927, when he graduated from the University he now heads. Petrovskii has clearly followed his own counsel that "a man must be more than a specialist, a man must be a man." Today he not only sits on the Presidium of the Academy of Sciences of the U.S.S.R., but is a delegate to the Supreme Soviet and a member of its Commission on Foreign Relations. That's all the more impressive because Petrovskii is not a member of the Communist party. Indeed, talking with him, one hears the same sorts of concerns, the same sorts of aspirations as one hears from great educators throughout the world. The central problems of educating young men seem to transcend political philosophy. Yet there are national differences, and those in Moscow we found to be fascinating soon after we got past the obvious preliminaries.

Just how big is the Moscow State University?

We have about 16,000 full-time undergraduate students, about 2,000 postgraduate students, and about 10,000 evening and correspondence students.

What fraction of these are in the sciences?

We have about 9,000 full-time students in science and about 7,000 in the humanities. We have more part-time students in humanities than in science. In some of our faculties, we have evening students, but no correspondence students, for instance, in physics and in chemistry. In these fields the students need laboratory work, and, of course, they can't do this at home.

Most of our full-time students receive scholarships, and they must not engage in other activities. The part-time students work in factories, laboratories or offices, and study in our university only in the evening. However, they have two months a year paid leave for more intensive study. Most students in physics and chemistry are full-time students.

At the Massachusetts Institute of Technology, where I

studied, the most popular course in recent years has been physics. Is this true at Moscow State University?

Maybe the situation in our university is the same. But, for instance, our faculty of mathematics is as large as our department of physics.

In what ways has your curriculum changed in recent years to match the developments that have taken place in science?

The curriculum in our university has two parts. The first part is devoted to the study of fundamental questions of science. These fundamental questions of science do not change very quickly, so these courses do not change very quickly. However, they have changed from thirty years ago when I was a student; there have been great changes.

Even in the fundamentals?

Yes, even in the fundamentals. Now, about senior courses, the fourth and fifth years of studying. There we do not have a firm curriculum. Each student has a special tutor and he, with the student, chooses special courses. These courses change very quickly. Each year, the special courses are different.

The standard university course in Russia takes five years— as against three years in Britain or four years in the U.S. The graduate is more or less equivalent to a holder of the U.S. master's degree.

Can you give me some examples? Take, for example, mathematics, which has been so influenced by the advent of the electronic computer. In what ways has the mathematics faculty at the Moscow State University responded to this change in mathematics?

All of our students in mathematics now have access to work with computers. All students. But we have students who study electronic computers as their specialty.

What is the nature of this experience that they get? Do they write programs, or do they merely watch while the professor programs?

They have special practice, as in a laboratory. They solve some problems and write programs as well. In addition all our students practice during the year or half-year when they work in scientific institutes. But, as you know, the most important part of mathematical education is not in computers. The best computer centers prefer to receive a good mathematician, who does not have special preparation in computers, but who is a good mathematician. They say they can prepare him to work on the computer very quickly.

What do you do to get good mathematicians?

We start with the pupils of the middle school (you say high school in your country). We have, each year, a special mathematical "Olympics." The first stage of this competition is held in towns all over our country. The best pupils come to Moscow, and there they must solve special problems. This year, we chose forty of the most gifted pupils to live near Moscow for one month with some of our most well-known mathematicians and very many of our young mathematicians. From this group of forty promising mathematicians we choose about twenty and receive them in a special school for gifted young mathematicians and physicists. This school is attached to our university here in Moscow.

Let me understand. This is a middle school?

Yes. And some of these pupils from this middle school will go to our university.

I wonder whether you have done here at Moscow State University what has been done at MIT, particularly under Professor Zacharias and Professor Friedman, namely, examine the teaching of the middle schools, to see whether the curriculum that is being used there is attuned to the needs of today and does reflect the modern understanding of mathematics and physics? Do you know the programs of which I speak?

No, I do not, but it is very interesting. We think about a program for middle schools. We ask whether our recent program suits well. It is not clear. I know that in your country various mathematicians and various teachers study this problem. In our country we also study this problem. It would be interesting to receive some knowledge about your luck. Glenn Seaborg was in our university; he said that in your country physicists think about middle-school programs in physics and the chemists about new chemistry courses.

I gather by implication that the curriculum in your middle schools in mathematics today is probably quite the way it was thirty-five years ago when you went to the middle school.

I think that the curriculum for middle schools in mathematics is about the same.

Has it been possible, at the Moscow State University, to provide the latest computers for your students? Or are they working with models which, while good for practice, are perhaps a few computer generations old?

We have computers of different sizes. And our students work on several computers.

Does it include the latest models? I wonder, you see, about the ability of the University to compete with the institutes, with other laboratories, for physical facilities.

A very important question. I can't say that we have laboratories in all branches of science as good as in research institutes of the Academy of Sciences. But in some branches, we have good equipment. And we propose to organize branches—filials—of our faculties at scientific institutes. We have such a branch at the Dubna Institute of Nuclear Research. Our senior students live in Dubna, and they learn there. Our leading scientists in nuclear physics teach these students.

This is the first, started some years ago. But this is only the first and not the last; we propose to organize another. It is very important that our more gifted and talented students learn from great scientists, and that they work in very good laboratories. Very important. In your country, all science is represented in the universities. But I read some time ago that many great scientists in your universities do not teach. I think that it is very important that great scientists teach.

Yes. And everyone at the Moscow State University teaches, even though he may have his own research?

We have very many well-known scientists who teach at our university. We have very close affiliation with the Academy of Sciences. There are many people who will work in an institute of the Academy and our faculty at the same time.

In the physics faculty, what fraction of the professors would you say are also in an institute?

Professors, I think about 30 per cent.

The others teach only?

In our university, teachers must not only teach but must also do scientific work of their own. In our university, each professor is elected every five years, and this election takes place in this very place, in the hall of the university council. We make a decision with regard to scientific work of this professor, not only his talent as a teacher.

This is not always good, is it? Sometimes this is bad.

Maybe.

You must have a Russian equivalent of the great American college expression that's grown out of this situation: Publish or Perish.

The most severe judges for scientists are his colleagues. They decide whether this scientist works—really works. It is not necessary to publish anything.

. . . but it is necessary to be competent.

Yes. Our scientific council, which consists of mathematicians, physicists, chemists, biologists, zoologists, decides every question about election on the basis of recommendation of special committees, committees of well-known specialists.

Is it frequent that a man is not re-elected?

Rarely, but sometimes it happens.

A great problem in English universities is the limited number of professorships that are available. It restricts the expansion of English scientific education. Is there a problem of this kind in Soviet institutions?

In our country, we receive a number of places for teachers and professors that corresponds to the number of students. For each ten students, we receive approximately one teacher. Each year the number of students rises, and, therefore, we receive new chairs for professors. One thing limits the numbers of our students—building space. Now we have two times more students as was planned when this school was built. Our full-time students study in two shifts, morning and late afternoon. This is not good, we know, but we must have many students.

I'm amazed, because I have never seen bigger university buildings. Do you have plans, then, to build new buildings?

We will build, but not very much. Our ministry is organizing new universities in other cities of our country. We have forty-two universities in our country, and this is apart from more specialized institutions that prepare doctors or engineers.

Where, incidentally, do you train engineers?

We have different institutes that prepare engineers. Some institutes provide extensive scientific preparation. Some institutes that prepare engineers have a narrow curriculum.

I would like to go deeper into this question of research at the university. For example, in nuclear physics, do you have any large equipment here at the university? MIT, say, has a cyclotron, several Van de Graaff generators, and now has built, in association with Harvard University, a rather large electron accelerator of six billion volts.

We have some devices of that kind, but they are not very big.

You feel, then, that there is a need—this is perhaps why you set up the branch at Dubna—to get a closer connection between the research frontier and the student doing advanced work. We're talking now of the graduate student—the man who is going for his doctorate, or whatever it is called here.

No, I mean here not only graduate students but also students of senior courses. A very large part of our senior students participate in scientific research. Every year about two hundred articles by our students are published in reports of our Academy of Sciences.

Such a student has already received his first college university degree, and is doing graduate work?

By the time of graduation from the University many students have *already* done scientific work.

In that respect your students would be ahead of ours, because typically our student will do research for his thesis, but only for that. He would not be likely to have published a paper until he has received, or is at least close to, his doctorate.

But, I take it, your student, in addition to the thesis that I presume he works on, works in an institute laboratory and, in collaboration with the scientists there, does work at a publishable level.

Sometimes, not always, the thesis of our students is scientific work. But our students study for five years as undergraduate students. And our postgraduate students study for three years. In your country, I am told, it is more like four and four—so the total amount is not very different.

I understand that you have here on this great campus principally the faculties of science and geography. The faculties of the humanities are downtown. I wonder what this means in terms of the amount of training in the humanities that a student of science receives? How much history and philosophy does the man learn who enrolls here at the Lenin Hills campus to study physics?

All our students in science study also humanities. They study history of our country after the revolution. They study philosophy and political economy. And all students study one foreign language, usually English, for several years.

Have you felt the need to increase the amount of humanities? Or is it perhaps decreasing because there is so much more science and mathematics to teach?

I feel there is need. I think that it would be very good for the professors in humanities to deliver special lectures for students in science and vice versa. Not obligatory, voluntary. What we call facultative courses. We will arrange this. It is very important, I think.

Do you, in concert with the faculty, decide the courses or the programs, or is there another, higher level—perhaps at the Ministry of Education—to which you must appeal and discuss your programs?

In the University, we decide the curriculum in obligatory courses, for all students of each faculty. But the special courses, which change every year, the faculty decides—the scientific council of the faculty decides. In practice, though, the professors decide.

A great argument rages in our country about the suitability of the graduate of the universities. For example, Bell Telephone Laboratories, which hires many of our university graduates, runs a training program for students who come from the universities, because their education is not sufficiently attuned to the needs of the modern telephone system. What do you hear from your industries and institutes about the graduates of the Moscow State University?

We do not prepare engineers; we prepare mathematicians, physicists, chemists, and so forth. Most of our graduates in science work in industry. Most of them. Therefore we send the projects of our curriculum to different ministries, and we receive their remarks. We pay great attention to their remarks.

We have a similar thing, but much less formal. The universities and the companies talk to each other, but there is no formal submission of planned curricula. Can you give me some examples of what has flowed from this relationship? Have you perhaps added a course in chemistry, because, say, the synthetic fiber industry felt it was necessary?

In some cases we received certain remarks, for instance from the State Committee for Chemistry.

Is this the Committee for the Coordination of Scientific Research?

No. This is the State Committee for Chemistry, which supervises the chemical industry of our country.

Of which ministry?

It is an independent committee, like a ministry.

Can you give me an example of what they say? Have they caused you to change your curriculum?

I will give you one example. About ten years ago, we had no specialty in semiconductors. But industry said they needed specialists in this field. Now we have a special chair for semiconductors occupied by Victor S. Vavilov, the son of the late president of the Academy of Sciences. He is a very gifted scientist who also works in the physical institute of the Academy of Sciences.

How much contact do you have with presidents of uni-

versities in the United States? Do you correspond with them or see them?

I have more contact with American scientists. Recently, we saw in our university very many distinguished American mathematicians on their way to a meeting in Tiflis and Novosibirsk. We have more connection with scientists than with the education authorities of universities. It is very important to visit each other.

What are your major problems—the things that you stay awake at night thinking about?

My most important task . . . to improve and teach the scientific work especially in the new branches of science.

But we have very many students; our university is a big university. I can't know each student, but I understand that each student is a man, each student needs attention. Now, each student, from the end of the third course, has a special tutor, who cares about him. I think this is very important. When a young man begins to live his own life by himself, he needs special attention, and my task is to organize the attention for students from good teachers. Each student is a man—not only a mathematician, or a physicist, but he is a man. The best of our professors are concerned, not only for preparation in science but also for preparation in life.

Let me tell you what a great impression our Professors P. S. Alexandroff and A. N. Kolmogoroff have made on me. They like music very much. Professor P. Alexandroff has a tape recorder and he taught his students to hear good music. I myself began to like good music from Alexandroff. And I began to ski under the influence of A. Kolmogoroff. I am not very old. It is always interesting for me.

I think it is very important. A man *must be more than* a specialist, a man must be a man. . . .

Lloyd V. Berkner

*C*alls *for drastic increases in the production of science PhD's had become commonplace by the end of 1962, when we interviewed Lloyd V. Berkner in the suite which is permanently reserved for him at New York's distinguished Waldorf-Astoria Hotel. What was new at that time was Berkner's outspoken advocacy of increased PhD production not only in the established graduate schools of the Northeast, upper Midwest, and California, but in such unlikely looking, industrially underdeveloped, educationally underendowed regions as Texas. Berkner was among the first to argue that the industrial and economic progress of any such underdeveloped region depended as much on the presence—in the region itself—of centers of research and educational excellence as it did on the availability of venture capital. This thesis is now widely accepted—among regional planners and by federal fund-granting agencies at any rate. Prodded by congressmen from the more remote constituencies, agencies like the Department of Defense and the National Aeronautics and Space Administration are committed to wider geographic dispersal of applied research and development contracts. The National Science Foundation, chief federal patron of basic research and education in the sciences, embarked in 1965 on a potentially more far-reaching program. Aiming its seed money at good, but not quite excellent, schools already in existence in the less-favored regions, the NSF seeks to turn them into new centers of educational excellence.*

That Berkner's advocacy should have borne fruit so rapidly is no surprise; given his prestige and influence among industrial, government, and academic science administrators the result could have hardly been otherwise. What did surprise us, however, was Berkner's personal involvement in and personal approach to solving the problems he was being so articulate about.

In dress, bearing, and speech he was as distinguished as his Waldorf surroundings; he looked every inch the national and international statesman of science that his reputation made him out to be and was clearly accustomed to moving in an urbane and cosmopolitan environment. Yet two years before we met him, Berkner had quit the job he had held for ten years—president of Associated Universities, the consortium of schools that runs the Brookhaven National Laboratory on Long Island, New York—to become the first head *of a Dallas, Texas, organization known as the Graduate Research Center of the Southwest.*

From advance notices, it was hard to tell whether this was to be merely another research institute (how blasé we have become!) or whether it might turn out to be the precursor of a major new university. Today, it is still mostly a contract research center—something like the Mellon Institute in Pittsburgh, not yet granting degrees as the Rockefeller Institute began to do even before it became a university. In either case, Berkner's switch had surprised us. For him, either alternative sounded like relatively small potatoes. True, heading a research institute or a university would not be a bad job for a man whose only earned degree is the bachelor's, University of Minnesota, 1927. But this modest first credential has since been augmented by seven DSc's, one DEng, one PhD, and one LLD, all honorary.

Berkner began his remarkable career straightforwardly enough. His early training in electrical engineering was followed by further work in physics. He went on to imbibe deeply, as he is fond of putting it, of that heady combination of electronics, geology, meteorology, and a dash of astronomy, that nowadays is called environmental science.

Berkner went to the antarctic with the first Byrd expedition in 1928, spent the thirties doing pioneer work on the propagation of radio waves through the electrically conducting layers of the earth's atmosphere, and worked on radar for the Navy (he's a rear admiral in the Reserve) during World War II. He has served on the President's Scientific Advisory Committee (under Eisenhower), and is the acknowledged "father" of the International Geophysical Year of the late 1950's. Until a few months before we interviewed him, Berkner had also been chairman of the Space Science Board, a group set up by the U.S. National Academy of Sciences to advise on the scientific goals of the space program. He is a past president of the American Geophysical Union, the International Scientific Radio Union, and the International Council of Scientific Unions; the last is a voluntary non-governmental "United Nations" of national scientific organizations in just about every field. To a man with such a back-

341

ground it would seem that even booming Dallas must seem provincial. Our curiosity piqued, we got directly to the point and asked:

Recently you spoke of your work at the Graduate Research Center as something of a sociological experiment. In what sense did you mean that?

There's a social problem I first became aware of during my frequent visits to Dallas in 1956 and 1957. I had been living in the East for thirty-five years and had acquired the attitudes of the average Easterner. But when one lives away from the East, one begins to realize there are important forces at work in the rest of the country.

You mean specifically in Texas?

No, I think Dallas is typical of the larger share of the country . . . outside the industrialized areas.

What was taking you there at that time?

I had some interest in one or two of the industrial companies that had developed down there after the war, and I was watching. . . .

You are a member of the board of Texas Instruments, I believe.

That's right; that was one of the principal reasons I was down there. They're a very interesting company, and they are typical of the sort of growth emerging out of science today. . . .

A growth in some sense limited by sociological conditions in the area?

Not to date. I think you have to look at this problem that worries me as a long-range one. I don't think that up to date the Southwest has suffered particularly—and when I say the Southwest I might as well be speaking of the South or the Mountain States or any of the thirty-eight or forty non-industrialized states, the states that up to the mid-century depended primarily upon agriculture and natural resources.

You're concerned that they can't do that any longer?

I'd like to make three points, which may make my approach a little clearer. The first is that a major part of the country is being affected by the population explosion in a very special, a very particular way. The population of the U.S. as a whole is growing 1.8 per cent per year, while the population of the South and Southwest is growing much more rapidly, about 3 per cent per year. Now the character of that regional growth is not a uniform distribution over the area; it's concentrated in the cities. The new population is going into a few cities that you can count on your two hands a couple of times.

This is conspicuous in California.

I'd say California had achieved a substantial industrialization before this change began—California experienced it much earlier than the rest of the country.

In these other areas, then, you're talking about a postwar phenomenon?

Yes, like the second factor I want to point to. That's the demonstration that occurred during the war—a very profound demonstration—that science has become powerful enough to revolutionize any technology if it is applied consistently to that technology. Now this was not true of science at the turn of the century or even as late as 1925. Since the time of the Babylonians, most technology emerged out of crafts, out of what we already knew how to do. Only since about the turn of the century have we witnessed entirely new technical procedures being introduced out of science. And these were almost accidental—the Edisons and the Marconis introducing rather rare phenomena which developed into major industries. But now there's this second postwar discovery, that science is now strong enough to revolutionize any technology, any technology at all.

So you have a population explosion concentrated in cities outside the industrial areas. You have a change in the effect of science. There was a third point, you said?

It's quite clear that these growing cities have a problem of developing their industrial capabilities to meet the challenge of this new flow of population. And it's quite clear that they must do this, not in terms of conventional industry

343

but in terms of the new industries growing out of the new technology. And for this—and here's my third point—they require very large numbers of people who control knowledge at its outer limits.

Statistically speaking, lots of PhD's.

Exactly. And remember that in 1950 a PhD, essentially, was needed only for teaching. I would doubt that in 1950 more than a hundred PhD's were employed in the Dallas-Fort Worth area. Now it's eight hundred at the very least, and has risen from almost nothing to several hundred just in the El Paso area. One finds it in every city—in order to remain competitive, in order to retain the capacity to innovate, business finds it essential to employ large numbers of people trained to the boundaries of knowledge.

And your concern is where the Southwest will get them?

If you look at the bachelor's degree level, the educational capabilities of the country are about uniform. The number of bachelor's degrees per million population each year is almost uniform. But at the graduate level one finds an entirely different story. There are ten states which grant on

the order of a hundred PhD's per million population. These states you know well—Massachusetts grants a hundred and forty per million I believe, New York with about an even hundred, Wisconsin, Minnesota, California down toward seventy. The industrialized states. And the rest of the states grant about thirty PhD's per million population per year, plus or minus about twenty.

Is it necessarily a bad thing to have some regional specialization of this sort?

I think it's bad. There are a whole variety of reasons, nowadays, why it's essential that every metropolitan area have some high intellectual capability. Now there's a second interesting thing you get out of digging around in the situation. Back in 1920, about ten big universities produced about two-thirds of all our PhD's; these were predominantly private universities. By 1940, this number had grown—twenty universities produced two-thirds of the doctorates. The increase was primarily in the public group—Illinois, Minnesota, Wisconsin, Ohio State—these are very clear.

Well now—from 1940 to 1962 one sees a very striking phenomenon. In 1962, twenty universities still produce two-thirds of the PhD degrees. No large university has been added.

Of course, the twenty have each grown.

The twenty have grown—but of the 10,240 PhD's that will be produced this year, some 7,000 will be produced by these twenty. It's a structure of a few very large, very good universities, and the small ones not growing as rapidly as the large ones. It's a very disturbing matter that no new universities have emerged as great graduate institutions— since we now see that a metropolitan area requires a great university if it is to provide the intellectual skills that have become essential for the economic and social welfare of the community.

Ph.D. output in 1966: about 18,000 in all fields.

Don't you think perhaps the regional research institutes that are springing up around the country may be an answer?

These are very useful institutions, because they fit into the area of what I would call transition between the basic sciences and industrial application. Nevertheless, I think the purely research institution cannot provide all the capabilities which the graduate institution provides to the community —a means of retreading the engineers and scientists in the community, a means of consultation with the faculties in a wide variety of specialties, and, of course, a source of PhD's.

Do the doctorates really have to be granted locally?

If you survey what happens to high school graduates, you find that in the states having the big graduate schools, about fifteen graduates per thousand will go on to their doctorates, in the other states only about five. The existence of graduate schools within a community tends to create the aspirations of children. The conclusion is quite unambiguous—unless there is a graduate school near you, it is unlikely that you will go through to get your doctoral degree. Not that you will necessarily attend that university, but that the community attitudes are changed.

Of course that's not just a Southwestern problem. . . .

Some five years ago I first began to detect this stirring—

not just in the Southwest but in the West and some areas of the North, and in the Southwest—a feeling that something was seriously wrong, that something needed to be done. This has moved very rapidly in the last five years. I point out to you that today in Oregon there's a real state movement to create a graduate school in Portland supported by the two state universities. Then, of course, the lack of a graduate school in San Diego is very apparent, and the campus at La Jolla has been changed with Herb York coming in . . . this is a very important experiment. In Florida there's a tremendous drive toward creation of institutions of advanced learning. At the Southern Governors' Conference, this was the major subject discussed this year—how could the Southern states acquire graduate schools?

Is there an answer to that?

It's by no means clear how you get a good graduate school. The fact that none have emerged in twenty years is a very frightening specter; apparently the old method is no longer tenable. There's where I come to Herb York's experiment. What he is doing in La Jolla is creating a graduate school from the top. This may be the way. It's very doubtful that a newly emerging undergraduate institution can find the strength to build a graduate school in less than a century or two; we don't have time.

Is that the pattern you want to follow in Texas?

NSF seed money, however, went to privately endowed Rice University in Houston in the summer of 1965.

It's not altogether clear to us how the graduate schools will be developed in the Southwest. Clearly the University of Texas has emerged to the point where it may become a great graduate school if it receives strong state support; I think in another two decades it will probably become the Columbia of the Southwest.

Does that put it in competition with such a center as yours?

Not any more than you would say MIT and Harvard are competitive. What you have to ask yourself is: How many universities will a region like the six Southwestern states require over the next fifteen years? If your objective is to reach a level of a hundred PhD's per million population . . . and the population, which is now twenty million, will reach thirty million by the time you can do anything . . .

this would mean you'd need 3,000 per year. To get that many doctors you must have 60,000 students in your graduate schools. You must have 15,000 faculty members. Quite clearly you are not talking about one new university; you are talking about ten or twenty.

And how do you see the Graduate Research Center fitting into this?

We're starting very much like La Jolla, with the development of a series of units we call laboratories. Our emphasis is not yet on graduate education at all. We are still collecting together some very skilled research talent. The basis for any graduate education is the assembly of high talent in basic research. Our first students will be postdoctoral fellows. We already have some postdoctorals, about half from the U.S. and half from abroad. Our first laboratory is well under way; this is the Laboratory of Earth and Planetary Science.

Is it the first because of the importance of the aerospace industries in the Southwest?

In part, and in part because the Southwest has more skills in the earth sciences; I felt that I should develop something in the areas of our greatest skills.

Will the laboratory do any industrial research at all—the applied kind of basic research—perhaps like the division of industrial research at MIT?

My own attitude is that the laboratory must maintain very close relationships with industry in the region. The best way to kill a good idea is to patent it inside a non-profit institution. If you want the benefits of your research to reach the public in the form of technology, you must maintain relationships with industry.

And yet the relationship sometimes seems to cause headaches at MIT. Can it get too close?

Does it really? I know some people worry, but are you sure whether this is good or bad? I point out to you that transition from science to industry is a most difficult problem, and that some interrelationship is essential if transition is to be effective.

You're not afraid of the relationship?

I'm not afraid of it. I point out to you that the Soviet Union tried to maintain this ivory tower attitude by separating the Academy from industry—and in April of 1961 they had to reorganize their whole system, simply because ideas from science were not getting into industry.

Many educators feel doubtful about whether you can have an educationally valid graduate institution in which graduate students don't have to deal with things like laboratory instruction of undergraduates.

I'm not going to deny that undergraduates are a very good thing around a university. The question is how to get them: Do you start with them, or do you end with them?

You said you planned a series of laboratories.

We're actively planning four at present: earth and planetary science, and a laboratory of electronics, which we will probably start in the field of biomedical electronics. The third lab will be in material sciences, largely devoted to solid-state phenomena. The fourth—the most difficult probably—will be molecular science.

Molecular biology?

I didn't say molecular biology. I said molecular science, which is an area that is hardly touched at all now. We know that there are certain phenomena in purely inorganic processes that are not dissimilar to the processes of molecular life in biology. These need studying. There are many questions and very few answers. This is the laboratory we see least clearly. My instinct tells me I should do the easiest jobs first—then the more difficult become easier.

It's rather striking that you describe your organization in terms of interdisciplinary fields. You don't talk about your department of physics.

It's the job of a university graduate school to have departments of physics and chemistry and so on. But when one is in postdoctoral research, one should stress the interdisciplinary aspects and not simply perpetuate the schizophrenia among university departments.

But this postdoctoral work is simply a starting point?

Simply a starting point. How the graduate school will develop in Dallas we don't know, but . . .

In postdoctoral students, is it a buyers' market or a sellers'? Do you have to hunt for them?

There are many posts available for every doctoral graduate. To get them, you have to go about building one of the best groups in the world in each area. Right now, I think I have the best group in the world on upper atmospheric meteorology.

Do these students pay tuition?

No, they become members of the staff. This idea of starting with postdoctoral students emerges from an experiment we did at Brookhaven, starting in 1948, of having postdoctoral research associates. Out of this we learned that a period of postdoctoral training is the best way of producing a teacher—and that is going to be our greatest need in the future.

Richard Morse

*M*ost politicians have cast hopeful eyes at the technical world, certain that there must be solutions to complex public problems lurking there. Similarly, most technical folk are convinced that technical "know-how" could help in the public arena if only the civil servants would listen to their ideas. Except at the federal level, the two somehow never seem to get together. And this is too bad, for it's a fact that many Americans still like to solve their problems as close to home as possible.

There's a relatively new movement afoot—termed regional development—that may tap this traditional American impulse and redress the balance. The idea is quite simple. In every region of the U.S.—be it a large city or groups of cities, states or groups of states—there is plenty of technical talent in hand; industries, universities, and non-profit research organizations all have abundant technical skills that could be turned to regional problems—from urban transportation to water pollution.

The trick is to get local talent focusing on such problems. This means that mechanisms must be found to bring technical men and civil servants together, to define the problems, and to get willing minds to work on them—in short, to show that money can as well be made regionally as it can by solving problems for, say, the Defense Department. What's needed is the guidance of men who have grown up in the federal-industrial realm, and yet who are stimulated by the concept of local initiative.

One such man is Richard S. Morse, a New Englander with an abiding affection for his region. He comes well equipped for the unusual needs of regional development. Trained in physics, he is currently senior lecturer at MIT's Sloan School of Management. He served as Director of Research and Assistant Secretary of the Army from 1959 to 1961, after a nineteen-year career as head of National Research Corporation in Cambridge and its many offspring, including Vacuum Metals and Minute Maid. He consults to two departments of the federal government—Defense and Commerce—and is board chairman of Cryotronics Corporation, a new Rockefeller-Mellon venture in the ultra-low-temperature field.

Morse's current interest in regional development was stimulated by his participation on the Commerce Department's Technical Advisory Board, which he joined at its birth several years ago. The board, he told us, has been concerned with the civilian sector of the economy "and particularly the use of science and technology to promote economic growth." Our first question, then, turned on this point.

Tell us first why you are thinking about the civilian *utilization of technical people—people who are now working in space and defense.*

If you look at the defense and space programs, you see that we are beginning to get a fairly radical change. Barring an all-out expansion in Vietnam, or a technical breakthrough in the anti-ICBM program or submarine warfare, we have essentially completed our task in terms of developing a military capability based on mass retaliation as a means to deter all-out war. And to some extent this is true in the space program. We've got the fundamental work done. On the other hand, we have developed a lot of skills, management methods . . . the whole concept of the systems approach to massive problems. And we've got a lot of technology. We should make a bigger effort to apply this technology and use these people more effectively in the civilian economy.

How do you view the role of scientists and engineers in this effort?

It's a sad commentary that our scientists and engineers—and the academic-government community—need a Sputnik to challenge their imagination, to initiate massive public programs, such as the space effort. The cities, towns, and regions of the country have far more important—and potentially exciting—problems to attack. And it is high time we got on with the job.

You're thinking of the big urban problems, such as transportation . . .

This country kills 50,000 people a year in auto accidents . . . and maims several hundred thousand. Our coastal waters south of Cape Cod are so dirty that sailing is no fun. Los Angeles is now unlivable for any rational human being, because of traffic and smog. Our rivers are polluted, and what may be a permanent weather shift threatens the water supply of the Northeast. Here are some *real* opportunities for the scientific community—rather than post-lunar projects.

But you are not proposing that the federal government take the initiative?

I don't think there is any doubt that the federal government is going to be involved. But being a sort of free-enterprise kind of guy, I would rather see some local initiative applied. The kinds of problems we now have are really *regional* problems—let's say transportation, or pollution, or highway safety, or the development of marine or fresh water resources. These are fairly gigantic problems, regional problems. It's not possible for, say, a village or town or city or county—or even a state—to attack this kind of problem.

Take marine resources as an example. How does your "regional approach" apply to the development of marine resources?

This is a problem that must be attacked on a fairly large scale. You cannot look on it on a single-state basis. Whatever you do in Rhode Island will affect what you do in Massachusetts. Now it so happens that New England has about one-half the continental shelf of the U.S. It certainly doesn't make any sense for one New England state to become heavily involved in, say, the development of a new method of artificially growing lobsters or shellfish. You can only go at some of these marine problems by looking at the entire system—the entire marine environment—on a fairly large scale. In this particular case you've got to look at navigation problems, dredging problems, stream pollution—possibly air pollution—and you've probably got to go out and design and build some experimental ships employing advanced technology and creative engineering.

The whole area of ocean engineering . . .

Yes. But to date, most oceanographic work has lacked input from industry. And certainly there has been a lack of input from marketing.

Because nobody has figured out how to make any money out of oceanography.

But that's because there is no mechanism—to date—that can be applied to get industrial input into this field. Now we have the necessary assets, right here in New England. We have all the technical talents and facilities that are necessary.

But they're focused in different directions.

They're doing other things. We don't need any more laboratories or research facilities. We don't need more universities. We've just got to find a mechanism which can use these talents.

You're saying you have plenty of scientists and engineers, but too few people who know how to put science and engineering to work.

Take New England . . . In the state governments—and I think this is generally true throughout the country—you do not have the technical competence to do these jobs. The so-called development departments of most states are concerned with trying to attract business to the area. They're not concerned with using modern technology or the system management approach on state or regional problems. And frankly, I don't think the states are going to be able to get that technical competence. Now this presents a problem to the federal government. It has no communicating means—it has no way to get at these regional problems in working with the states.

The level of both management and technical ability at the federal level is considerably higher than at the state level. If NASA wants to take on a regional problem—or HEW or the Department of Commerce—there is nobody at the state level they can effectively talk to. You don't have systems-oriented people at the state level. You don't have an organizational structure that combines management competence, scientific competence, and—I'll add the word—entrepreneurship from industry. We've got to find some means of using the experienced people we have in industry and in our academic institutions . . . some means whereby they can work on regional problems in collaboration with the federal government.

This is another way of saying there's got to be a clear way for a man to make a dollar . . . in the process of doing these things.

If you find the mechanism for attacking regional problems at the local level—if you find a more effective means of utilizing our academic, industrial, and financial talents—then you will encourage industry to take the initiative. First, you've got to get a demonstration project under way. Then industry will come in—the profit incentive will cause the next step.

Then you have the problem of getting any group of states to work together—even when you do have the talent in those states.

Many states are now talking about this problem and searching for solutions. The only alternative—I'm afraid—is even greater domination by the federal government in the administration and funding of projects that can more effectively be operated nearer to the local level.

When several states begin to think "region," how do they bring the technical people into the early thinking? What kind of organization has to be set up?

One form of organization would be a non-profit regional development corporation. It would be established with appropriate technical management, with representatives from the states involved, industry, and the universities. It would serve as a systems manager to attack regional problems . . . and it would serve as the go-between between the federal agency and the governors of the region. It would have a competent technical staff—out from under civil service and political influence. And it would have appropriate representation from industry, the academic, labor, and the financial community. I don't know any other way to do this.

Sort of a regional RAND Corporation, in other words?

An acronym for research and development; a "think factory" established by the Air Force after World War II.

Yes. This is the technique the federal government has used, for various reasons. And by and large, the idea has served a useful function. But nobody has done this for regional development work.

In the states, I can see problems of provincialism—of self-interest. Will Maine object if it thinks New Hampshire is getting more than Maine is?

Oh, everybody is provincial. But I think it is very important that this corporation avoid duplicating the efforts of the member states—wherever the necessary competence exists in a member state or industrial or academic organizations. I think it is important that the corporation avoid building up a big staff. As a systems manager, it would subcontract its funds—whether federal or federal-state matching—wherever it could find the best people and facilities, whether in the area or outside. It would retain enough in-house competence to manage programs, initiate review studies and prepare proposals.

But I still worry about self-interest. If the project is marine resources, I can hear all but one of the New England states saying yes. But I hear Vermont saying, "No. Why should we support that stuff? We have no continental shelf."

Well, actually, Vermont is one of the greatest proponents of regional collaboration. Governor Hoff takes the position that he does not have the technical facilities of the greater Boston area. So he turns out to be the most vocal about the need for the six New England states to get together. Such an organization would help make the technical talents in one area more readily available in other parts of the region. This concept is in direct line with the objectives of the recently passed Technical Services Act for example.

Provides federal matching grants to help states help industries apply the latest results from science and technology.

How is New England industry responding to your idea? Will you have industrial support?

As a matter of fact, several of our largest industrial firms have said they would be willing to join with their competitors in an effort to utilize their backgrounds—much of it space-defense background—in attacking regional problems. During the past year, some eight or ten representatives from the

New England industrial, financial, and academic communities have been studying the regional problems on a volunteer basis. The theory is that business will subsequently evolve from this.

A question directed specifically at marine resources: If an organization such as you propose is in fact set up, how does this organization attack the marine resources problem?

Well, purely by way of example, the Russians have long had better trawlers than ours—more efficient, larger, better instrumented. I can see a situation where it might be useful to combine the ideas and inventions which have evolved out of submarine warfare—and out of advanced electronics— with the problems of catching fish. At present, there is an interface here which isn't being attended . . . an interface, in the sense that the man who builds the boat isn't concerned with the system of catching fish.

The talents available—such as those people who are expert in anti-submarine warfare research—are not now available to anybody who wants to catch more fish. Maybe the fishing group doesn't even know such talents exist. This is what I mean by a systems management approach with a dash of entrepreneurship.

I can foresee one serious delay—the usual pleas from the cautious: "Wait. First we've got to study this. We've got to research that."

We've had *all* the studies and paper reports on regional development we need. We don't need any more research. And we don't need any more science. We need an operating management mechanism for utilizing the technology that is here right now, for the good of the region.

Is any region, so far as you know, close to creating such a mechanism?

Well, California has initiated several study contracts—in mental health, hospital design, transportation, air pollution. Governor Brown is attempting to utilize the talents of California's aerospace industry and has enlisted the services of Systems Development Corporation as a sort of program supervisor. Now, in New England, there's the New England Council—which may be the only regional organization of its type in the country. The Council itself cannot be the mechanism—it doesn't have the resources or technical staff to do the job I'm talking about—but it does serve as a communications link between the governors and the industrial and academic communities. I can say that the Council would like to help at least in promoting an idea of this kind and now has established a committee for science and technology.

It's hard for me to see how you weave entrepreneurship into the idea. Take New England's transportation problems, for instance: When you set out to get some new technology— new hardware—you're not going to shop around New England for it. You're going to shop the world.

Well, that may be. But we have some aggressive companies in New England who are concerned with this regional problem of transportation. And MIT is undertaking a creative study for the Department of Commerce relating to new approaches to the high-speed train problem. As a matter of fact, the companies have supplied people on loan, to work with me on the question: What should we do? These companies view it this way: "We're defense-oriented at the moment. But we can see an urgent future need for the kinds of people and talents we now have—when these larger regional problems begin to get more attention." Also, these companies see something else: "We're also in the hardware business. And we'll take our chances. If we can become associated with some of these civilian programs, we're reasonably certain to get some business out of it. We'll take that gamble." This is what I mean by entrepreneurship.

That implies you are not going to wait around for a transportation company to solve the transportation problem.

Look, the railroads look at conventional railroads. The automobile industry doesn't even think about transportation, highway safety, or traffic control. It thinks about selling cars in quantity, cars designed to be obsolete in appearance at an early age—if they run that long. Now somebody's got to make a good high-speed train sometime. Lord knows, we've never had one yet in this country. The Japanese have been far ahead of us. There's going to be a change—and a massive change—in transportation within our lifetime. The total regional system may include hovercraft, maybe hydrofoils,

VTOL planes, maybe 300-mph trains. I'm not suggesting what it will be. An aggressive company with an enlightened management that is systems-oriented should *right now* be concerned with regional development in the transportation field.

VTOL =
vertical take-off *and* landing.

Right now, it seems to me, you need a prototype—you need a "success story." What is that one idea that looks most promising?

I think the marine resources approach looks as interesting as any. If we can get two or three of New England's best electronics companies—if we can get them to develop instruments for fishing trawlers. They're willing to spend some of their own money, because they can see down the line a repetitive, profitable business.

Maybe this is the opening wedge to the exploitation of the oceans.

Maybe so. We're spending a substantial amount of money on oceanographic research in this country. We're collecting data and we're writing reports and we're studying the temperature of the water in the Indian Ocean, and we have a marine program to drill a hole a long ways into the earth under the ocean in search of scientific data—all at a pretty good rate. But very few industrialists or investors can figure out how to make any money out of this research. I think eventually they will, but first we've got to find a means for bringing the entrepreneur-industrial part of our society into the program. And I think you do this jointly—with federal support and regional support, with strong input from academic experts and from the industrial people who want to do something constructive in the field.

Atomic energy might provide a good example.

Certainly GE and Westinghouse would not be building profitable atomic power plants today if we hadn't had those demonstration power plants, funded by the federal government. It took ten to twenty years longer than a lot of people thought, but it is now paying off. This is the kind of thing we've got to do regionally.

Thomas Malone
and
Douglas Brooks

*H*artford Connecticut's recently renewed downtown area
—*the Constitution Plaza complex—is a significant example*

DOUGLAS BROOKS

*of an urban core brought back from dry rot to a bustling life
scaled to the size and soul of man. We went to the building
at the north end of the Plaza which houses the Travelers Research Center because we had learned that the Travelers Insurance Company was going to sink an initial quarter of a
million of its own dollars into its now independent not-for-
profit offspring. It wants the Center's hundred and fifty professionals—mathematicians, statisticians, weather scientists,
geophysicists, oceanographers—to bring the full power of
interdisciplinary scientific studies to bear on the ways in
which the natural environment and the man-made environment affect personal and national lives.*

*Ten years ago Thomas Malone, then a meteorology pro-
fessor at MIT, organized a small group of statistical and
weather scientists to do research aimed at covering the insurance company's actuarial and underwriting flank. He is
now director of research for the company and board chairman of the Research Center. Douglas Brooks, president of
the Research Center, is a meteorologist turned operations*

researcher. Earlier, he was director of research for the U.S. Naval Warfare Analysis Group.

Our first reaction was puzzled:

A while ago we heard Mr. Tooker, the president of the insurance company, talk in a speech of the need to know about urban stresses, air and water pollution, minority problems, things like that. Why should a hard-headed insurance man feel a need for a center to study such things?

MALONE: Because if the private sector doesn't understand what is going on here, it's going to be pre-empted by the government. Now maybe only the government can handle such problems. Maybe—and I stress the word maybe—providing needed protection, say, for an economic or racial minority is incompatible with the test of survival of a private enterprise—that it run at a profit. This interface between the legitimate function of government and the legitimate function of private enterprise is an important one. I think Tooker realizes that no one organization, no group, not even the whole nation in aggregate, is going to solve these problems overnight. Such problems are solved incrementally. The important thing is to get started. It was to permit this kind of incremental progress that our auto safety program was constructed.

What gives you the feeling that it is possible now to deal scientifically with such problems?

BROOKS: A number of us have a meteorological background. And there is a readiness now in the atmospheric sciences to deal with practical problems in which the atmosphere is an important element of a complex environment.

Where does that come from? How did you two get into this, say?

MALONE: Well, I got into it as a direct result of interaction with a very harsh environment. I grew up in South Dakota in the twenties and thirties . . . the dust bowl years. I'd go out in the spring full of vigor and with the smell of the new-turned soil . . . and then the drought would come along and I'd see our labor go to pot. As for the economic environment, this was during the depression years. For the social environment—we were a minority group, Irish Catholics in a Lutheran neighborhood. This is what stimulated my interest in meteorology, the impact of the physical environment on an already shaky economic environment.

BROOKS: The war years gave a tremendous boost to the field of meteorology—by the tremendous growth of air operations—and to many meteorologists. An equally significant development from the war years is the founding of operations research. This had the unique characteristic of bringing scientists out of their laboratories into operational organizations where real-world decisions are made. Finally, the computer now lets us handle really complex systems.

So out of all this you come to something like a broad study of auto safety. What can the sociologists tell you about that?

MALONE: It's not just the sociologists. It's the engineers who are dealing with the design of automobiles. It's the psychologists who talk about motivations of people who have accidents that may differentiate them from people who don't. Physiology—because there are reflexes involved here too. These people are each concerned with one or another component of the traffic problem. Each, we hope, can provide values for the parameters which describe that component— its variability, its statistics, its functional form. How the numbers are different in the state of Massachusetts, say, along the Massachusetts Turnpike, than they are on the network of roads which constitutes a city like Hartford here.

You are saying that someone has to put these components into the model of a system.

MALONE: Yes. You see the mathematical model builder can visualize the functional form of these components of the problem. But he doesn't know where to start. He needs the insight of the sociologist or the economist or the engineer before he can put the numbers in. But those numbers alone are not enough; that's a limitation of the way auto safety has been studied in most places so far.

BROOKS: You can build an entirely new traffic system, on paper. Actually, we're approaching this auto problem as a systems problem, not just as a matter of auto safety. One of the properties, but *only* one of the properties of a transportation system is its safety.

Operations research: the (usually) quantitative analysis of almost anything but love, perhaps. Arose during World War II when scientists applied mathematical techniques to analysis of submarine-warfare strategies, strategic bombing, and the like. Now very big also in industrial and economic studies.

Functional form: the ways in which the components relate to each other and in which, together, they relate to the total problem.

363

Where does that approach take you?

BROOKS: We can do the following, for example, which has never been done. We could go to the safety engineers, the driver-training experts, the highway engineers, and we could ask them what the ultimate success in their line might be. How safely can you design an auto—assuming that present research continues to its ultimate? How safely can you design a highway—assuming you go as far as the state of the art permits? How homogeneous can you make the behavior of drivers—assuming that you start driver training at the age of ten and carry it along through. We can put the ultimate improvement of each component into our model and find out what system safety is going to look like. And come to the conclusion, if that's warranted, that the present efforts are not good enough.

Of course now you are into value questions. What do you mean by "good enough"? And what are you willing to give up for auto safety? I suppose even a desire to beautify the surroundings can conflict with safety goals.

BROOKS: You can bring such questions in in the following way. You can say "suppose." Suppose a constraint existed on the use of riverbanks for highways, for instance, because riverbanks were reserved for parks.

There is still a decision problem.

MALONE: But the insurance company will not make this decision. Our task, as I see this project, is to point out the alternatives—to articulate the choices to be made through the mysterious processes by which our society does make such decisions.

I think if I were Mr. Tooker, I would say, "Look, we lost $20 million last year, or whatever it was, on auto accident claims. Don't tell me about parks along the riverbanks and people having picnics there . . . I want to cut that accident loss. Do something."

MALONE: This is not what Mr. Tooker has said to us. Such a short-term tactical problem does exist for the insurance company, but that is being dealt with by other means. What we have been asked to do is to deal with the strategy, the long-term aspects of the society in which the insurance company is going to be functioning in the decades to come. This is a basic-research program.

Isn't there any connection to the business?

MALONE: The link is the actuaries. If they have a better understanding of the milieu within which they carry on their insurance operations, they can make tactical adaptations.

But hasn't the actuarial problem been solved? You just increase the rate to balance the payout.

MALONE: Rate-making is simply one facet of the total marketing strategy which any company must have, whenever you commit yourself to serve a particular portion of the market. Unlike most companies, the insurance company undertakes contract commitments which don't mature for decades.

How much of this sort of thinking is going on abroad? There's an OR tradition in Britain, and there are insurance companies.

OR = operations research.

BROOKS: I'm unaware of any comprehensive assault on the question of what man's total environment ought to be.

Not even among the Soviet planners?

MALONE: I was in Moscow this summer. The problem hasn't quite reached the critical stage. I suspect the timing is the only thing that's really different.

BROOKS: Partly, the timeliness of a problem like this is a function of the degree of urbanization of a society, of the degree to which it is crowding its space and resources. Perhaps we are nearer these boundaries than they are.

MALONE: They have come to grips with certain aspects. In the reports to the Twentieth Congress they listed weather control and climate modification as major scientific objectives, along with nuclear energy and space. In the arctic, they are getting the fundamental understanding for a very broad kind of climate modification. And they have done some extraordinarily effective work—if the results stand up—on hail suppression. Uncontrolled hailstorms are highly destructive of most standing crops.

So that, sooner or later, what you are doing here at Travelers Research Center is part of a worldwide program?

MALONE: Think of it this way. There has been very great progress in physical science; we're right on the threshold of similar progress in the life sciences. But we're not going to be able to do much with the knowledge unless this same take-off point is reached in a thrust through the social sciences. It is time to find a nucleus around which a synthesis of all these sciences can take place—and one is emerging in this concept of man and his interaction with natural and man-made environment. The urgency is underscored by the population explosion—in a fixed environment.

There are still choices to be made about that.

BROOKS: That is what we hope. And that is why it is a management problem and not merely a problem in science. You see, if we were looking at another species we would just extrapolate the growth curve—which looks exponential but is always an S—and be quite happy to see the S curve reach a plateau representing the physical starvation limit. Like a bacteria colony in a culture. And there are such limits for us, too, I'm sure. But we will be failing our duty to ourselves if we permit the development of our own species to reach that point. We'll be failing to use the one characteristic which sets us apart—the ability to project, to foresee, to take measures.

Exponential curve

S-curve

Company Presidents

The 1950's were the years in which science arrived on
Wall Street. During that time an unprecedented number of
new technical businesses were formed as the result of the
technological explosion in the wake of World War II and
the Korean War. Nearly all started out as small struggling
enterprises, occasionally even in the legendary garage; many
prospered in a way that exceeded the expectations of the
scientists and engineers who founded them. Many more,
however, failed to make it. The stock market shakeout of
1962 found them unable to raise the capital they needed and
taught their founders that it took something more than a
hot product and "onics" in their name to ensure success.
Some failed outright. Many more dissolved quietly into the
anonymity of merger, thereby attesting to how long the odds
are against the scientist turned businessman.

It was against this background that we began wondering
just what the problems were that a technical man faces in
building his own company. What must he do to succeed in
the business of science? So we invited five technical men
who had done just that to sit down with us, men now heading successful companies; we asked them to reflect on what
it had taken them to succeed and why they had tried in the
first place.

The men who joined us at our offices in New York ranged
in age from thirty-eight to fifty-seven. They had the polite,

KENNETH H. OLSEN   DENIS M. ROBINSON

soft-spoken authoritativeness of men who are not just self-confident and successful but also have a sensitivity to people and their problems that is greater than that of the typical engineer or scientist. Their company sales ranged from $1 million to $20 million—not so large that their founders might have forgotten the trials of starting and carrying along a small company.

Dr. Denis M. Robinson is president of High Voltage Engineering Corporation, Burlington, Massachusetts, a firm he founded in 1946 with two other scientists to build machines called particle accelerators. These machines produce precise and powerful beams of electrons, protons, neutrons, and x rays for a variety of applications in science, industry, and medicine.

Kenneth H. Olsen is president and co-founder of Digital Equipment Corporation, Maynard, Massachusetts, founded in 1957 to build digital computers and associated equipment.

Our youngest company, Hydronautics, Incorporated, Laurel, Maryland, was represented by Marshall P. Tulin, vice president and co-founder. The firm was started in 1959 to do research in hydrodynamics, which is the study of solid bodies moving through water and involves such things as ship hulls and hydrofoil skis.

Isaac L. Auerbach is president of Auerbach Corporation,

MARSHALL P. TULIN   ISAAC L. AUERBACH

the Philadelphia-headquartered organization he founded in
1957 to do design and consulting work in the field of in-
formation systems, which include systems that collect, store,
process, and retrieve information.

Dr. John V. N. Granger is president and one of the
founders of Granger Associates, a ten-year-old Palo Alto,
California, manufacturer of communications equipment.

The discussion began after a get-acquainted lunch, which
turned out to be a reunion of sorts for Granger and Robin-
son. We discovered they had last seen each other while work-
ing at the British Telecommunications Establishment in Eng-
land back in 1940.

We asked each of our guests to lead off by telling some-
thing of how he happened to become a businessman.

ROBINSON: It was after the war, and I was looking for
something new to start on. At the time I was a professor of
electrical engineering at Birmingham University, and I decided that my roots were back in the United States where I
had lived previously for about four years. So I came back
to the U.S. and my good luck was that, after looking at six
different jobs, I found that Dr. John Trump at MIT was
going to start up a company for which he already had the
name, and for which he had the product, and for which he

JOHN V. N. GRANGER

thought he had the application. He was wrong about where it would be applied, but he had the rest, and it happened to be in the application of high voltage to the generation of dc, which had been a particular interest of mine. I am continually amazed by the way in which we all choose our life careers. We do it on the most insufficient evidence, the way we make most of our decisions. I can actually date the occasion. John Trump was trying to interest me in all this, and I was very doubtful whether this was something too "chancy" for somebody nearly forty, who really had only one more throw of the dice. He wanted to make accelerators for generating x rays for cancer treatment. I went to some people I knew in that field and they were so intransigently opposed and narrow-minded about it that I decided to throw in my lot with him just on that.

OLSEN: I was an engineer at MIT and enjoyed it, and never thought of leaving. I enjoyed building things; in fact, this was an ambition of mine. The only thing that made me waver from staying at MIT forever was that what we were doing didn't seem to influence industry or the outside world. People smiled at us and said it was just academic, and so we just set about to show them.

Did it involve emotional stress to move from thinking of yourself as a technical man to thinking of yourself as a businessman?

OLSEN: Building things and building an organization take

very much the same type of planning and give the same feeling of success or creativity—at least that's been my reaction. Working out things so that other people can get things done gives me the same feeling of satisfaction.

TULIN: At the time I started Hydronautics with a colleague, we had both been with the Office of Naval Research for about five years. We were generally a little disaffected with our lives in the government. I know I became quite frustrated because my responsibilities were primarily for coordinating research, rather than doing research itself. I think we sensed a great deal was about to happen, or should happen, in the field of hydrodynamics, and that we could help bring these possibilities about. But I don't know if we would have had enough imagination to start a research business if the pattern hadn't been set before by a number of other people.

Imagination or courage?

TULIN: No, not courage. Perhaps we were simply foolhardy but I felt no danger whatsoever in taking this step. I think we had a taste for adventure, and I think that is crucial.

ROBINSON: You always think you can get back, don't you?

TULIN: No, I didn't even think about that. I was not going back to administration. I wanted to get into active research again. Anyway, we certainly didn't seriously consider that we would fail entirely.

AUERBACH: At the time I left Burroughs, I had an excellent position responsible for most of the military R and D, with an excellent future, but felt that I was not learning any more and was not interested in just saturating out at this point in my career. The desire to control my own destiny and the destiny of a group of men was very great, and since I was basically a builder of new enterprises—particularly technical enterprises—the desire to do this on my own, rather than for other organizations, was very great. The question of courage was one that, quite frankly, never entered my mind. There was never a question of failure. I don't think if you consider the possibility of failure you can direct all of your energies to success. There has never been a question of failure in this enterprise from the day we started.

GRANGER: I was at Stanford Research Institute for seven years after the war with responsibility for most of their military and avionics activities. I got to be frustrated with this. Perhaps I was wrong in my attribution of the reasons. I thought it was because of a feeling that organizations like SRI had grown very rapidly, but on the basis of a service that was very limited and confined entirely to paper reports, and also a feeling that there had been a number of good ideas developed there, and some useful directions for moving forward, but nothing had really happened with most of them. I felt, along with some of my colleagues, that you ought to be able to prove these things, but I didn't have any very clear idea about how to do this. I finally came to the conclusion that the reason I hadn't been able to think of a good way to do it was because I hadn't had enough time, and the only way to get time was to quit the job. So, I quit and then set about to find a sensible alternative. The only one I could find that seemed sensible was to borrow some money from my father and start my own company.

As I listen, I have the feeling that each of you possesses an inordinate amount of creative drive. Do you feel you're as creative in building an organization as you might have been in continuing as technical people?

ROBINSON: Definitely. If you can get an extension of your own wishes and personality by organizing *other* people to do it, then that's really worth while. Furthermore, I think we all realize that the really creative period in most men's lives is subsiding by the time they are thirty. At least, it's true of many of us. I was never particularly inventive, so it was no great sacrifice for me. But for others of us this subsides, and you want to help others along the road that you had been helped along.

GRANGER: Nothing brings out the creativity in a man like the responsibility for signing paychecks.

AUERBACH: I'm not quite sure I attribute this to the diminishing of creative powers so much as to the force of younger men who have had the opportunity to learn those new things that were considered "impossible" when you went through school and that now are taken for granted. Younger men stand on the shoulders of those scientists who have gone before them, and they can reach higher more easily. The older creative scientist is often hampered by his own inventions—he knows too much about them. I agree, though, that there's a great deal of value to be gained in applying these same creative skills to people problems—they don't change as rapidly as science does.

ROBINSON: But I think that every one of us realizes how much more difficult it would be to stimulate these drives in other people if we had not been in the scientific community ourselves. We do not understand how a lawyer or an accountant, however skillful, could have done this stimulating job, and that's what makes our life in management worth while.

Is being president of your own company a management job in the sense you're using it?

ROBINSON: Yes. More than anything else, it is just that. And it is a tremendous mixture of skills that many of us had no idea we would find in ourselves. I think if we had known what we were facing, we would never have done it—we wouldn't have dared. Perhaps it is useful to be naïve.

OLSEN: You have to be naïve. Even an engineer, to start a project, has to have a certain naïveté or else he will never start.

ROBINSON: Yes, if he is fearful as we senior people have become—we don't dare any more. Young people do because they are not fearful.

AUERBACH: Knowing what you know today, would you start your business all over again?

ROBINSON: Today, I wouldn't dare.

AUERBACH: I can say that I would not want to expend *that* much energy and effort all over again. I mean, I have done it, and I'm very happy that I did it, but if you asked me to sell out and start all over again today, I would say it is not worth the effort.

But in no sense are you gentlemen coasting. I notice in all your company reports plans for acquisitions and growth.

AUERBACH: But you're over the first hurdle, you see. This is like having run the first lap of the race. You are now in the race, and what is nice about it is that you've got a few hundreds or fifties of people running with you. It's quite different than when you're running alone. The difficulty of going out and buying your own stationery and buying your own desk, you see, and arguing with the telephone company to put the extensions in—this level of thing is hardly creative, is hardly management, but it's almost necessary when you start, and to go down to that level again, obviously, I would not do today. I would look for other resources.

GRANGER: I agree with your proposition, but I would put the problem somewhat differently. I think the necessity that starting over again would face me with, and that would be a big barrier to ever attempting it, is the necessity to re-establish a pattern of personal relationships of the complexity that exists now in my company and exists in any organization.

ROBINSON: You've given yourself once fully. And this is almost like a marriage, or a first love. It's very difficult to do all that twice in one lifetime.

TULIN: I would like to strike a dissonant note. I agree there is plenty of room for creativity in business. But a really creative technical group is a very fragile thing, and I think there is danger in that management's eventual motivations may be quite different than they were initially. You can't con a smart group of people though. They know what *matters* to you and it makes a difference. We've felt change in ourselves. We've fought it. I've seen it in other people. I think business experience can have a sad effect eventually on creativity. You may survive—even prosper—but watch out. . . .

*Going back a minute, do the rest of you share the feeling that
the fact you began as technical people is crucial to what you
do now?*

AUERBACH: In my case, the answer is very simple. I could
not have started the business if I had not been technically
trained and I could not continue to function in the business
without that technical training, because when I am functioning in the capacity of a consultant, which I thoroughly
enjoy, I depend very heavily on my technical familiarity with
what's going on in the industry. But I must say that it becomes increasingly difficult to find the time—not the interest
or the motivation, but just the honest-to-God time—to do all
this and *still* perform the function of the president of the
organization, who must continue to represent his organization to the outside world, who must address himself to the
day-to-day and long-range business problems in planning for
growth.

OLSEN: I think having a technical background is exceedingly important in *starting* a company. Most of us are presidents, but I think if you look at the average company you'll
see presidents don't last this long. It's a dangerous job. It's
just like revolutionaries in politics. After a company goes
for a while, then a lawyer or an accountant might do a
better job, and while we may have been successful up to our
present levels perhaps when we're an order of magnitude
bigger it will be time for the accountant to run the organization—or that's the challenge we have before us.

*It occurs to me that being president and running a company
is just plain more fun than being a technical man.*

ROBINSON: It's more agony as well. I'm sure we all get fun
out of it, or we wouldn't be doing it. Presumably any of us
could take a much easier job that would give us as much
yield financially and would be far less disturbing to the
psyche and the body, but we don't do it, and I think we do
like the challenge and the excitement even when it gets us
down. But the agony goes with the fun.

GRANGER: Yes, it seems to me that it's more fun in the
sense that a gambler playing for thousand-dollar stakes is
getting more fun out of it than one playing for one-dollar

stakes, but inextricably the agony is there too. The thing that is characteristic of the chief-executive job is the risk entailed. All of us were technical people and grew up in a tradition— a very sound one—in which objectivity had as one of its advantages the notion that if the experiment failed, but was done objectively, it was still a worthwhile experiment and didn't detract in any way from your stature as a scientist or an engineer. But it certainly does detract when the experiment is a business enterprise; so when you become the chief executive you're playing an entirely different role.

This leads to a different sort of question. Just financially, is science a good business to be in? Those companies here which publish reports seem to be earning some 10 per cent before taxes; to most manufacturing companies that wouldn't look terribly attractive.

ROBINSON: In the case of our company, the return has not been on the profit after taxes but on the growth of the company; that has been very remunerative to its stockholders. On the basis of only $2 million which has been truly invested, we are doing about $18 million a year—and only about $1 million earnings after taxes. On the basis of turnover, it's not particularly attractive, but it's extremely attractive to the original stockholder. Whether it will continue to be is another matter; but we are still growing.

AUERBACH: When you start a new business and the investment is small, you reach a point where the return is great. When the company matures and starts to face the normal economic environment, the investment becomes more risky, because now you are putting your money on profitable return, based on scientific brains. And that is not necessarily their maximum skill. Maybe you need a financial man guiding you more heavily than in the early days. Over a long pull, a science-based company becomes less attractive; the goal is to get in at the early stages.

Has your road been a particularly smooth one?

ROBINSON: Heavens no. I don't believe anyone who says their road has been smooth. The first three years we completely went through our capital and in the second three years there were only three weeks where we were as much as a month's money ahead. There were many times—I can think of at least five—when we were within a few weeks of being right on our uppers—finished.

What saved you?

ROBINSON: All kinds of things, but above all, the fact that we had a product people wanted and an extraordinary devotion by the people in the company who worked as much as sixteen and eighteen hours a day, particularly when things got rough. This is something the large companies can't ask for and never get out of their people—or very seldom get. I told our people that building a new industry requires incomparably more from its people than keeping an established one going. Back in '47 and '48, the average pay was $3,500 a year, with no overtime being paid to engineers, and they were working sixty and seventy hours a week to make the thing go. Our company was able to grow by plowing back the high financial return from younger men with tremendous enthusiasm. They expected and got stock and other things which have made their lives very comfortable now.

Dr. Granger, you've had similar experiences. Can you describe your insides at that time?

GRANGER: You were much too busy to be deeply affected by it—at least consciously. In those periods, you don't know what will work, but you do know some things that can be done, and you know for certain that something must be done.

ROBINSON: For ten years I kept a diary and there are constant references to the fact that I couldn't sleep and my insides were in a tremendous uproar and I was furious with everybody and I would have to stop taking it so seriously and all those things. They were there all the time—at every crisis. But generally you're so busy, you ignore your symptoms until the crisis is over. Then you're furious with everybody for not realizing they were all nearly finished, and then your whole insides go . . . lack of sleep and so on. Long ago,

I predicted that I would have ulcers—and I don't have them. Why, I'll never know. But this is what I mean by the agony. I think it is really there, in one form or another.

AUERBACH: We had an experience that was just one of those strokes of good luck. We were actually in two businesses at once during our first three years. One was designing prototype equipment where we did carry an inventory, with technicians, benches, and everything that goes with this. In 1960 the electronics industry went through one of its downward cycles and this business went sour. Frankly, if it had been our only business we would have gone out of business; although we carried the staff for a number of months, eventually we had to decide—and with great reluctance—to close that manufacturing operation completely. We had only twenty-three men in it, but the question came of laying them off or finding things for them to do.

ROBINSON: And you certainly went through plenty of heart-search and agony, whether you felt it in the stomach or somewhere else.

AUERBACH: Oh, you feel it. It's quite traumatic to suddenly recognize that you have built this organization up and then to have the choice of either trying to convert these assets into a different kind of business or giving it up altogether.

You all indicated that at the beginning you went into this in part because there were some frustrations with the earlier jobs. Now, it is suggested there are frustrations in this job. What is the difference that keeps making you do this?

AUERBACH: You made these frustrations. These are your frustrations.

OLSEN: They're not really frustrations. They're challenges. They're under your control.

Are they really under your control? The picture always is that the president is some ultimate boss. Are you in fact?

ROBINSON: You're given the responsibility of trying to find the way out of the box you're in. You're always in a box of some sort. But in this job, when you think you know a way to get out of it, you can generally take the steps, whereas as part of a larger organization you're often subject to decisions that don't come in time for you to even begin. I'm one of the ones who didn't get into this because of frustrations in my previous job, but I do understand what these men are talking about. And I must say I agree that when I was doing personal research for a larger organization— and I had great freedom—many experiments didn't come to anything, but I never felt the same agonies about them. I felt disappointed, but it was all up in the top think tank— not anywhere else.

What do you do in your present role to ensure that the people who are working for you today, as you once worked for someone else with frustration, don't suffer that same frustration to the same extent?

AUERBACH: Many employees suffer frustrations that come about in two ways. One is lack of decisions being made, and the second is decisions being made that impose a hardship on getting the job done—boxing the situation through rules and regulations. For example, employing a draftsman to do some detail work often requires just as much energy and effort as getting a contract signed for a million dollars. Now I try to combat this kind of problem by delegating complete responsibility and authority to the men to operate their units on a profitable basis in accordance with a plan. They can hire; they can fire. The approvals I require are more to ensure that they are giving proper consideration to their decisions.

TULIN: We purposely avoided ordering or structuring our organization for an awfully long time. It's a funny thing, you know; people don't like that—they want order. So in a way they bring all these things on themselves. I have a contempt for order myself—I'm a very poor administrator, and I tend to fight administration. I think that helps, but now we're getting ordered to a certain extent, and I'm sure some frustrations exist. I think it helps a great deal here if you can maintain working contact with as many people as possible, and I think that consciousness of the problem is the crucial thing. As long as the organization is small enough so that management is really aware and concerned with the problem, you're all right.

As a final question, let's return to the point that so many companies disappear, and ask what it takes for a science company to succeed. Suppose your brother-in-law wanted to start a company—what would you tell him?

ROBINSON: Don't underprice! Assuming you've got something really salable and can get an edge for a time, then this would be my first advice. And don't tell me it's salable if you have to compete with IBM or GE or DuPont. Don't even think about it. And good pricing doesn't mean making 20 per cent before taxes. That's no use. You have to have 50 per cent to 70 per cent, in fact, so that you'll have 25 per cent over for the R and D of the future. That's what made the success in our case—I'm certain of it. But then there are also some routine things which are prerequisites that I'd like to enumerate as follows: patient venture capital, a bank that has some confidence, and a devoted team willing to work extremely long hours and, in the early years, at very low pay. Also a unified top management. We almost fissioned once, and for the sake of the organization I had to give up my whole plan and go in with the other two founders because they outvoted me—I was the president, but I had to swallow it. Also every science company has to have the ability somewhere in the organization to explain itself to others—to bankers, to Wall Street, to other scientists. And you have to have predictability as a management—on bank loans, payroll—even management availability. I've seen companies go sour, in my opinion, because you never knew where the president was, you couldn't reach him. I think this is highly important—you can go to Florida if everybody knows you're going, or be late in the mornings if everybody knows you're going to be late, but you mustn't just be odd about it, you have to be predictable.

AUERBACH: I'd like to reinforce that about loyalty. I think one of the major causes of the demise of many companies has been that they got three or four men together who were not loyal to each other and not devoted to the common cause and did not trust each other, then bickering, politicking, aspiration for control, and all that started. And when that happens you have to rout it out or just pray every night it doesn't destroy you. I also think it's very important for a new company to set a goal for itself of simply surviving. This way you don't take gambles—any one of which will knock you out of the ring. You always have enough staying power to come back the next day and try again. Also, understanding the market—that's one of the most important things for a new company. The best technical brains in the business won't bring success if you don't know how to price your product.

GRANGER: One thing your pricing has to support that's inevitable with a new company doing new things is the situation in which the goods you deliver are not as satisfactory to the customer as you promised they would be. Then you've got no recourse—you've got to follow through or be prepared to go out of business. And sometimes its damned expensive. It's never in the plan or budget, but you have to be prepared to do it. Another thing that causes failure is lack of flexibility. There are many companies that are started by bright young fellows who've got a good idea, but if that idea doesn't work out as they expected it to, they may get into real trouble, because they're inflexibly committed to it. And you just can't be inflexibly committed to anything if survival is one of your goals—which it's got to be.

TULIN: If someone came and asked me about going into a research business for himself, I would tell him that it was a silly idea unless he has *proven* capability in research and also a detailed prior knowledge of the market for his particular talents. These are crucial. It's necessary to have proven ability because when you say to people, "I think this should be done, and in this way . . ." they're very often not going to listen to you unless they know *who* you are. I think many failures are due to improper estimate of the market. They really didn't know . . . didn't have a realistic view of what was needed in a technical sense.

OLSEN: A business is not a democracy. There can be only one boss, and that helps the politicking question.

AUERBACH: Absolutely. One way of keeping politics out

is to have meetings of your senior people and make sure that at least they know what is going on. And make sure your door is always open to them, so that they can come in and gripe and get some of their complaints off their shoulders, so that they don't become cancerous. This is, I think, a very, very critical problem for a young company during its early years. Later on, you don't have the problem so much. There is a stability and there is an ongoing force that keeps you moving. But during the early years, when you are literally a handful of people, this can be extremely destructive.

ROBINSON: And if they get a hearing, they do not then go ahead and do this underground stuff—that's been my experience too. That's why I said the president must be available—and not put them off for two days. Because to the man himself, he is hurting with this—he's burning. You must see him within a couple of hours if possible. This is one of the chores. You often have to drop your own stuff to reason with him. I make it a rule never to put anyone off further than the next morning if they ask for me urgently. Incidentally, I'd like to add that we have ignored my own rules about pricing and competition three times—and failed at it miserably. The risk is tremendous, and it comes up and hits you if you accept these things. The particular products were underpriced, they were competitive they were underpriced because they were competitive. And we didn't have the edge. We were taken to the cleaners, and we're still fixing up the things we did wrong.

OLSEN: There's an interesting danger there. If you have a little bit of success, the outside world is so ready to encourage you to go into something else. They think you have a magic touch—and if you ever start listening to the flattery, after a while you start believing it, and then you are in trouble. The outside world—the flatterers—are probably the biggest danger.